Instructor's Resource Manual

WILLIAM ALEXANDER
James Madison University

JUDITH BECK
University of North Carolina – Asheville

LEO CONNOLLY
University of California – Santa Barbara

FIFTH EDITION

Astronomy

A Beginner's Guide to the Universe

CHAISSON | McMILLAN

PEARSON

Prentice
Hall

Upper Saddle River, NJ 07458

Project Manager: Christian Botting
Senior Editor: Erik Fahlgren
Editor-in-Chief, Science: Dan Kaveney
Editorial Assistants: Jessica Berta and Fran Falk
Executive Managing Editor: Kathleen Schiaparelli
Senior Managing Editor: Nicole M. Jackson
Assistant Managing Editor: Karen Bosch
Production Editor: Robert Merenoff
Supplement Cover Manager: Paul Gourhan
Supplement Cover Designer: Christopher Kossa
Manufacturing Buyer: Ilene Kahn
Manufacturing Manager: Alexis Heydt-Long

© 2007 Pearson Education, Inc.

Pearson Prentice Hall

Pearson Education, Inc.

Upper Saddle River, NJ 07458

Pearson Prentice Hall™ is a trademark of Pearson Education, Inc.

The author and publisher of this book have used their best efforts in preparing this book. These efforts include the development, research, and testing of the theories and programs to determine their effectiveness. The author and publisher make no warranty of any kind, expressed or implied, with regard to these programs or the documentation contained in this book. The author and publisher shall not be liable in any event for incidental or consequential damages in connection with, or arising out of, the furnishing, performance, or use of these programs.

Printed in the United States of America

10 9 8 7 6 5 4 3 2 1

ISBN 0-13-187173-0

Pearson Education Ltd., *London*
Pearson Education Australia Pty. Ltd., *Sydney*
Pearson Education Singapore, Pte. Ltd.
Pearson Education North Asia Ltd., *Hong Kong*
Pearson Education Canada, Inc., *Toronto*
Pearson Educación de Mexico, S.A. de C.V.
Pearson Education—Japan, *Tokyo*
Pearson Education Malaysia, Pte. Ltd.

Instructor's Resource Manual
To accompany *ASTRONOMY: A Beginner's Guide to the Universe, 5th edition,*
By Eric Chaisson and Steve McMillan

Table of Contents

Introduction

Welcome to the Instructor's Resource Manual (IRM) for the Chaisson/McMillan textbook *ASTRONOMY: A Beginner's Guide to the Universe, 5th edition*. The ideas and suggestions for teaching astronomy presented in this manual are based on personal experiences in the classroom as well as on conversations with colleagues and mentors pursuing the art and science of teaching astronomy. Teaching a course is a cooperative enterprise that actively involves the students and the instructor; as such, the ideas in this manual are also shaped by the suggestions and responses of students. With this updated IRM for the 5th edition, there has been an effort to incorporate a learner-centered approach to supplement a more traditional college-level astronomy pedagogy. A note should be made regarding the use of the term "weight" in the IRM. I have expressed weight in terms of Newtons, not in terms of "equivalent mass" which is used to some extent in the main text. This will affect a few of the problem solutions. I hope you find this manual helpful as you further develop your own unique approach to teaching and learning.

Teaching Introductory Astronomy

Who are your students and why are they taking this course? These are the first questions you as an instructor need to answer in order to successfully plan and conduct an introductory astronomy course. Perhaps one reason students are taking the course is to fulfill a general education or divisional requirement. If so, it is important for you to recognize that many will not be science majors and may not have much experience with college level science. If that is the case, you will probably want to include and emphasize more conceptual ideas about the pursuit of scientific knowledge and the practice of science. Use discussions of historical and contemporary figures to help you present the human side of science. Many non-science students view science as a collection of dry facts; this course is your opportunity to show them the process of science, and the splendor involved in finding out more about the cosmos.

Math is a very powerful tool for examining scientific concepts, even on the introductory level. Make sure you know the level of mathematics ability of your students and if there is any math prerequisite to the course. Consider giving your students a mathematical pretest on the first day of class. Even though your students might not be thrilled with this, it will give you a better sense of abilities of your students. Quantitative problems are included at the end of each chapter in the text; assign or do in class those that you judge to be at the appropriate level for your students. If you are teaching astronomy as a general education course, you may well have some students in your class who avoid math at all costs. Demonstrate mathematical applications, and present math as a useful tool and as a way of describing and investigating nature and the universe in which we live.

Many students enter an introductory astronomy class already fascinated by the subject, even if they do not yet know much about it. Capitalize on their interest and enthusiasm! Consider passing out index cards on the first day of class, to see what students are interested in. Although you might not cover UFOs and time travel, it's still interesting to see what students are interested in and it can inform your goals for the course. In teaching astronomy, you have the opportunity to present some of the most bizarre, immense, baffling, and complex structures and ideas in science. Challenge your students to engage with and question these ideas. Present the study of astronomy as a human endeavor, as a quest for understanding, and as an enriching, exciting experience. Your students will hopefully reward you by rising to the occasion! However, sometimes student expectations of an astronomy class can exceed any instructor's abilities. This is where taking a survey of your students can help to inform you of these expectations.

Over the past few years there have been efforts to learn more about how college students learn astronomy in an effort to affect classroom instruction. Much of this research is highlighted in the online journal, *Astronomy Education Review* (AER) which can be found at http://aer.noao.edu/. An example of this research is *Lecture-Tutorials for Introductory Astronomy* by Jeffrey Adams that is suggested extensively throughout the IRM. The key idea of these lecture tutorials is the engagement of the students in order to make the classroom more student-centered. Another text that is mentioned in the IRM that also encourages student engagement is *Peer Instruction for Astronomy* by Paul Green. These new approaches to teaching college astronomy aren't without controversy because within the AER this has been a sometimes heated debate about what should be the emphasis of a first course in astronomy. In essence, should the "basics" such as lunar phases and seasons be emphasized, or should frontiers of astronomy such as black holes and galaxy formation be highlighted? As for me, I think a balanced approach is appropriate, but others would disagree. At the heart of this debate is who speaks for introductory astronomy. Do the astronomers or the astronomy education community speak for what constitutes an introductory astronomy class? It's ultimately the responsibility of the instructor to understand their own institutional goals for their astronomy class. To this end, each instructor should be aware of the body of knowledge concerning the teaching of introductory astronomy.

Course Organization and Structure

Lectures, discussions, and presentations

The **daily structure** of your course will depend upon several factors, including class size, resources available to you, and your own teaching style. For a small class, you may engage in frequent discussions, question/answer sessions, and/or student presentations on specific topics. If you have a large lecture class, you will probably not have extended class discussions and there will not be time for every student to do a presentation. But astronomy education research has shown that lecture tutorials can be very useful to foster student engagement even with large lecture classes. There are a number of ways you can encourage an interactive atmosphere with your students. Students tend to find demonstrations and models particularly engaging when their peers are involved, so ask individuals to come forward to help you with presentations. Even in large classes you can encourage questions from your students; sometimes they are insightful, which adds tremendously to your presentation, and other times students' questions can point out misconceptions you may not otherwise recognize and address.

For some topics you can ask students to make predictions or guesses and then write a few of them on the board. This technique not only gets students more involved in the class, it also helps them apply knowledge they have gained to new situations and avoid seeing astronomy as a string of unrelated numbers. As an example, consider the study of the planets. First you will introduce the solar system as a whole and then you will concentrate on Earth, followed by the rest of the planets in order. When you get to Venus, ask students to write down their best guesses for Venus's distance from the Sun, orbital period, rotational period, density, and temperature. For some of these items they should be able to make pretty good guesses; the distance must be less than one A.U. and the orbital period less than 1 year. Since Venus is a terrestrial planet, they will have a good idea what its density is. For other items, such as length of day and temperature, they will probably be way off, which will help you make important points about special characteristics of Venus. The process of making educated guesses for various properties usually makes the numbers more meaningful for students and gives them practice in estimation and reasoning skills.

Astronomy is a very visual science. Take advantage of the large collection of **slides or transparencies** made available by the textbook publisher. You may wish to augment your collection by purchasing other educational slide sets. There are many different ways you can employ the images. For instance, you may wish to break the lecture in the middle each day, dim the lights, and have a slide show concerning the topic of the day. Or, you can save all the images for the end of class to use as a conclusion and review. Finally, you may choose to have the slides interspersed throughout the lecture. Include images of people if possible, both historical figures (Galileo, Annie Jump Cannon, Edwin Hubble) and contemporary astronomers (Margaret Geller, Murray Gell-Mann) to illustrate the human side of astronomy.

If you are teaching in a "smart classroom," you can access the Companion Website and show animations illustrating particular concepts. Other **Websites** can also be employed. For instance, when discussing the Sun, you can bring up current photos of the Sun to show the locations of sunspots. Even after moving on to other topics, you can take a minute at the beginning of class each day for a week to view the Sun so students can watch the motion of the sunspots and even estimate the rotational period of the Sun. Be sure to plan your Website "fieldtrips" ahead of time and check the locations before class, so you do not spend class time surfing or hunting down broken links.

Demonstrations, models, and visualizations add an important dimension to any science class. Models are particularly helpful in astronomy, which deals with dimensions and distances that are hard for students (or anyone else!) to comprehend. Demonstrations enliven presentations and help students understand (and remember) concepts.

Finally, whatever balance of lecture, demonstration, interaction, and visual presentation you decide is right for you, make sure your own enthusiasm for the subject shines through. Your fascination with and passion for astronomy will leave a lasting impression on your students, and will aid in their learning at least as much as demonstrations and slide shows will.

Evaluation

Consider using a variety of methods to evaluate your students. Possibilities include homework, quizzes, tests, laboratory exercises, written assignments, and projects. You may also choose to require attendance and therefore have it contribute to a final grade. Personally I think attendance is critical for not only the individual student, but also for the class as a whole. I think that a student is not only responsible for their own learning of the material, but their responsibility extends to the entire classroom to be there to engage in discussions and to participate in group learning activities. So, not only should the struggling student attend class, but also the more "advanced" student as well. Whatever your policies regarding grading, make sure that they are clearly stated in the syllabus and applied fairly and consistently. Remember also that evaluations not only help you assign grades to students, they also help you keep your finger on the pulse of a class. For both the students' sake and your own, do not wait until midterm to give students feedback in the form of a grade. If the class averages for the first few quizzes are extremely low, then you know you are not getting across to students and can determine what needs to be changed.

There are many ways to encourage and motivate students to keep up with class. Homework and quizzes are two of the most common methods. Each chapter in the textbook includes 10 numerical problems and 15 review and discussion questions. Subsets of these can be assigned for **homework**. The problems range from fairly simple to quite complicated; use those that are appropriate for the level of your students. You may wish to use some of the problems as in-class exercises; many are excellent extensions and applications of material covered in the chapter, and provide an opportunity to further investigate specific topics. Also encourage students to try the "Conceptual Self Test" questions at the end of each chapter. Students can check their own answers in the back of the textbook to assess their level of understanding. The online exercises provided on the Companion Website provide another powerful tool for students to use to test their understanding and prepare for tests.

Quizzes provide another way to encourage students to stay engaged and caught up. A relatively simple and short quiz given at the beginning of class once or twice a week can ask the students questions about the last class (which encourages them to look over their notes) or questions about the material to be covered that day (which encourages them to read the material before coming to class). Alternatively, use technology and give a quiz via computer that must be completed before class. The in-class quiz can also be used as an attendance check and as an incentive to get to class on time; the Web quiz allows you more class time for new material. A short quiz given at the end of a class period is yet another option; it can be used to assess student understanding of the day's material and as an attendance check.

Class size will probably have some influence on the format of your **tests**. Very large classes usually dictate the necessity of multiple-choice and other objective-question tests. For smaller classes, you may opt to include some discussion or essay questions. Since visual images are an important part of an astronomy class, consider including some identification or other questions based on images. For a semester (15-week) course, two tests instead of a single midterm are usually the most effective. Prentice Hall Custom Test provides the opportunity for online testing, tailored to your specific needs.

The student **writing questions,** written in large part by Leo Connolly, included in this manual are intended to encourage writing as a regular course activity. Many campuses are emphasizing writing across the curriculum, and these exercises provide an opportunity for student writing in the sciences. There are generally five questions included per chapter in this manual; you can also make up your own to tie in with class discussions or personal interests. The questions are intended to stimulate creativity, imagination, and critical thinking. Avoid assigning questions that require students to repeat what they have just read or that may have canned answers found on the internet.

Small-group or individual **projects** can be an excellent experience for students in an astronomy course. Observing projects can range from one-night to semester-long assignments. Examples include tracking the motion of a planet with respect to the background stars, drawing the moon's phases, plotting the motions of the moons of Jupiter, observing and sketching astronomical objects, and following the motion of the Sun by measuring daily shadow lengths or sunrise and sunset positions along the horizon. Non-observing projects are also possible. For instance, throughout the course models are very useful for illustrating various concepts. Small groups of students can be assigned different modeling projects to design and construct. Possibilities include models of the solar system, the interior of the Earth, the layers of the jovian planets, the Milky Way, the Local Group, etc.

Exactly how you determine final grades will depend on your personal preference, whether or not the course has a laboratory component, and institutional culture. In particular, check to see if there are expectations regarding what percentage of the final grade is determined by the final exam. Three possible grading schemes are given below.

Scheme 1: One-semester course with lab
   Labs and Projects 15%; Homework and Quizzes 20%; Tests (2 @ 20%) 40%; Final Exam 25%
   Grading scale: A: 90–100, B: 80–89, C: 70–79, D: 60–69, F: 0–59

Scheme 2: One-quarter course with lab
   Labs and Projects 20%; Homework and Quizzes 25%; Midterm 25%; Final Exam 30%
   Grading scale: A: 92–100, B: 82–90, C: 72–80, D: 62–70, F: 0–60
   (In this scheme, a gap is left between the letter-grade ranges for the discretion of the instructor. Often, borderline cases are decided primarily by student performance on the final exam.)

Scheme 3: Semester or quarter course without lab
   Homework and Projects 20%; Quizzes 15%; Tests (1 or 2) 30%; Final Exam 35%
   Grading scale: A: 90–100, B: 80–89, C: 70–79, D: 60–69, F: 0–59

Sample schedules

The textbook is ideal for use with a one-quarter, one-semester, or two-quarter course. Sample schedules for all three formats are presented in the following tables. They assume a 15-week semester or a 10-week quarter with a separate final exam period at the end of the course. One midterm exam per quarter and two exams in the semester format have been included in the schedules. Alternatively, the 2-quarter schedule could be used as a 2-semester schedule if supplemental activities such as writing assignments, sky observations or group projects. The content for the 10-week quarter would be distributed into a 15-week semester so that there would be more time for the various supplemental activities.

Sample Schedule for 1-Quarter Course	
Week #	Chapter or Activity
1	E-1
2	2-3
3	4-5
4	6-7
5	8-9
6	Midterm &10
7	11-12
8	13-14
9	15-16
10	17-18 and review for final

Sample Schedule for a 1-Semester Course	
Week #	Chapter or Activity
1	E-1
2	2
3	3
4	4
5	5
6	6 and exam
7	7-8
8	9
9	10
10	11-12
11	13
12	14 and exam
13	15-16
14	17
15	18 and review for final

Sample Schedule for a 2-Quarter Course (or 2- 15-Week Semester Course with Supplemental Activities)			
First quarter		Second quarter	
Week #	Chapter or Activity	Week #	Chapter or Activity
1	E-1	1	10
2	2	2	11
3	3	3	12
4	4	4	13
5	Review and midterm	5	Review and midterm
6	5	6	14
7	6	7	15
8	7	8	16
9	8	9	17
10	9 and review for final	10	18 and review for final

Syllabus

It is important to provide your students with a clear syllabus at the beginning of the course. Include your office hours and contact information, course objectives, goals and expectations, grading criteria, resource information, a schedule, and general policies, including issues from plagiarism and cheating to snow days and absences due to campus-related activities. You may also wish to include hints and suggestions for success. The following is a list of some possible suggestions for students; you will undoubtedly have some favorites of your own to include.

- Prepare for class; read material in the text *before* the lecture.
- Use your resources, including the text and the Companion Website.
- Don't miss class; get notes from someone if you have an unavoidable absence.
- Review and practice math as necessary.
- Participate in class.
- Keep up with homework and projects.
- Form a study group.
- Practice, practice, practice.
- Let me know how you're doing!

Teaching Resources

Supplementary materials

In addition to this IRM, there are a number of other resources available from the publisher. Over 250 of the figures and tables from the text are reproduced as *transparencies* for instructor use. A *test item file* is also available. An e-book *CD*, including a hyperlinked electronic version of the text, is included free with every textbook. Be sure to visit the *Companion Website* (linked from the site http://www.prenhall.com/chaisson) and encourage your students to take advantage of the excellent resources available there. See the text preface for more details on these and other resources. Two software packages are also made available for demonstrating and charting the night sky. These include **Starry Night Pro** and **Sky Chart III**. Helpful hints on how to use these software packages are discussed throughout this IRM.

Organizations and publications

Two publications that emphasize a student-centered approach to teaching introductory astronomy are *Lecture Tutorials for Introductory Astronomy* by Adams, Prather, and Slater and *Peer Instruction for Astronomy* by Paul Green. Both of these books are available from Prentice Hall.

The *Astronomy Education Review* is a peer-reviewed online journal for astronomy education research and also includes reviews of textbooks as well as position papers related to astronomy education. It can be found at http://aer.noao.edu/.

The two publications *Sky & Telescope* (http://skyandtelescope.com/) and *Astronomy* (http://www.astronomy.com/home.asp) are excellent magazine resources for both instructors and students of astronomy. In addition to interesting and current articles, each issue contains a sky chart for the month and suggestions for observing.

The American Association of Physics Teachers (AAPT) publishes the *American Journal of Physics* and *The Physics Teacher*, which often contain articles related to teaching astronomy as well as to teaching physics. In addition, AAPT sponsors workshops and meetings on teaching innovations. (http://www.aapt.org)

NASA provides a wealth of resources for students and educators. Visit their Website at http://www.nasa.gov for news, educational opportunities, products, photos, videos, announcements, and just about anything you can imagine related to the space agency.

Monthly star maps can be downloaded from http://www.skymaps.com/. The maps are easily downloaded via pdf format and are updated each month showing naked-eye planets and comets. There are also links on the site to purchase interesting books, charts, and posters.

The Astronomical Society of the Pacific (ASP) has many excellent educational materials related to astronomy, including slide sets, videos, and models. Visit http://www.astrosociety.org/ or call 800-335-2624. The Website contains astronomy news as well as products for sale.

The Harvard Smithsonian Center of Astrophysics has developed *Project Star Hands-On Science Materials* appropriate for introductory college astronomy classes and labs. Examples of their materials include refracting telescope kits, spectrometer kits, and celestial sphere kits. The products are available at Learning Technologies, Inc., 40 Cameron Avenue, Somerville, MA, 02144. http://www.starlab.com.

Several companies supply scientific equipment and materials for demonstrations and labs. If you do not already have a favorite, try Edmund Scientific, which has a good selection of astronomy-related products. (See http://www.scientificsonline.com.) Fisher Scientific (http://www.fishersci.com/) and Sargent-Welch (http://www.sargentwelch.com/) are also good choices.

Organization of the IRM

The rest of this manual is organized by chapter. In each section you will find a chapter outline, summary, list of major concepts, teaching suggestions and demonstrations, answers to the end-of-chapter questions, and solutions to the end-of-chapter problems. At the end of each IRM chapter is a list of the transparencies available as well as suggested readings pertaining to the chapter content and ideas for some materials that may be useful for demonstrations. Each section concludes with space for your notes.

A Final Word

Earlier editions of the IRM to accompany the main textbook were prepared solely by Dr. Leo Connolly of the California State University, San Bernardino and later editions by Dr. Judith Beck of UNC, Ashville. The current edition incorporates much of their earlier work including most of the student writing questions and many of the responses to review and discussion questions. In addition, I have kept many of their excellent ideas, teaching suggestions, and problem solutions in the text of the current manual. I am grateful to both of them for generously allowing me to continue to use the wealth of material and ideas they have collected into previous editions of this manual in my preparation of the current edition.

I would like to thank Christian Botting of Prentice Hall for his guidance and support during this project. I also would like to thank Ed Prather and Tim Slater of the University of Arizona, Randy Bell, Ed Murphy and Robert Tai of the University of Virginia, Tom Statler and Joe Shields of Ohio University, as well as all of my colleagues at James Madison University for their influence on my teaching.

This manual is dedicated to my wife, Dawn Alexander, whose love and encouragement helped me to see this project through.

William R. Alexander
Department of Physics
James Madison University
alexanwr@jmu.edu
February 2006

Exploring the Heavens
Introduction

Outline

E.1 The "Obvious" View
E.2 Earth's Orbital Motion
E.3 The Motion of the Moon
E.4 The Measurement of Distance
E.5 Scientific Theory and the Scientific Method

Summary

The Prologue covers the view from Earth, including constellations, the celestial sphere, and the apparent motions of the Sun and stars. The actual motions of Earth that give rise to those apparent motions are then discussed. The chapter concludes with angular measurements and distance determinations.

Major Concepts

- The view from Earth
  - Constellations
  - The celestial sphere
- Earth's orbital motion
  - Rotation
  - Revolution
  - Precession
- Motion of the Moon
  - Lunar phases
  - Eclipses
- Measuring distance
  - Triangulation
  - Angular measure
  - Parallax
- Scientific theory and the scientific method
  - Observation
  - Theory
  - Prediction

Teaching Suggestions and Demonstrations

One of the challenges in studying astronomy is developing the ability to view the universe from different perspectives, primarily the perspective we have from Earth, where we see the Sun and stars rise in the east and set in the west, and the perspective from outside, where we see Earth spinning on its axis and orbiting the Sun. Use plenty of models and diagrams in teaching this introductory material in order to help your students practice shifting viewpoints. Lots of new vocabulary is introduced in this chapter; take the time to define new terms.

There has been an emphasis among the astronomy educational research community that teaching approaches in college astronomy classes should be more learner-centered. An easy way to start to incorporate this approach is the book *Lecture Tutorials for Introductory Astronomy* by Adams. This book contains many in-class exercises that students work on in small groups. There are exercises on positional **astronomy, solar vs. sidereal day, seasonal stars**, the **ecliptic**, and **phases of the Moon** as well as additional topics that will be mentioned throughout this book. It takes a lot of consideration to decide how to use such materials, but research shows that it will benefit most students for the classroom to be more learner-centered.

Section E.1

Your students will all have heard of **constellations** and will probably be able to name at least a few. Emphasize that the stars in a given constellation are probably not physically close to each other in space; they just appear close to each other as seen from Earth. The stars in each constellation were grouped together by observers in ancient times, and we continue to use nearly the same groupings today. You can pass out or project a sky chart without constellations drawn in and challenge students to make up their own.

Asking students what their zodiacal sign can be a good way for the students to feel connected to the sky, even though very few might actually follow astrology. Personally I don't make it a practice to "debunk" astrology. I think it's a good thing that students know the name of at least one constellation. Consider using **Starry Night Pro** to demonstrate how the zodiacal constellations lie across or near the ecliptic line. Show how the sky view will change during the year. Be sure to let students know that their zodiacal constellation is associated with where the Sun was located when they were born, but it's about a month off due to precession of the equinoxes. This is illustrated in Figure E.8.

It is also interesting to compare names of northern and southern constellations. The northern constellations are typically named for animals and mythological characters. The Southern Hemisphere sky includes constellations such as the telescope, the microscope, and the octant. Ask your students if they can explain the difference. The **constellation names** we have inherited today derive from northern observers. The northern constellation names, therefore, date from ancient times, but the southern ones date from the early travels made by northern explorers to the Southern Hemisphere.

If you have time, explain a few of the **myths** that involve whole families of constellations. The story of Orion, Taurus, and the Pleiades is a good one, as is the story of Cassiopeia, Cepheus, Andromeda, Cetus, and Perseus. These are all constellations your students can find in the night sky, depending on the time of year you are teaching the course. Provide star charts and encourage your students to find major constellations in the night sky throughout the course.

The concept of the **celestial sphere** is an important one. We are missing *depth perception* when we look out at the night sky. If you have one, bring in a transparent model of the celestial sphere with Earth inside and point out the **north and south celestial poles** and **the celestial equator**. This is a good time to discuss Polaris and clear up any misconceptions; often, introductory astronomy students believe the North Star must be the brightest star in the sky.

Introduce students to **right ascension** and **declination** by comparing these to latitude and longitude. Emphasize that the celestial coordinates are attached to the sky. Over the course of a night, stars move from east to west and the coordinate system moves with them. Look up the coordinates of a few well-known stars (including Polaris) and help students determine their positions. Ask students to compare the two different methods of describing star locations, by coordinates and by constellation, and discuss the advantages of each.

Section E.2

Students usually know the terms **rotation** and **revolution** but often confuse them, so take a few moments to define these terms. In my own teaching I find myself using the word "orbit" instead of "revolution" so that I won't mistakenly use the wrong word. Students will also probably know that Earth takes a day to turn on its axis and a year to orbit the Sun, but will not know the difference between a **solar day** and a **sidereal day**, or a **tropical year** and a **sidereal year**. Use lots of diagrams, such as Figure E.7, to help explain. Models also help. Demonstrate rotation and revolution with globes, or bring students to the front of the class to model Earth's motions. For instance, one student can spin around (slowly) while also orbiting another. Ask the class to concentrate on one point on the Earth, say, the spinning student's nose, and imagine when it is lit and when it is dark. Use this model to explain day and night, sidereal vs. solar days, and why different constellations are visible in the night sky during different months.

Figure E.9 is also an important one. Make sure students understand that it shows the *apparent* **path of the Sun** on the celestial sphere. Use models of Earth and the Sun (or just two spheres) to help explain how Earth's tilt changes the position of the Sun in the sky as Earth orbits the Sun. Emphasize that the **solstices** and **equinoxes** can each refer to both a point in time *and* a point in space. The summer solstice, for instance, is the point on the ecliptic where the Sun is at its northernmost point, but we also use the term to refer to the time and day when the Sun is at that point. Students will be most familiar with the latter meaning, and know that the summer solstice occurs around June 21.

Begin your discussion of **seasons** with an informal, multiple-choice pre-quiz. If you'd like to make this pre-assessment a bit more formal, author Paul Green discusses more ideas in his book *Peer Instruction for Astronomy* starting on page 11. He also includes **"concept tests"** for the **seasons** as well as the **celestial sphere** and **time conventions** used in astronomy that can be used throughout the lecture. These can be used in conjunction with additional **"clicker questions"** that are provided with the instructor materials. During your lecture, ask students what causes the seasons, and include in the answer choices both the correct response, namely, Earth's tilt, and a common misconception, the distance from Earth to the Sun. If significant numbers of students choose the distance answer, make sure you address this misconception and explain why the different distances from Earth to the Sun do not affect the seasons. Many students are surprised to find that, in fact, the Earth is *farthest* from the Sun during the Northern Hemisphere summer. Bring in a flashlight and shine it directly down on a tabletop or on the floor, and then shine it at an angle to show how the angle of the Sun's rays affect solar heating. Go back to your model of Earth orbiting the Sun to show how the length of time the Sun is up in the sky also changes as the seasons change.

A gyroscope or top makes a good demonstration of **precession**. Find Vega on a star chart and point it out to students to help them get a sense of the scale of the change. Precession is also responsible for the fact that the zodiac constellations no longer correspond to their astrological dates. The heliacal rising of Sirius, in the constellation Canis Major, was an important date in the ancient agricultural calendar, but this no longer occurs on the same date today.

Section E.3

(**DEMO ⚡**) Demonstrate the **Moon's phases** by shining a flashlight on a ball. You can also paint one half of a Ping-Pong ball black and have students hold it at arm's length with different amounts of the black side facing them. For different positions of the Moon, ask students how much of the surface of the Moon is lit, and how much of the lit surface can be seen from Earth. Emphasize that half the surface is always receiving light, but we just do not see it all. Before showing Figure E.13, demonstrate and discuss with students when one particular phase, first quarter, say, will rise and set. Then ask them to predict rising and setting times of the other phases. This exercise provides an excellent opportunity for students to practice changing viewpoints as discussed in the previous chapter. Consider assigning students a project to track the Moon's phases. For instance, you can ask them to look for the Moon each (clear) night for a month, sketch its shape, and note the time and position in the sky. For best results, you should do this demo in a very dark room. Even with all the lights turned out, there will still be a lot of light reflected from the walls. It's best to use a classroom with dark walls, but this might be a difficult task. You should always try out a demo in the room that you'll be teaching before you do the demo in front of a class.

Once your students have a good grasp of phases, they should have no trouble understanding the causes of **eclipses**. Some points that you may need to clarify include why we do not have a solar eclipse every new Moon and a lunar eclipse every full Moon, and why a lunar eclipse lasts a while and can be seen from about half Earth's surface, but a solar eclipse can be seen only from a narrow band and lasts only a short time for any particular observer. A scale model using two spheres (for Earth and the Moon) and a strong light source (for the Sun) can help clarify points about lunar eclipses. Show pictures of the Sun during a solar eclipse and try to convey some of the excitement and awe inspired by eclipses. In addition to being spectacular events to watch, solar eclipses provide Earth-bound astronomers a rare opportunity to study the Sun's corona.

Section E.4

Figure E.21 illustrates an excellent demonstration of **parallax** that you can have your students try in class. Instruct them to hold up a finger (or pencil), close one eye, and line their finger up with some object on the far wall of the classroom. When they sight on their finger with the *other* eye open instead, it lines up at a different position. Ask students to try the exercise several times with their finger at different distances from their eyes to determine the relationship between the distance and the amount of shift. Figure P.11 shows this method applied to astronomy using Earth's diameter as a baseline. Challenge students to come up with a method where observers restricted to the surface of Earth can create an even longer baseline in order to measure parallaxes of more distant stars. (Observations can be made at different points in Earth's orbit around the Sun.) Even with the diameter of Earth's orbit as a baseline, the parallax method only works for the stars in the solar neighborhood.

Angular measure is very important to astronomy. Discuss *More Precisely E-1* carefully. Demonstrate angular measure by holding up a penny. At a distance of about 1 meter, a penny subtends an angle of about 1 degree. Students can hold up a penny and see what objects at different distances in the classroom have an angular size of about 1 degree. Also have students try this at night and estimate the angular size of the Moon, half a degree. *More Precisely E-2* discusses finding the **distances** to (and diameters of) astronomical objects. Go over angular measurements and then try several examples. Many problems throughout the text use the equations in this section, so it is worth spending some time with them to ensure student understanding.

Section E.5

Since many of your students are likely to have had minimal exposure to science, this section is worthwhile focusing on for class discussions. This discussion might be very timely due to the recent controversies concerning the teaching of "**intelligent design**" in public schools in the U.S. In introducing the **scientific method**, refer to Figure E.22 now as well as throughout the semester. Remind the students that science is a process rather than some fixed set of ideas or laws. This is a **STRENGTH**, not a weakness. Sometimes those that might challenge the validity of science using non-scientific arguments often try to exploit the tentative nature of science. The strength of science rests on the fact that it does not rely on the authority of political or religious systems nor on the interpretation of texts, ancient or otherwise. Ask the students to provide examples of ideas in their own minds that have changed once additional data or knowledge had become known to them. In my own opinion, I think science is a way that we (as humans) can sense the world around us and make predictions that can be tested and verified. At the heart of this process is the fact that the universe is inherently knowable. When discussing the nature of science, it is easy to fall into the philosophy of science. This can become a very exhaustive discussion, so make sure to have certain specific goals in mind so that you can move on to other topics when you've completed them.

Student Writing Questions

1. What was the tiniest object you have ever seen? The largest? The longest distance you have ever traveled? What is the largest number of objects you have ever knowingly encountered? (You may encounter lots of bacteria but not knowingly.) What was the longest you ever spent doing one activity? How do the largest and the smallest of these compare? How do the distances compare to the size of Earth? To the distance to the Moon? How does your time spent in one class compare to your lifetime?

2. Describe in metric units the room in which you do most of your studying. How big is it? What is the size of your desk? The TV or radio? How heavy are your books? The dimensions of your bed? Choose objects that have a range in sizes.

3. Test your horoscope. Each day, write two or three sentences about the most significant events that occurred to you that day. Cut out or copy your horoscope for that day and save. Continue this daily for about three weeks and make sure you write down your daily events before you read the horoscope. After three weeks, check what you wrote and your horoscope for each day to see whether there is a match. Count the number of hits and misses. Discuss the results and whether there is any significance to the number of hits. Are horoscopes truly predictive?

4. Find a location to view the night sky with as little interference as possible. Do this on as clear a night as possible. What do you see? Look all over and make note of the brightest stars. Are there any planets? How can you tell? Is the Moon out? What does it look like? What sort of details can you see on its surface?

5. What would it be like to live with only one functional eye? How would this change your perception of everything around you? What would pose the greatest difficulty to you? The least? You might actually try this first and then write about it. Did you get used to not having both eyes? Is parallax the only effect you miss with only one eye?

6. Describe an ordinary situation in which people regularly apply the scientific method, even though they are not aware they are doing so. Relate the situation to the three basic steps in the scientific method: gather data, form theory, and test theory.

7. Compare and contrast science as a way of knowing with some other way of knowing, such as social science, art, philosophy, or religion. How do these disciplines differ, how might they be similar?

Answers to End of Chapter Exercises

Review and Discussion

1. The Earth's diameter is about 110th that of the Sun. The Earth is about 10^{14} times smaller than the Milky Way Galaxy and about 10^{18} times smaller than the Universe.

2. A constellation is a pattern of stars that appear together in the sky although they are generally not close together in space. Many constellations are named after mythological figures or animals. Each constellation covers a specific area on the celestial sphere, and stars are designated by the constellation to which they belong.

3. Earth's rotation makes the Sun and stars appear to rise in the east and set in the west.

4. A solar day (measured by the Sun) is about 3.9 minutes longer than a sidereal day (measured by the stars). As Earth rotates on its axis, it also moves forward in its orbit so it has to rotate a little farther than one full turn to bring the Sun back to the same position in the sky.

5. One orbit of the Sun corresponds to one year, so a person's age in years equals the number of times he or she has orbited the Sun.

6. Because Earth revolves around the Sun, Earth's dark side (away from the Sun) faces a different direction at different times in Earth's orbit. The stars visible in the winter night sky are behind the Sun in the summer and therefore not visible.

7. Seasons are caused by the tilt of Earth's axis with respect to the plane of its orbit. The hemisphere tilted toward the Sun has summer, because the Sun appears higher in the sky and therefore the Sun is up longer and its rays are more direct. Both the length of time the Sun is in the sky and the angle of the rays contribute to increased heating.

8. Precession is the slow shift in the orientation of Earth's rotation axis. It is caused by the combined gravitational pulls of the Moon and the Sun.

9. Only a portion of the hemisphere of the Moon that is lit by the Sun may be facing Earth. For instance, during a full Moon, the entire lit portion faces Earth, but during a new Moon, the entire lit hemisphere is facing away from Earth, so we see none of it.

10. A lunar eclipse occurs when Earth's shadow falls on the Moon. A solar eclipse occurs when the Moon passes directly in front of the Sun, blocking its light so that shadow of the Moon falls on Earth. The Moon's orbit is slightly inclined with respect to the ecliptic, so Earth, the Moon, and the Sun are not precisely lined up every full and new Moon.

11. Since neither Mercury nor Venus have moons, it would have to be Mars or other outer planets. However the moons of Mars are too small to cover the solar disc as seen from the surface of Mars, as shown in problem #10 of Chapter 6. Eclipses as seen from the cloud tops of Jupiter is the topic for problem #5 in Chapter 8.

12. Parallax is the apparent shift in position of a foreground object with respect to the background as the observer's position changes. For example, as you drive down the road, a telephone pole along the road will line up with different points in the distant landscape.

13. When using triangulation, the longer the baseline, the greater the shift in position, or the greater the parallax angle. Objects in space are so far away that their shifts are very small. A long baseline will increase the chance that the shift will at least be measurable.

14. The diameter of an object can be determined if both the distance to the object and its angular diameter are known.

15. The scientific method obtains truths that rely on empirical data obtained in a naturalistic way using our senses. Religion, on the other hand, relies on truths that are divinely revealed.

Conceptual Self-Test

True or False? 1. F 2. F 3. T 4. F 5. T 6. T 7. F

Multiple Choice 8. b 9. b 10. c 11. a 12. c 13. d 14. b 15. a

Problems

1. The year 10,000 A.D. is about 8000 years from now, which is about 0.3 of the total precessional period of 26,000 years. Because there are 12 constellations in the zodiac, this corresponds to about 3½ constellations. If the vernal equinox is just now entering Aquarius, then it will be in the latter half of Scorpio in 10,000 A.D. (See Figure E.8.)

2. The distance Earth moves in a year is the circumference of its orbit:
$$C = 2\pi r = 2\pi(1.5 \times 10^8 \text{ km}) = 9.42 \times 10^8 \text{ km}.$$
A day is 1/365 of a year, so the distance Earth moves in a day is:
$$9.42 \times 10^8 \text{ km} / 365 = 2.58 \times 10^6 \text{ km}.$$
An hour is 1/24 of this, so the distance Earth moves in an hour is:
$$2.58 \times 10^6 \text{ km} / 24 = 1.08 \times 10^5 \text{ km}.$$
Finally, in a second, the Earth moves: $1.08 \times 10^5 \text{ km} / 3600 = 29.9 \text{ km}.$

3. The sidereal day would be the same, but the solar day would change in length because the Earth is still orbiting the Sun at roughly 1 degree per day. Normally the Earth must rotate an extra 1 degree after it reaches an entire sidereal day as shown in Figure E.7. This means that it takes about 3.9 extra minutes for the Earth to reach the position for a solar day, so a solar day is 3.9 minutes longer than a sidereal day. If the direction of rotation is changed, then it will take ~3.9 minutes less to reach a solar day than it would a sidereal day. In this case, the solar day will be ~3.9 minutes shorter than the sidereal day, which remains the same. The difference in the solar day would be:
$3.9 \text{ min} \times 2 \cong 8 \text{ min}$

4. Let's assume that the Moon is in a circular orbit with an orbital period of 27.3, which is the sidereal period. We'll assume that it moves through 360 degrees in these 27.3 days. Convert 27.3 days to seconds: 27.3 days = 2358720 seconds. The calculations should be done using ratios.

(a) $\dfrac{360°}{2358720 \text{ sec}} = \dfrac{X°}{3600 \text{ sec}} \Rightarrow X° = 0.5° = 33' / hour$

(b) $\dfrac{360°}{2358720 \text{ sec}} = \dfrac{X°}{60 \text{ sec}} \Rightarrow X° = 0.01° = 0.55' = 33'' / min$

(c) $\dfrac{360°}{2358720 \text{ sec}} = \dfrac{X°}{1 \text{ sec}} \Rightarrow X° = 0.00015° = 0.01' = 0.55'' / sec$

$$\frac{360°}{2358720 \sec} = \frac{0.5°}{T \sec} \Rightarrow T = 3276 \sec = 55 \min / 0.5°$$

5. Calculate the circumference of the lunar orbit, then divide by the sidereal period (27.3 days) converted to seconds. 27.3 days = 2358720 seconds.

$$\frac{3.14 \times 2 \times 384,000 \text{ km}}{2358720 \sec} = 1.0 km/s$$

6. Use the relationship given in *More Precisely E-2*:

$$dist. = baseline \times \frac{(360°/2\pi)}{parallax}$$

(a) $dist. = 1000 \text{ km} \times \dfrac{(360°/2\pi)}{1°} = 57,300 \text{ km}$

(b) $dist. = 1000 \text{ km} \times \dfrac{(360°/2\pi)}{(1/60)°} = 3.44 \times 10^6 \text{ km}$

(c) $dist. = 1000 \text{ km} \times \dfrac{(360°/2\pi)}{(1/3600)°} = 2.06 \times 10^8 \text{ km}.$

7. At an arm's length, a person's thumb covers about twice the angular size of the full Moon. Since the full Moon is 0.5 degrees, a person's thumb is ~1 degree at arm's length.

8. From *More Precisely P-2*:

$$diameter = dist. \times \frac{angular\ diameter}{57.3°} = 45,000,000 \text{ km} \times \frac{(55/3600)°}{57.3°} = 12,000 \text{ km}.$$

9. The diameter of an object in space is proportional to the distance times the angular diameter. If both the Moon and the Sun have the same angular diameter, then the ratio of their diameters will be equal to the ratio of their distances:

$$\frac{diameter_{sun}}{diameter_{moon}} = \frac{dist_{sun}}{dist_{moon}} = \frac{150,000,000 \text{ km}}{384,000 \text{ km}} = 391.$$

10. Using *Discovery E-1*, if the Earth was flat, the angle with respect to the shaft of the well would always be zero, as long as the Sun is far enough way so that the Sun's rays are parallel when they reach the Earth. In *Discovery E-1*, the angle is caused by the roundness of the Earth.

Resource Information

Student CD Media Resources

Interactive Student Tutorials
Phases of the Moon

Movies/Animations
Summer and Winter Solstice
The Equinoxes

The Earth's Seasons
Solar Eclipse in Indiana

Transparencies

Materials

Some basic materials helpful for demonstrations in this chapter include a globe (showing the tilt of Earth's axis), a flashlight, a gyroscope, and at least two different-size balls. (Styrofoam balls work well; you can use toothpicks stuck in the poles to show the axes.)

"Star wheels" or "star finders" are adjustable circular star charts that enable you to show the stars for any particular night and time. These are very helpful for explaining the apparent motions of the stars during the course of a night or the course of a year because you can rotate the wheel to represent passing time. Edmund Scientific has inexpensive cardboard ones sold in bulk packs.

Project Star has a Celestial Sphere Kit (PS-02) for modeling the apparent daily motion of the stars and the Sun.

Balls and a strong flashlight are helpful in demonstrating lunar phases.

The Powers of Ten video and CD-ROM provide an excellent introduction to the sizes of things in the universe and an engaging exploration of scale. (Available from Astronomical Society of the Pacific.)

Suggested Readings

Allen, Richard Hinckley. *Star Names: Their Lore and Meaning.* Dover Publications, New York. A reprinting (with corrections) of a work first published in 1899. It has fascinating information and more detail than you will ever need to know.

Berman, Bob. "Five-five-uh-oh." *Astronomy* (5 May 2000). p. 93. Discusses the effects of the planetary alignment of May 2000, and provides arguments against astrology.

Byrd, Deborah. "The starry sky: Libra." *Astronomy* (May 1995). p. 63. A short article about the constellation Libra, which is home to the autumnal equinox.

Dunlop, S., and Tirion, W. *How to Identify the Night Sky*. Collins. 2004. I particularly like this reference because the star maps include an adjacent star field image which is good for practicing constellation identification.

Gianopoulos, Andrea. "Reasons for the seasons." *Astronomy* (7 July 1999). p. 74. Discusses activities to do with children to explain the seasons.

Gurshtein, Alexander A. "In search of the first constellations." *Sky & Telescope* (June 1997). p. 46. A fairly detailed discussion of the origin and history of constellations.

Hobby, David. "Portrait of the shortest day." *Sky & Telescope* (6 June 1998). p. 46. Displays and discusses making a photograph of the Sun's path across the sky on the winter solstice.

Kanipe, Jeff. "Tilt-a-whirl astronomy: the seasons explained." *Astronomy* (Mar 1996). p. 50. Describes the apparent daily and annual motions of the Sun across our sky.

Krupp, E. C. "Slithering toward solstice." *Sky & Telescope* (6 June 2000). p. 86. Discusses the symbolism of snakes, serpents, and solstices.

Krupp, E. C. "Springing down the banister: vernal equinox festival at Chichen Itza pyramid, Mexico." *Sky & Telescope* (Mar 1996). p. 59. A fun description of a vernal equinox festival held at Chichen Itza.

Kuhn, T.S. *The Structure of Scientific Revolutions 3rd edition*. University of Chicago Press, Chicago, 1996. This is a reprinting of the classic 1962 work which discusses the philosophy and nature of science. This is a must for those who want to delve deeper into the philosophy of science.

MacRobert, Alan M. "Understanding celestial coordinates." *Sky & Telescope* (Sept 1995). p. 38. Describes the celestial coordinate system.

Panek, Richard. "That sneaky solstice." *Natural History* (5 June 2000). p. 20. Describes the meaning of the solstice, and discusses why the earliest sunrise does not happen on the solstice.

Ratcliffe, Martin, and Shaffer, Rick. "First views: old sol celebrates the solstice." *Astronomy* (25 Dec 1997). p. 71. Discusses the analemma and how it demonstrates the offset between dates of earliest/latest rising/setting of the sun and the solstices.

Rey, H. A. *The Stars: A New Way to See Them*. Houghton Mifflin, Boston, 1962. One of my favorite books for introducing constellations. Rey uses diagrams that make the groupings of stars actually look like what they are supposed to represent!

Ryan, Jay. "SkyWise: equinox." *Sky & Telescope* (3 Mar 2000). p. 114. Comic strip drawing illustrating the equinoxes.

Ryan, Jay. "SkyWise: latest sunrise earliest sunset." *Sky & Telescope* (6 Dec 1998). p. 124. Cartoon strip illustrating why the date of the earliest sunset is not exactly the winter solstice.

Trefil, James. "Architects of time." *Astronomy* (9 Sept 1999). p. 48. Discusses history of astronomical timekeeping, from Stonehenge to pulsars.

Notes and Ideas

Class time spent on material: Estimated:_____   *Actual:_____*

Demonstration and activity materials:

Notes for next time:

Chapter 1: The Copernican Revolution
The Birth of Modern Science

Outline

Summary

Chapter 1 continues the view from Earth begun in the "Exploring" by the apparent motions of the planets. The historical development of astronomy from Copernicus through Newton is considered next. The chapter ends with a thorough discussion of Kepler's laws of planetary motion and Newton's laws of motion and gravity.

Major Concepts

- The planets' motions
  - Wanderers among the stars
  - Retrograde motion
- Geocentric models of the universe
  - Aristotle
  - Ptolemy
- History of modern astronomy and heliocentric models
  - Copernicus
  - Brahe
  - Galileo
  - Kepler
- Kepler's laws of planetary motion
- Isaac Newton
  - Laws of motion
  - Gravity

Teaching Suggestions and Demonstrations

At the beginning of this chapter, give your students a copy of a current star chart showing positions of any visible planets. Better yet, have your students make their own using **Sky Chart III**. Encourage them to observe the planets over the course of the semester and the Moon over the course of a month and notice how these move with respect to the stars.

Sections 1.1 and 1.2

Humans have looked at the sky and tried to unravel the motions of the stars and planets since early times. The evolution of our understanding of the structure of the universe is a remarkable story of **scientific process**, where each successive model took care of some problem of the previous model. Ptolemy, for instance, introduced epicycles to account for retrograde motion that could not be explained by the

Aristotelian universe. Kepler changed the shape of the orbits from circles, as shown in Copernicus' model, to ellipses.

(DEMO⌁) This section is particularly suited for using **Starry Night Pro** to demonstrate the **retrograde motion** of the superior planets. Mars will be the best planet to use, because the retrograde motion happens over just a few months. Jupiter and Saturn will both work since they are visible as they move through the constellations. The trick with this simulation is that you should center on the planet and then change the time intervals to multiple days. It takes some practice, but will make for a good demo in class and will likely be more effective than showing a static image. You should have the students mark the relative positions of both Earth and Mars in their orbits during the retrograde interval. Students should understand that the retrograde motion is associated with the Earth overtaking Mars in its orbit.

Students accept the **heliocentric model** without question, and they tend to forget just how hard it was for people to give up the **geocentric model**. The reason is obvious; go outside at night and observe the sky over a period of time. It sure *looks* like the stars are going around Earth, and it certainly does not *feel* like Earth is moving! Reluctance to demote Earth from its position at the center of the universe resulted in Ptolemy's complicated and intricate model, which still failed after a long time to accurately predict the positions of the planets. Moving to a heliocentric system and changing the orbits from circles to ellipses greatly simplified the model. As discussed in the text, simplicity is a desirable characteristic in scientific models; ask students to think of other examples of scientific advancement where successive models increased simplicity.

Tycho Brahe actually had a model of his own that combined aspects of the heliocentric model with geocentrism. He kept Earth in its central position, but placed the other planets in orbit around the Sun, which itself orbited Earth. Brahe's model was largely ignored, and he is remembered today for his contributions in the form of vast quantities of observational data (that predated the telescope), which laid the foundation for Kepler's work. Interestingly, Brahe's main argument for keeping Earth in the center was the lack of observed stellar parallax. Brahe had a good point; he just couldn't conceive of stellar distances so great that the corresponding parallaxes would be too small to be observed without precise instruments. In fact, the first successful parallax measurements were made in 1838 by Wilhelm Bessel.

Before discussing **Galileo's observations with the telescope**, go over the prevailing worldview of his time and emphasize some of its major characteristics. This background will help students understand just how dramatic Galileo's discoveries were. The Aristotelian view maintained not only that all astronomical objects orbited Earth, but that they did so in perfect circles. Earth was flawed, but heavenly objects were perfect, unblemished, and unchanging. Further, Aristotle's view had been inextricably linked with Christianity through "medieval scholasticism," so contradicting Aristotle was extremely serious as it was equivalent to contradicting the Roman Catholic Church. Galileo's discoveries gave evidence that objects not only orbited something other than Earth (Jupiter's moons, phases of Venus) but also that heavenly bodies were not unblemished (sunspots, mountains on the Moon). Galileo's experiments with falling bodies also directly contradicted the Aristotelian view, which maintained that heavier objects fall faster than do lighter ones.

If Jupiter is visible at night when you are teaching the course, encourage your students to view Jupiter through binoculars from a reasonably dark site. The four **Galilean moons** are visible in binoculars, and students can follow their motions over the course of a week or so to re-create Galileo's observations. (DEMO⌁) The orbital motion of the Galilean moons can be demonstrated using **Starry Night Pro**. You'll need to zoom in on Jupiter until the moons are visible. Then you can advance through time and watch the moons orbit. When you initially see the moons it's not necessarily apparent which moon is which, so **Starry Night Pro** can be used to identify them.

It will probably surprise students that Galileo and **Kepler** were contemporaries. In terms of conceptual development, it seems that Galileo built upon and provided evidence for Copernicus' heliocentric model, and then Kepler refined the heliocentric theory with details about the orbits of the planets. In fact, Galileo and Kepler were working at the same time. Galileo was placed under house arrest for promoting the heliocentric model and was forced to declare that it was useful as a mathematical tool only, not as a description of reality. Meanwhile, at the same time, Kepler was not only assuming that the planets orbit the Sun, but he was describing their actual paths and speeds in those orbits. Point out to students the differences in societies at the time that resulted is these very different climates for debate and discussion.

Throughout your discussion of the **historical development** and final acceptance of the Copernican system, sprinkle in interesting details of the lives of the people involved. Copernicus' theory was not even published until he lay on his deathbed. Brahe wore metal noses after he had his nose cut off in a duel. Galileo was a flamboyant character who loved to engage in debate. He published in Italian and often expressed his ideas in dialogue form, to make them accessible to both the common man and the scholar.

Sections 1.4 and 1.5

Begin your discussion of **Kepler's laws of planetary motion** by drawing an ellipse on the board or overhead, using the method shown in Figure E.22. Define the various parts of an ellipse and show how a circle is the special case of an ellipse with an eccentricity of 0. Have students draw ellipses with the same eccentricities as the planets and point out that most of the planetary orbits are nearly circular. (See Table 1.1 for data.) Extend Kepler's second law to comets, and ask students to describe the relative speeds of a comet with a very elliptical orbit when it is close to the Sun and when it is far away.

Finally, for Kepler's third law, pick one or two planets and use the semi-major axes given in Table 1.1 to calculate the periods. Compare to the periods given in the Appendix on planetary orbital properties. Review the mathematical meaning of "squaring" and "cubing." Many students will confuse a^3 with $3a$. The more mathematically-aware students are often concerned that the units of the third law do not work out correctly. When it is said that the constant of proportionality is one, that does not imply that there are no units associated with the constant. In fact, the constant is 1 yrs^2/AU^3, but for convenience we rarely show it.

(DEMO⚡) To demonstrate **orbital motion**, whirl around a ball on a string in a horizontal circle. In the demonstration, the tension in the string provides the centripetal force. In the case of a planet, gravity is the centripetal force. Ask students to predict what would happen if the force suddenly "turned off"; demonstrate by letting go of the string. Note that if you shorten the string that the period will also shorten, much like **Kepler's third law.** For instructors that might be skilled with a yo-yo, the trick "around the world" can be used instead of the ball and string for this demo. To shorten the string, simply have a second yo-yo that already has a shorter string prepared.

Try using "Observing Retrograde Motion" and "Orbital Period and Distance" from the book, *Lecture Tutorials for Introductory Astronomy* by Adams. These two exercises are particularly good and help to reinforce material that you have covered in lecture. Be sure to consider how much time to devote to these exercises, since they normally take more class time than you'd estimate.

Newton's laws of motion are extremely important and not necessarily intuitive. Give plenty of examples of each. For instance, ask students to imagine an airplane trip on a beautiful day with no turbulence. If you throw a peanut up in the air, does it hit the person behind you or fall back in your lap? Also consider the motion of Earth. If you jump up in the air, does the wall of the classroom slam into you? (Galileo already had a pretty good idea of the notion of inertia when he argued against the geocentric view and used ships at sea as an example.) Emphasize to students that Newton's laws divide objects into the two categories of *accelerating* and *nonaccelerating*, instead of *moving* and *not moving*. An object moving at a constant velocity (that is, in a straight line and at a constant speed) is like an object at rest in that both have no net force acting on them.

Define **acceleration** carefully and calculate an acceleration with which students are familiar, such as the acceleration of a car merging onto the highway. You can use first units that make sense, such as miles per hour per second, and then convert to the more standard meters per second squared to help students gain a feel for the acceleration due to Earth's gravity. Students often confuse acceleration and velocity, so be sure to distinguish between the two carefully. You can demonstrate Newton's third law and the role of mass by attaching a rope to a rolling chair and asking a student to pull it across the floor. Then sit in the chair and repeat. Ask the student to compare (qualitatively) the force used to accelerate the empty chair with the force applied to the chair with occupant.

(DEMO!) Use an air track with carts or an air hockey table with pucks to demonstrate Newton's laws, if possible. Seeing the behavior of objects in a nearly frictionless environment will help students overcome Aristotelian misconceptions about motion.

Newton's law of gravitation is explained in *More Precisely 1-1*. To examine the significance of the various terms, ask students what would happen to the force of gravity between Earth and the Sun if the mass of Earth doubled or if the distance between them doubled. Students often confuse the force of gravity with acceleration due to gravity. Derive the expression for acceleration due to gravity and show that it is consistent with Galileo's experiments regarding the motion of falling bodies. Also emphasize that Earth alone does not "have" gravity; gravity is a force *between* two objects. For instance, the weight of an object is the force between it and Earth when the two are in contact. Calculate the weight of a 70-kg person on Earth and on the Moon and compare. It is important to distinguish the difference between weight and mass of an object. The mass of an object is expressed in kilograms, but the weight is a force and is calculated by the mass times the acceleration due to gravity. For a 70-kg person, their weight is 686 newtons (or kg x m/s^2). The weight varies from planet to planet because the acceleration due to gravity changes because it is a function of the mass and size of the planet. Use Figure 1.19 to help explain how gravity is responsible for objects falling as well as objects orbiting. Ask your students to picture the Moon as constantly falling towards the Earth and missing!

Student Writing Questions

1. Try to identify at least one star that you can see at night. Look up information on it such as its distance and how its properties compare to the Sun. What would it be like to live on a planet orbiting this star?

2. Mars is a planet with several similarities to Earth: its day is about the same length and it is tilted in a way that causes seasons to occur. But its orbital period is significantly longer. Imagine people born and raised on Mars. They might use the Martian year rather than an Earth year to measure time. How long are the seasons on Mars, as measured in Earth units? How old would you currently be in Martian years? Do you think time would actually pass differently for you if you lived on Mars? There are 669.5 Martian days in a Martian year. What kind of calendar would you design? How would you define months and weeks and how many would you want to make?

3. Kepler's accomplishments, with his three laws of orbital motion, cannot be overstated. What is more amazing is the way in which he had to make all calculations by hand, without the aid of the modern instruments we usually take for granted. How did he do this? Go to the library and look up a biography of Kepler and investigate how Kepler went about this monumental task of taking

Tycho Brahe's observations and turning them into these three laws. Did he use mathematical tricks and shortcuts?

4. Describe what it would be like to live without any gravity. What would be easier? Harder? Impossible? Fun? Annoying? Do you think you would like to live like this for an extended period of time?

Answers to End of Chapter Exercises

Review and Discussion

1. The geocentric model of the universe placed Earth in the center with all the other astronomical bodies orbiting it. Ptolemy's model also included epicycles to explain retrograde motion.

2. The Ptolemaic model was extremely complicated and intricate. It was missing simplicity, a quality often taken to be an indicator of truth. The geocentric insistence that Earth was in the center of the universe was the major flaw in the model.

3. Copernicus "rediscovered" and refined the heliocentric model of the universe, in which the Sun is at the center and Earth spins on its axis while orbiting the Sun.

4. The realization that Earth is not the center of the universe is known as "the Copernican Revolution."

5. Four of Galileo's discoveries are considered the most important in terms of refuting Aristotelian philosophy and therefore supporting Copernicus. These are: (1) the discovery of mountains and valleys on the Moon, (2) the discovery of sunspots, (3) the discovery of the moons of Jupiter, and (4) the discovery that Venus goes through phases that can only be explained by its motion around the Sun.

6. Galileo performed experiments to test his ideas, rather than using logic alone. For instance, Aristotelians argued that heavier objects would fall faster. After all, it was "logical." Galileo actually performed experiments on falling bodies to investigate them.

7. Kepler's first law: The planets travel along orbits that are elliptical, with the Sun at one focus. Kepler's second law: A planet sweeps out equal areas of the ellipse in equal time intervals. Kepler's third law: The square of a planet's period is proportional to the cube of its semi-major axis.

8. Tycho Brahe made the most accurate positional measurements in astronomy prior to the invention of the telescope. These positional observations of the planets were used by Kepler to devise his three laws of planetary motion.

9. His laws were based on observations.

10. Radar can be used to find the distance from Earth to Venus. Also, Kepler's laws can be used to find the distance from Venus to the Sun in terms of Earth's distance, that is, in astronomical units. Combining these pieces of information yields the distance of Earth to the Sun. (See Figure 1.14.)

11. Newton modified Kepler's first law to state that each planet orbits the Sun in an ellipse, with the *center of mass of the Sun–planet system* (instead of the center of the Sun) at one focus of the ellipse.

Newton modified Kepler's third law to state that the period squared is proportional to the semi-major axis cubed *divided by the total mass of the system.*

12. Even though the force between the baseball and Earth are equal, the acceleration of the baseball is much greater than the acceleration of the Earth, so the baseball moves more.

13. The acceleration due to gravity on the Moon is about one-sixth what it is on Earth. When a ball is thrown upward on the Moon, the force pulling it down is less, so the ball goes higher.

14. According to Newton, the Earth is in orbit around the Sun because the Sun-Earth gravitational force is causing the Earth to accelerate towards the Sun, but the Earth has a sufficient tangential velocity that Earth is continually "falling around" the Sun.

15. If the Sun's gravity were somehow "turned off," Earth would move in a straight line, tangential to its orbital path, through space instead of orbiting the Sun.

Concept Self-Test

True or False? 1. F   2. F   3. F   4. F   5. F   6. F   7. F   8. T

Multiple Choice 9. d   10. c   11. c   12. a   13. c   14. b   15. b

Problems

1. The ratio of one arc minute to 360 degrees will be the same as the ratio of the corresponding distance to the circumference of the whole circle.

$$\frac{(1/60)^\circ}{360^\circ} = \frac{x}{2\pi(dist.)}$$

(a) At the distance of the Moon, $x = \dfrac{(1/60)^\circ \times 2\pi(384,000 \text{ km})}{360^\circ} = 110 \text{ km}.$

(b) Using the distance of the Sun (1.5×10^8 km), the result becomes 44,000 km.

(c) At closest approach, Saturn and Earth are (9.5 A.U. − 1.0 A.U.) = 8.5 A.U. apart. Converting to km and substituting this distance into the equation in part (a) results in:

$$x = \frac{(1/60)^\circ \times 2\pi(8.5\text{A.U.})(1.5 \times 10^8 \text{ km/A.U.})}{360^\circ} = 3.7 \times 10^5 \text{ km}.$$

2. Use $d = vt$ and remember that the radar travels at the speed of light and is making a round trip.

$$t = d/v = \frac{2 \times 0.7 \text{ A.U.} \times 1.50 \times 10^8 \text{ km/A.U.}}{3 \times 10^5 \text{ km/s}} = 700 \text{ s}.$$

3. The Earth has an average orbital speed of 29.79 km/s = 2,573,856 km/day. Mars has an average orbital speed of 24.1 km/s or 2,082,240 km/day. The separation is 0.5 A.U. or 7.45 x 10⁷ km. Let's assume that the motion during one day can be approximated as linear motion, then in one day the Earth moves 2,573,856 km and Mars moves 2,082,240 km. The difference is 491,616 km. We can

treat the parallax angle as if it's the angular diameter of 491,616 km as seen from 7.45 x 10^7 km. Using the formula developed in *More Precisely E-2*, we obtain the following:

$$\frac{Parallax°}{360°} = \frac{491616\text{km}}{2 \times 3.14 \times 7.45 \times 10^7 \text{ km}} \Rightarrow Parallax° = 0.37° = 23' \text{ Mars moves in retrograde}$$

4. (a) The semi-major axis will be half the major axis, which is the sum of the perihelion and aphelion distances: $\quad a = \dfrac{(2.0 \text{ A.U.} + 4.0 \text{ A.U.})}{2} = 3.0 \text{ A.U.}$

    (b) From Figure 1.12, the eccentricity can be calculated from the perihelion (or aphelion) distance and the semi-major axis:
    $$perihelion = a(1-e) \quad \text{so} \quad e = 1 - p/a = 1 - 2/3 = 1/3 = 0.33.$$

    (c) Finally, use Kepler's third law, $P^2 = a^3$ to calculate the period:
    $$P = \sqrt{a^3} = \sqrt{(3.0)^3} = 5.2 \text{ years.}$$

5. From Kepler's third law, $P^2 = a^3$ so a $= \sqrt[3]{P^2} = \sqrt[3]{76^2} = 17.9$ A.U.

    The major axis is therefore 2×17.9 A.U. $= 35.8$ A.U. The aphelion distance plus the perihelion distance is the major axis, so the aphelion distance is the major axis minus the perihelion distance:
    $$\text{aphelion} = 35.8 \text{ A.U.} - 0.6 \text{ A.U.} = 35 \text{ A.U.}$$

6. The perihelion distance of any planet is given by $perihelion = a(1-e)$. Use the data from Table 1.1 to calculate this distance for both Pluto and Neptune:

    Pluto: $\quad perihelion = a(1-e) = 39.48(1 - 0.249) = 29.6$ A.U.

    Neptune: $\quad perihelion = a(1-e) = 30.07(1 - 0.009) = 29.8$ A.U.

    Therefore, Pluto is closer to the Sun at perihelion than Neptune ever is.

7. Use the modified version of Kepler's third law, $P^2 = a^3/M_{total}$, where the period is in Earth years, the semi-major axis is in A.U., and the mass is in solar masses. Because Callisto's mass is negligible, the total mass of the Jupiter/Callisto system is just the mass of Jupiter.

    $$M_{Jupiter} = a^3 / P^2 = \frac{[(1.88 \times 10^6 \text{ km})/(1.50 \times 10^8 \text{ km/A.U.})]^3}{[(16.7 \text{ days})/(365 \text{ days/yr})]^2} = 9.40 \times 10^{-4} \text{ solar masses} = 1.87 \times 10^{27} \text{ kg.}$$

8. The acceleration due to gravity is inversely proportional to the square of the distance from the center of Earth. Therefore, $\quad \dfrac{g_h}{9.80 \text{ m/s}^2} = \dfrac{(r)^2}{(r+h)^2}$, or $g_h = \dfrac{(r)^2}{(r+h)^2}(9.80 \text{ m/s}^2)$, where r = the radius of Earth, h = the altitude, and g_h = the acceleration due to gravity at that altitude.

    (a) $g_h = \dfrac{(6.40 \times 10^6 \text{ m})^2}{(6.40 \times 10^6 \text{ m} + 100,000 \text{ m})^2}(9.80 \text{ m/s}^2) = 9.50 \text{ m/s}^2$

    (b) $g_h = \dfrac{(6.40 \times 10^6 \text{ m})^2}{(6.40 \times 10^6 \text{ m} + 1,000,000 \text{ m})^2}(9.80 \text{ m/s}^2) = 7.33 \text{ m/s}^2$

(c) $g_h = \dfrac{(6.40 \times 10^6 \, \text{m})^2}{(6.40 \times 10^6 \, \text{m} + 10{,}000{,}000 \, \text{m})^2} (9.80 \, \text{m/s}^2) = 1.49 \, \text{m/s}^2.$

9. For a 70.0-kg person:

$F = \dfrac{GMm}{r^2} = \dfrac{(6.67 \times 10^{-11} \, \text{Nm}^2 / \text{kg}^2)(5.97 \times 10^{24} \, \text{kg})(70 \text{kg})}{(6.40 \times 10^6 \, \text{m})^2} = 681 \, \text{N} \times (1 \, \text{lb}/4.45 \, \text{N}) = 153 \, \text{lb}.$

We typically call this force the person's *weight*.

10. The speed of a satellite in a circular orbit is given in *More Precisely 1-2* as: $v = \sqrt{GM/r}$

For the satellite in orbit about the Moon, this becomes:

$v = \sqrt{(6.67 \times 10^{-11} \, \text{Nm}^2 / \text{kg}^2)(7.3 \times 10^{22} \, \text{kg}) \Big/ (1.70 \times 10^6 \, \text{m})} = 1700 \, \text{m/s} = 1.7 \, \text{km/s}.$

Resource Information

Student CD Media Resources

Interactive Student Tutorials
None

Movies/Animations
Retrograde Motion of Mars
Geocentric Solar System
Heliocentric Solar System
Thought-Experiments in Pisa
Earth Captures a Temporary Moon

Transparencies

16.	Figure 1.1	Planetary Motions
17.	Figure 1.2	Geocentric Model
	Figure 1.3	Ptolemy's Model
18.	Figure 1.5	Retrograde Motion
19.	Figure 1.7	Galilean Moons
20.	Figure 1.8	Venus Phases
21.	Figure 1.11	Ellipse
22.	Figure 1.12	Orbital Properties
	Figure 1.13	Kepler's Second Law
23.	Table 1.1	Some Planetary Properties
	Figure 1.14	Astronomical Unit
24.	Figure 1.16	Newton's First Law
	Figure 1.17	Gravity
25.	Figure 1.18	Gravitational Force
26.	Figure 1.19	Sun's Gravity
	Figure 1.21	Orbits

Materials

The *Sky Calendar* from Abrams Planetarium is a very helpful resource for keeping up with interesting events to watch in the sky. See www.pa.msu.edu/abrams/diary.html for the online version and for subscription information.

Balls and string are helpful in demonstrating orbital motion.

Two air track systems, one for use with a computer interface, and one stand-alone, are available from Fisher Scientific.

Suggested Readings

Bernhard, K. and Bernhard, J. "Mechanics in a Wheelchair." *The Physics Teacher* (December 1999), p. 555. Describes a kinesthetic experience of Newton's laws.

Brown, Jeanette. "It's just a phase." *Astronomy* (Apr 1999). p. 76. Describes an activity designed to demonstrate the phases of the moon.

Christianson, John Robert. *On Tycho's Island: Tycho and His Assistants, 1570-1601.* Cambridge University Press, 1999. This is a scholarly work of the life and times of Tycho Brahe. Not only his relationship to Kepler is highlighted, but other collaborations that Tycho fostered.

Ehgamberdiev, Shuhrat. "The astronomical school of Ulugh Beg." *Sky & Telescope* (Nov 1995). p. 38. Describes astronomical observations made by a 15th-century Mongol prince.

Ferrguson, K. *Tycho & Kepler.* Walker & Company, New York, 2002. A lively account of the tumultuous collaboration between two great astronomers who together would change our view of the solar system.

Gettrust, E. "An Extraordinary Demonstration of Newton's Third Law." *The Physics Teacher* (October 2001), p. 392. A description of an apparatus using magnets and force probes to demonstrate that the action and reaction forces are equal in magnitude.

Gould, Stephen Jay. "The sharp-eyed lynx, outfoxed by nature. Part one: Galileo Galilei and the three globes of Saturn." *Natural History* (May 1998). p. 16. Discusses the life and work of Galileo.

Hiscock, Philip. "Once in a blue moon." *Sky & Telescope* (Mar 1999). p. 52. Discussion of the meaning of the term "blue moon."

Kemp, Martin. "Kepler's cosmos." *Nature* (May 14, 1998). p. 123. Describes ancient cultures' image of the cosmos.

Kemp, Martin. "Maculate moons: Galileo and the lunar mountains." *Nature* (Sept 9 1999). p. 116. Discusses Galileo's observations of features on the Moon.

Krupp, E. C. "Designated authority." *Sky & Telescope* (May 1997). p. 66. Discusses the role of the "official" astronomer in ancient cultures.

Krupp, E. C. "From here to eternity: Egyptian astronomy and monuments." *Sky & Telescope* (Feb 2000). p. 87. Discusses the depiction of the stars and sky in ancient Egyptian monuments.

Krupp, E. C. "Stairway to the stars: the Jantar Mantar, or 'House of Instruments,' in Jaipur, India." *Sky & Telescope* (Sept 1995). p. 56. Describes an 18th-century Indian monument which was used to track the motions of the Sun.

Morris, R. *Dismantling the Universe: The Nature of Scientific Discovery.* Simon and Schuster, New York, 1983. Chapter 4 covers the story of Brahe, Kepler, and Galileo.

Olson, Donald W. and Sinnott, Roger W. "Blue-moon mystery solved." *Sky and Telescope* (Mar 1999). p. 55. Discussion of the meaning of the term "blue moon."

Olson, Donald W. and Fienberg, Richard Tresch; Sinnott, Roger W. "What's a blue moon?" *Sky & Telescope* (May 1999). p. 36. Even more discussion about the interesting history of the term "blue moon."

Panek, Richard. "Venusian testimony." *Natural History* (June 1999). p. 68. Discusses Galileo's observations of the phases of Venus.

Sobel, Dava. *Galileo's Daughter.* Walker & Company, New York, 1999. A very readable, detailed account of Galileo's work, with fascinating details about his personal life, his scientific contributions, and the interactions between them.

Stephenson, F. Richard. "Early Chinese observations and modern astronomy." *Sky & Telescope* (Feb 1999). p. 48. Discusses ancient Chinese astronomical observations, and how they can be connected to modern science.

Sullivant, Rosemary. "An unlikely revolutionary: Nicolas Copernicus." *Astronomy* (Oct 1999). p. 52. Discusses the life and scientific works of Copernicus.

Sullivant, Rosemary. "When the apple falls: Sir Isaac Newton." *Astronomy* (Apr 1998). p. 54. Discusses Newton, his life, and his scientific works.

Toepker, T. "Babies and the Moon." *The Physics Teacher* (April 2000). p. 242. Contains a graph of birth data to dispel the popular myth that more babies are born under a full moon.

Trefil, James. "Rounding the Earth." *Astronomy* (Aug. 2000). p. 40. Describes some of the astronomical knowledge of ancient Egyptian, Greek, and Near Eastern cultures.

Vogt, E. "Elementary Derivation of Kepler's Laws." *American Journal of Physics* (April 1996). p. 392. For your more advanced students, here is a proof of Kepler's laws that follows from conservation of energy and angular momentum, with further discussion.

Westfall, Richard S. *The Life of Isaac Newton.* Cambridge University Press, Reprint edition, 1994. This is a condensed version of a larger biography of Newton from the same author. This work is very scholarly and highlights Newton's experimental approach to understanding the universe.

Williams, K. "Inexpensive Demonstrator of Newton's First Law." *The Physics Teacher* (February 2000). p. 80. Uses a Downy® Ball fabric-softener dispenser!

Notes and Ideas

Class time spent on material: Estimated:_____   Actual:_____

Demonstration and activity materials:

Notes for next time:

Chapter 2: Light and Matter
The Inner Workings of the Cosmos

Outline

Summary

Chapter 2 deals with the extremely important topics of electromagnetic radiation and spectra. After an introduction to waves in general, the chapter discusses electromagnetic waves and the various parts of the electromagnetic spectrum. Continuous, emission, and absorption spectra are described and explained. The chapter ends with the Doppler effect and its use to determine radial velocities.

Major Concepts

- Waves
  - Wavelength, frequency, speed
  - Electromagnetic waves
- The electromagnetic spectrum
  - Full range of radiation
  - Visible light
  - Blackbody spectrum
  - Radiation laws
- Spectra and spectral lines
  - Emission
  - Absorption
  - Photons
  - Hydrogen spectrum
  - More complex spectra
  - Analysis of spectral lines
- The Doppler effect

Teaching Suggestions and Demonstrations

The first section of this chapter makes the excellent point that "virtually all we know about the universe beyond Earth's atmosphere has been gleaned from the analysis of electromagnetic radiation received from afar." Contrast the work of an astronomer to the work of a biologist, chemist, or environmental scientist. Astronomers can rarely touch, manipulate, or experiment directly upon their objects of interest. (An exception, of course, is the study of solar system material such as Moon rocks or meteorites.) Impress upon students the fundamental importance of *light* (or rather, all forms of electromagnetic radiation) to astronomers. This chapter will help students learn how to analyze the information contained in light.

Sections 2.1 through 2.4

(DEMO实) Demonstrate **wave motion** with a long Slinky®. Give the Slinky a quick shake at one end and have students watch the pulse travel to the other end. Tie a bit a red yarn to a coil in the Slinky and ask students to compare the motion of the pulse with the motion of the yarn. The pulse moves from one end to the other; the yarn just moves up and down. A wave is the propagation of a disturbance, not of the material or medium through which the wave travels. In fact, electromagnetic waves don't even need a medium in order to propagate. Contrast electromagnetic waves with mechanical waves and sound waves. Emphasize that the **speed of electromagnetic waves** in a vacuum is constant and is equal to wavelength times frequency. Try some examples. Students can calculate the wavelength of an FM radio wave and compare it to the wavelength of, say, red light.

Spend some time going over Figure 2.9. It is an excellent representation of the full range of the **electromagnetic spectrum**. Students will tend to think that visible light is somehow special or different. Point out that it is just one range of the wavelengths of electromagnetic radiation. We divide the electromagnetic spectrum into different areas not based on inherent differences in the radiation itself, but rather by differences in how we perceive it. We detect visible light with our eyes. Infrared is felt as heat, and ultraviolet gives us sunburns. Discuss the opacity of Earth's atmosphere and the major windows in the atmosphere that allow us to observe in certain wavelength ranges. Shine a light through a prism or diffraction grating to demonstrate the visible spectrum.

Ask students to estimate the classroom temperature in degrees Fahrenheit. Check with a thermometer if you have one available. Then, ask them to quickly estimate the temperature in degrees Celsius and in **kelvin**. Chances are, they will have a harder time with these estimations! Convert the room temperature and a couple of other familiar temperatures to both Celsius and kelvin to help students get a feel for these scales.

Use Figure 2.11 to discuss **blackbody curves**. Point out that as the temperature of a blackbody increases, two things happen. The glowing body emits more radiation at all wavelengths, so more total energy is emitted (Stefan's law). Also, the peak of the curve shifts to shorter wavelengths or higher frequencies (Wien's law). Students may be surprised that therefore a blue star actually emits more radiation at red wavelengths than a red star does! Try using the exercise "Blackbody Radiation" from *Lecture Tutorials for Introductory Astronomy* by Adams. Be sure to consider how much time to devote to this exercise, since it normally takes more class time than you'd estimate.

(DEMO实) Connect a filament light bulb to a variable power supply. Allow students to observe the light produced at various levels of power. Relate this qualitatively to temperature. As power is increased, the filament first glows a dull red, then orange, yellow, and white. Have a student hold a hand up to the bulb and comment on the amount of infrared coming from the bulb as well. At low temperatures, most of the energy comes out in the form of infrared and very little as visible light. Make a special effort to show your students that the intensity of the bulb changes much more than the color does. This is because the intensity (or the total energy radiated) is proportional to temperature to the 4th power. The color (or λ_{max}), on the other hand, is inversely proportional to the temperature to the 1st power, and changes relatively little compared to the intensity.

Sections 2.5 through 2.6

Spectra are critical to the understanding of astronomical objects, so it pays to spend some time ensuring that students understand these sections. First, you will have to mention the wave–particle duality of light. In the first part of the chapter, light is considered a wave. However, to discuss the formation of spectral lines, we consider the particle nature of light. If students have *no* trouble with the idea that light can be both particle and wave, then they are probably not paying attention! If you have time, briefly mention some of the important experiments that helped to develop this idea.

In discussing the **model of the atom**, you can use an analogy of a staircase. If someone is standing halfway up the staircase, she can jump down 1 step, 2 steps, or even 5 steps. However, she cannot jump down, for example, 3½ steps. Likewise, she can move up only a whole number of steps. There is no place to land "in between" steps, just as there are no energy levels "in between" the sharply defined energy states in an atom. (To make the analogy fit a little better, have students imagine a staircase in a fun house where the steps get closer and closer together as they get farther from the bottom!) The staircase analogy can be used to explain emission and absorption lines. When the person jumps down, he emits a bundle of energy equal to the difference in energies of the two levels. For the atom, the "bundle of energy" emitted is the photon.

Demonstration diffraction-grating glasses are very inexpensive and work fairly well. Hand them out to your students and let them view the classroom lights or light coming in the windows. Set up spectral tubes of various elements and have the students view the **emission spectra**. They should be able to easily identify the four hydrogen Balmer lines. They will also notice that other elements have more spectral lines, as expected from the discussion on more complex spectra. If you don't have a selection of spectral tubes, you can improvise by sending students across campus or out into the community to look at "neon" signs (which are mostly *not* neon) with the diffraction-grating glasses. Sodium and mercury parking-lot lights also work well.

Go over **Kirchhoff's laws** (see Figure 2.17) carefully and explain each in terms of the atoms absorbing and emitting photons. Also, discuss astronomical applications of each. Make sure students understand the connection between and the formation of absorption and emission spectra. Show the **solar spectrum** (Figure 2.15) to demonstrate the complexity of real spectra and the wealth of information they contain. If you have time, engage students in an exercise to identify lines in the solar spectrum. Project the solar spectrum on a screen, establish a wavelength scale, and determine the wavelengths of various lines. Then, identify the lines by comparing them to known elemental lines. Try using the exercise "Types of Spectra" from *Lecture Tutorials for Introductory Astronomy* by Adams. Be sure to consider how much time to devote to this exercise, since it normally takes more class time than you'd estimate.

Section 2.7

Students will most likely be familiar with the **Doppler effect** applied to sound. See if someone in the class can imitate the sound of a siren approaching, passing, and then receding from an observer. As an analogy, imagine a person in a boat in the middle of a pond dropping pebbles into the water at a constant frequency. The frequency and wavelength of the ripples that reach an observer on the shore will depend on whether the rowboat is stationary, moving toward the shore, or moving away from the shore. A Nerf® ball with a beeper or bell embedded inside it makes a nice demonstration. Students throw the ball back and forth while the class listens to the sound and compares it to the sound they hear when the ball is stationary.

The Doppler effect applies to light waves as well as to sound waves. Use the equation introduced in this section to try a few examples with students. Point out that the shift in wavelength or frequency can only determine the velocity of the object *toward* or *away from* the observer, not the transverse velocity.

At this point in the course, students will understand how **spectra** can be used to determine composition, surface temperature, and radial velocity. As a preview of coming attractions and to emphasize the importance of spectra, go over the list at the end of Section 2.6 to introduce students to other characteristics of astronomical objects that can be determined from spectra.

Section 2.8

Spectral line analysis can be used to measure the following quantities related to an astronomical object: Composition, temperature, radial velocity, rotation rate, and magnetic field strength. **(DEMO⚡)** An everyday example of spectral technology is the use of **IR thermometers**. Medical thermometers have become very reasonable in price and are very quick, because they are making an IR measurement, oftentimes on the forehead. Try bringing an IR thermometer to class to use as a demonstration.

Student Writing Questions

1. You are on a team of experts that is proposing the launching of a space telescope. With regard to the atmospheric blockage of parts of the spectrum, in what ways can you justify making astronomical observations from space?

2. Choose one of the 92 naturally occurring elements. Conduct a library research of this element and give a description of it, where it commonly occurs in nature, any uses it may have, and how it was discovered. In your description include its atomic structure, melting and boiling points, chemical activity, and whether it is common or rare.

3. What types of electromagnetic waves do you use on a regular basis? Think carefully about this because there may be hidden uses that you are not immediately aware of. How is your long-distance telephone call transmitted? How does your cable TV service receive its signals? How many of these uses would not have existed 25 years ago? 50 years ago? 100 years ago?

4. Imagine being able to see in a different part of the spectrum than the visible. What would it be like? How would your perception of your world be different from how it is now? Would there be advantages and/or disadvantages?

5. Pick an item that is colorful. Describe in detail why it appears colorful; which colors are being reflected and which absorbed? When we say "the shirt is red," is the shirt really red?

6. Select various sources of artificial lighting, like a computer screen, calculator display, or glow-in-the-dark posters. Describe, in terms of Kirchhoff's laws, how each is able to emit light.

Answers to End of Chapter Exercises

Review and Discussion

1. The wave period is a measurement of the amount of time needed for a wave to repeat itself at some point in space. The wavelength is the distance between any two consecutive positions in the wave, such as from peak to peak. The amplitude is the maximum height or depth of the wave above or

below the undisturbed state. The wave frequency is the number of waves that pass a point per unit of time, usually waves per second.

2. The electric force is similar to the gravitational force in that it drops off by the inverse square of the distance. It is different in that it can be either attractive or repulsive; unlike charges attract and like charges repel. If the number of positive and negative charges are equal in an object, it appears to be neutral and have no electric force. Gravity is always present and is never neutralized.

3. A star contains many charged particles that are moving. This motion creates waves in the electric fields of the charged particles, and these waves propagate or move outward and away from the star. Traveling at the speed of light, a few of these waves will finally reach a person's eye, which also contains charged particles. The waves make the charged particles move, and this motion is sensed by nerves and transmitted to the brain as an image of the star.

4. Radio waves, infrared radiation, visible light, ultraviolet radiation, X-rays, and gamma rays are all electromagnetic radiation and move at the speed of light in a vacuum. They differ only by their wavelengths (or frequencies), from longest wavelength (radio waves) to shortest wavelength (gamma rays).

5. The parts of the electromagnetic spectrum for which Earth's atmosphere is transparent are the visible (when it isn't cloudy!), parts of the infrared, and the radio, particularly for waves between about 1 centimeter and 10 meters.

6. A blackbody is an idealized object that absorbs all radiation falling on it. It also reemits all this radiation. The radiation emitted occurs at all wavelengths but peaks at a wavelength that depends on the temperature of the blackbody. The hotter the temperature, the shorter the wavelength of the peak radiation.

7. Even with clouds, the day-night cycle is quite evident. The lunar cycle would be evident from the light given off by the Moon, although it might not be clear what the object is that causes the lunar cycle. Radio radiation easily penetrates clouds. Little would be known about stars because their radiation is mostly at visible wavelengths.

8. As the coal cools off, its temperature decreases. According to Wien's law, more and more of its radiation will be emitted at longer and longer wavelengths. According to Stefan's law, it will emit less and less radiation as it cools. The net result is that it gets fainter and redder with time.

9. Spectroscopy is the observation and study of spectra. Because light is about the only information received from astronomical objects, this light is the source of all the information about those objects. Spectroscopy is the detailed study of this light and allows many properties of objects to be determined.

10. The spectrum emitted by a blackbody is known as a continuous spectrum. Light is emitted at all wavelengths, but the amount of light emitted at each wavelength varies and depends on the temperature of the blackbody. A continuous spectrum looks like a rainbow. An absorption spectrum appears like a continuous spectrum but with specific wavelengths missing. Dark vertical lines or bands, which can be quite narrow or very broad, are found throughout the spectrum.

11. The normal condition for atoms is one in which the number of electrons equals the number of protons in the nucleus. The electrons are in their lowest energy level. When an atom is excited, an

electron is found in a higher energy orbital. The precisely defined energy states or energy levels are referred to as *orbitals*. They are the regions occupied by electrons surrounding the nucleus.

12. In order for a photon to be absorbed, it must have an energy that is precisely equal to the energy difference between two energy levels, the lower level of which is occupied by an electron. The atom absorbs the photon, and the electron moves to the higher energy level. Very quickly thereafter the electron moves back down to the lower energy level by emitting a photon of energy equal to the energy difference between the two levels.

13. The emission lines will provide information about the composition, abundance, density, temperature, and motion of the particles in the cloud.

14. The Doppler effect is the change in the wavelength (or frequency) of a wave caused by the motion of the source of the wave. We perceive radiation at a different frequency than the source emits because of the motion of the source with respect to us.

15. Radial velocities of objects can be determined using the relationship:

$$\frac{\text{apparent } \lambda}{\text{true } \lambda} = 1 + \frac{\text{recessional velocity}}{\text{wave speed}}$$

In the case of spectra, the wave speed is the speed of light. Transverse velocities cannot be determined from the Doppler effect.

Conceptual Self-Test

True or False? 1. F 2. T 3. T 4. F 5. T 6. T 7. T

Multiple Choice 8. a 9. d 10. a 11. b 12. c 13. d 14. a 15. d

Problems

1. The relationship between frequency, wavelength, and wave velocity is $\lambda f = v$.
   Using the data given, the speed of sound in water is $v = (5.77 \text{ m})(256 \text{ Hz}) = 1480$ m/s.

2. Radio signals travel at c, the speed of light. Using the same relationship as in problem 1,
   $$\lambda = v/f = (3 \times 10^8 \text{ m/s})/(100 \times 10^6 \text{ Hz}) = 3.0 \text{ m}.$$

3. Earth's diameter is 12,756 km.
   $$f = c/\lambda = (300,000 \text{ km/s})/(12,800 \text{ km}) = 23 \text{ Hz}$$
   This wave would be in the radio frequency range.

4. Wien's law states that the peak wavelength is inversely proportional to the temperature. Comparing 200 to 650 nm gives a factor of 3.25; therefore, the object with a peak wavelength of 200 nm must be 3.25 times hotter than the object that peaks at 650 nm.

   Stefan's law states that the energy radiated is proportional to T^4. If the hotter object is 3.25 times hotter than the cooler object, it must radiate $(3.25)^4 = 112$ times as much energy as the cooler object.

5. Convert from Celsius to Kelvin: 37 + 273 = 310 K. Using Wien's law, $\lambda_{max} = 0.29/T$, with T in kelvin and the wavelength in centimeters. For 310 K, this gives $\lambda_{max} = 0.00094$ cm = 9.4 μm. This is in the infrared.

6. The Sun's temperature is about 5800 K. Using the Stefan-Boltzman equation from *More Precisely 2-2* gives $F = \sigma T^4 = 5.67 \times 10^{-8}$ W/m^2·K^4 × (5800 K)^4 = 6.4×10^7 W/m^2. The surface area of the Sun is $A = 4\pi r^2 = 4\pi(696,000,000 \text{ m})^2 = 6.1 \times 10^{18}$ m^2. Multiplying these two results gives the total solar power output of 3.9×10^{26} W.

7. $E = hf$, so energy is proportional to frequency. Find the frequency of a 1-nm gamma ray: $f = c/\lambda = (3 \times 10^8 \text{ m/s})/(1 \times 10^{-9} \text{ m}) = 3 \times 10^{17}$ Hz. The 10-MHz radio photon has a frequency of 10^7 Hz. The ratio of these two frequencies is 3×10^{17} Hz / 10^7 Hz = 3×10^{10}.

8. For an atom in the second *excited* state, there are three possible different photons corresponding to the transitions 3→2, 2→1, and 3→1, where "1" is the ground state. The wavelengths of these photons are 656 nm, 122 nm, and 103 nm. From the third excited state there are 6 possibilities, including the three already listed and 4→3 (1876 nm), 4→2 (486 nm), and 4→1 (97.3 nm). The Bohr model equation $E_n = -13.6$ eV/n^2 can be used to find the energy of each level. The energy of the emitted photon is the difference in energies of the two levels, and corresponding wavelength is $\lambda = hc/E$.

9. The H-α line has a wavelength of 656.3 nm. Using the Doppler formula from Section 2.7 gives:
$$\frac{656 \text{ nm}}{656.3} = 1 + \frac{v}{c}$$
Solving for v gives a result of -1.37×10^5 m/s, which is 137 km/s approaching.

10. The true wavelength must be exactly 3.00000 m. Using the Doppler formula:
$$\frac{3.00036}{3.00000} = 1 + \frac{v}{c} \qquad \text{gives} \qquad v = 36 \text{ km/s}.$$
The spacecraft is moving a distance equal to one circumference at this speed. The period of the orbit can therefore be determined. Use velocity = distance / time, or time = distance / velocity:
$$T = 2\pi \times (100,000 \text{ km}) / (36 \text{ km/s}) = 17,450 \text{ s}.$$
To use Kepler's third law, change units to years and A.U. There are 3.15×10^7 seconds in a year, so this period is 0.000553 yr. The orbital radius is 100,000 / 150,000,000 = 0.000667 A.U. Kepler's third law is: $P^2 = \dfrac{a^3}{M}$, so: $0.000553^2 = \dfrac{0.000667^3}{M}$, which yields $M = 0.000970$ solar masses. In kilograms, $M = (0.000979)(1.99 \times 10^{30} \text{ kg}) = 1.93 \times 10^{27}$ kg.

Resource Information

Student CD Media Resources

Interactive Student Tutorials
Continuous Spectra and Blackbody Radiation
Emission Spectra
Absorption Spectra

Movies/Animations
Infrared Image of Comet Fragment Impact with Jupiter
Classical Hydrogen Atom I
Classical Hydrogen Atom II
Doppler Effect

Transparencies

27.	Figure 2.2	Water Wave
	Figure 2.3	Wave Properties
28.	Figure 2.4	Wave Behavior
29.	Figure 2.5	Charged Particles
30.	Figure 2.6	Magnetism
	Figure 2.7	Electromagnetic Wave
31.	Figure 2.8	Visible Spectrum
	Figure 2.9	Electromagnetic Spectrum
32.	MP 2-1	The Kelvin Temperature Scale
33.	Figure 2.11	Blackbody Curves
34.	Figure 2.12	Spectrascope
	Figure 2.13	Emission Spectra
35.	Figure 2.14	Elemental Emission
	Figure 2.15	Solar Spectrum
36.	Figure 2.16	Absorption Spectra
	Figure 2.17	Kirchhoff's Laws
37.	Figure 2.18	Classical Atom
	Figure 2.19	Modern Atom
38	Figure 2.20	Atomic Excitation
39.	Figure 2.21	Helium and Carbon
40.	Figure 2.22	Hydrogen Spectra
41.	Figure 2.23	Doppler Effect
	Figure 2.24	Doppler Shift

Materials

Diffraction-grating glasses can be ordered from Fisher Science Education. They are listed as diffraction viewing glasses, catalogue number NCS48814 for individual glasses, or catalogue number NCS48814A for a package of 10. As an alternative, Edmund Scientific has diffraction-grating film available for purchase by the roll (item CR30521-16).

Eight different spectral tubes (items SE-9461 through SE-9468) and a spectral tube power supply and mount (item SE-9460) are available from Pasco.

A super Slinky® is available from Fisher Scientific, model number S42162.

One example of a "Doppler ball" is the Vortex Mega Howler, available from Toys R Us or other toy stores.

A medical IR thermometer, available from drug stores.

Suggested Readings

Ambrose, B., Heron, P., Vokos, S., and McDermott, L. "Student Understanding of Light as an Electromagnetic Wave: Relating the Formalism to Physical Phenomena." *American Journal of Physics* (October 1999). p. 891. Development and modification of tutorials to address student difficulty with the wave nature of light.

Collins, D. "Video Spectroscopy — Emission, Absorption, and Flash." *The Physics Teacher* (December 2000). p. 561. Uses a diffraction grating attached to a color video camera to display spectra.

Dibble, W. "A Pedagogical Note on the Doppler-Effect Formulas." *The Physics Teacher* (September 2000). p. 362. A quick and simple derivation for the Doppler-effect formulas useful at the introductory level.

Englert, Berhold Georg, Scully, Marlan O., and Walther, Herbert. "The duality in matter and light." *Scientific American* (Dec 1994). p. 86. Describe experimental work which supports the idea of wave-particle duality.

Goldberg, Leo. "Atomic spectroscopy and astrophysics." *Physics Today* (Aug 1988). p. 38. A review of atomic spectroscopy and its role in the development of modern astrophysics.

Helfand, David J. "Seeing the whole symphony." *Natural History* (Feb 2000). p. 84. Discusses the electromagnetic spectrum and astronomy at wavelengths other than the visible.

Itano, Wayne M. and Ramsey, Norman F. "Accurate measurement of time." *Scientific American* (July 1993). p. 56. Describes how knowledge of atomic energy levels is used for accurate timekeeping.

Kaler, James B. "Beyond the rainbow." *Astronomy* (Sept 2000). p. 38. Gives a nice overview of the different parts of the electromagnetic spectrum, and talks about the relation between the temperature of an object and the type of radiation it emits.

Marangos, Jon. "Faster than a speeding photon." *Nature* (July 20, 2000). p. 243. Describes how parts of a wave pulse can seem to travel faster than the speed of light.

Palmquist, B. "Interactive Spectra Demonstration." *The Physics Teacher* (March 2002). p. 140. A creative method for modeling emission, absorption, and continuous spectra that involves throwing balls and jumping on chairs!

Thomsen, Volker. "Signals from communications satellites." *The Physics Teacher* (April 1996). p. 218. Discusses the Doppler shift observed in signals from satellites.

Watson, Andrew. "Physicists trap photons and count them one by one." *Science* (April 5 1996). p. 34. Describes an experiment which directly measures individual photons.

Western, Arthur B. "Star colors for relativistic space travelers." *The Physics Teacher* (March 1997). p. 160. Discusses how stars would appear to an observer traveling near the speed of light.

Notes and Ideas

Class time spent on material: Estimated:_____   Actual:_____

Demonstration and activity materials:

Notes for next time:

Chapter 3: Telescopes
The Tools of Astronomy

Outline

3.1   Optical Telescopes
3.2   Telescope Size
3.3   High-Resolution Astronomy
3.4   Radio Astronomy
3.5   Other Astronomies

Summary

Chapter 3 begins with a discussion of optical telescopes. The two types, reflectors and refractors, are diagrammed and described, and the advantages of reflectors over refractors are discussed. The importance of telescope size in improving light-gathering power and resolving power is explained. Modern detectors and advancements in telescope design that help reduce the effects of seeing are also described. The chapter ends with a discussion of radio astronomy as well as astronomy at IR, UV, and high-energy wavelengths.

Major Concepts

- Optical telescopes
  - Reflectors and refractors
  - Reflecting telescope designs
  - Advantages of reflectors
- Telescope size
  - Light-gathering power
  - Resolving power
- Seeing
- Detectors
- New telescope designs
- Astronomy at other wavelengths
  - Radio and radio interferometry
  - Infrared
  - Ultraviolet
  - High-energy: X-ray and gamma ray

Teaching Suggestions and Demonstrations

(DEMO⚡**)** Having the opportunity to observe with a telescope, even a small one, is probably the best way to engender student interest in telescopes. If possible, arrange some observing nights for your students. Seeing Saturn's rings or the Moon's craters for the first time through a telescope never fails to make an impression! You should practice with the specific telescope you'll use with your class before you actually meet with your students. This is important even if you have a lot of experience with telescopes. Some of the newer computer-controlled telescopes can be quite a challenge if you try to rush your observing session. From my own personal experience, I've found the computer hand controllers to be far from user-friendly.

Section 3.1

(DEMO⚡) You can begin your discussion of telescopes by bringing in several **lenses and mirrors** and showing students how these form images. One important idea is that a converging lens causes parallel light rays to focus at a point. Ask your students if any of them ever tried to start a fire by focusing sunlight! If your classroom has windows, you can focus an image of a window on a piece of paper and ask your students to describe it. One thing they will notice is that it is upside-down! Use two different lenses with equal focal lengths but different diameters. A common student misconception is that larger diameter lenses produce larger magnifications. Show your students that the two lenses with equal focal lengths produce images that are magnified the same amount, but that the image from the larger diameter lens is brighter and shows more detail, because the lens collects more light.

(DEMO⚡) Also use a light bulb as the object of a **converging lens**. Draw a black arrow on the bulb so that the orientation of the image will be easy to determine. Show how the image distance and size changes with changing object distance. To demonstrate **chromatic aberration**, use two differently-colored bulbs and show that the image distance is different for the two.

Pass around a large **concave mirror** and have students look into it while holding it at varying distances. For instance, when you hold the mirror very close you will see a magnified, upright image of your face. This corresponds to the virtual image formed when the object is inside the focal length. With the mirror at a greater distance, the image is real and inverted.

(DEMO⚡) To create a makeshift **telescope**, stick two lenses on a meter stick with clay and sight through them. If possible, students can experiment with different lenses and different distances between them to investigate the types of images that are created. If you have access to an astronomical telescope, bring it to class and talk about its various parts. You can point out the primary mirror or lens, the eyepiece, and the mount. Show students how the telescope is positioned, and point out that once an astronomical object is found in the field of view of a telescope it won't stay there, unless the telescope has a tracking system. Although students are all well aware of the rotation of Earth, many are still amazed by how quickly stars move out of the field of view of a telescope. Discuss equatorial and alt-azimuth mount designs and the advantages of each.

(DEMO⚡) Bring out the concave mirror again and have students imagine designing a telescope around it. Trace the light path from an imaginary or real source and position yourself to observe at the prime focus. Students will notice that you are then blocking the incoming light! Ask them to think of ways to overcome this problem and show Figure 3.5, which illustrates different **reflecting telescope** designs. As pointed out in the text, all large modern telescopes are reflectors. Challenge your students to come up with reasons for this fact before you go over the excellent list given in this section.

Sections 3.2 and 3.3

Students will likely know that larger telescopes are better, at least for research purposes, but many will probably think that the reason has to do with magnification. It doesn't; instead, larger-diameter telescopes have improved **light-gathering power** and **resolving power**. Light-gathering power is proportional to the square of the diameter and is important because so many astronomical objects are faint. The angular resolution of a telescope is inversely proportional to the diameter (for a given wavelength of light), which means that larger-diameter telescopes are capable of seeing more detail. Have students calculate the resolving power of the telescope you brought into class and compare it to one of the Keck telescopes. They can also calculate how much brighter an image in the Keck telescope would be compared to an image of the same object viewed with the smaller telescope for an equal exposure time.

To introduce diffraction-limited optics, shine a laser through a pinhole and project the diffraction pattern on the wall or a screen. Discuss **angular resolution** of telescopes. As an analogy, have students imagine driving at night on a long, level, straight road. The headlights of an approaching car appear as one spot when the car is very distant, but can be resolved into two separate lights as the car gets closer. Draw pairs of black dots with different separations on white paper and have students determine the distances at which they can just resolve each pair. Students who wear glasses can try this both with and without their glasses, to see how corrective optics can improve resolving power.

"Stars twinkle, planets don't" is a saying your students may well have heard regarding how to tell planets from stars in the night sky. "**Seeing**" is the phenomena responsible for the old trick. Stars twinkle as their point images are bounced around by the changes in temperature and density in the atmosphere. Planets have disk shapes, and as the disks are moved slightly they continue to overlap, giving a more constant image. To demonstrate the effects of seeing, place a hot plate set on high just under the light projected by a slide projector. Show a slide with lots of stars in it and watch how the images become distorted.

New **detector and telescope designs** have been motivated by the desire to obtain better images, to view ever fainter objects, and to overcome the limitations of seeing. Look at the history of telescope design as a progression of improvements, many of which have been ingenious. Discuss CCDs, active optics, and adaptive optics, and ask students what limitations these new technologies are helping to overcome and how.

Sections 3.4 and 3.5

Radio telescopes have both advantages and disadvantages when compared to optical telescopes. For instance, radio astronomers do not need to wait until nighttime to observe! In fact, radio telescopes can observe the radio sky in cloudy and even rainy conditions, if the observations are occurring at longer radio wavelengths. Angular resolution of radio telescopes tends to be poor, however, because of the long wavelength of radio waves. Discuss how this shortcoming has been addressed through technologies that allow larger dishes and through interferometry. Most importantly, radio telescopes give us a whole new view of the universe, as many of the objects that are bright in the radio portion of the spectrum are not necessarily bright in the optical. Also, radio waves penetrate dust clouds, so we can investigate objects even if they are obscured in the optical.

Other astronomies, including infrared, ultraviolet, and high energy (X-ray and gamma ray), are likewise opening up new realms in astronomical observing. Spend time going through Table 3.1 to compare the general considerations for observing in each different wavelength range and the types of objects observed. Figure 3.31, showing the Milky Way Galaxy in five different wavelength ranges, is an excellent illustration of the wealth of information available through observations in different ranges. Point out the electromagnetic spectrum icon that indicates the wavelength range of each photo. These icons are used throughout the text, and students should pay attention to them as they view images of astronomical objects. Try using the exercise "Telescopes and Earth's Atmosphere" from *Lecture Tutorials for Introductory Astronomy* by Adams. Be sure to consider how much time to devote to this exercise, since it normally takes more class time than you'd estimate. This exercise can be a great extension of the material covered in the text. The Adams exercise illustrates the main reason for space-based astronomy which is to place the telescope above the Earth's atmosphere which entirely blocks certain parts of the electromagnetic spectrum.

Student Writing Questions

1. The next great observatory will have telescopes that can observe from the radio part of the spectrum through to ultraviolet light. You have been given the choice of locating this observatory on a high mountain peak on Earth, in Earth orbit, or on the far side of the Moon. Write a proposal that justifies the best site for this observatory. (You may want to read ahead on some information about the Moon in Chapter 5.) Don't worry about what the cost of running an observatory might be at any of these locations; just concern yourself with the most ideal observing location.

2. In this question, you can now worry about the cost of running an observatory at one of the locations given in the first question. What will make one location more expensive than another? Cost-benefit ratios are often discussed in this regard; i.e., are higher costs justified by some significant benefits? What would you propose?

3. The Hubble Space Telescope is operated remotely from Earth. What would be the advantages or disadvantages of having humans working at the telescope while in orbit? Do you think this would be cost-effective?

4. What do you think the next generation of telescopes will be? What can't be done now that needs to be done? Where will this be done from, Earth or space? Will the costs be worth it?

5. One of the next great challenges in observational astronomy will be to image planets around another star. Suppose there is a solar system like our own at a distance of 10 pc. What size telescope, working at what wavelength, would be necessary to just barely image Jupiter and Earth? If a single telescope is impractical, what might be used instead?

Answers to End of Chapter Exercises

Review and Discussion

1. There are three main advantages of the reflecting telescope over refracting telescopes. When light passes through a lens, light of different wavelengths focuses at slightly different places. This is known as *chromatic aberration* and can produce seriously out-of-focus images. It is not easy to correct when making large lenses. However, it is not a problem with mirrors. A second problem with lenses is that the glass lens absorbs certain wavelengths of light that the astronomer needs to observe. In the infrared, for instance, glass is not transparent like it is for visible light. In the infrared, the glass lens blocks light from entering the telescope. Because mirrors reflect the incoming radiation rather than let it pass through, this is not a problem with reflecting telescopes. Lastly, it is advantageous to have large mirrors or lenses for astronomical telescopes. Large lenses can only be supported on their edges, and so they tend to sag under their own weight, changing their curvatures and therefore focusing properties. Mirrors can be supported from behind because the light does not need to pass through. Also, a large lens is difficult to make perfect all the way through. Mirrors, however, only have to be perfect on the surface.

2. The largest telescopes are reflecting telescopes. Examples include the VLT (Very Large Telescope) in Chile and the two Keck telescopes in Hawaii.

3. "Seeing" is the blurring in the image of an object, such as a star, as its light passes through Earth's atmosphere. Instead of the star image being very small, limited by the diffraction of the telescope, the image is blurred to many times this size. Earth's atmosphere is not homogeneous; it is turbulent

and contains layers of varying temperatures and density. Light passing through these layers is refracted into many slightly different paths. Fortunately for astronomers, Earth's atmosphere is really rather thin, and so the images are not completely blurred to uselessness.

4. The *Hubble Space Telescope* is not affected by seeing because it orbits above Earth's atmosphere. It can also observe at wavelengths that are absorbed by Earth's atmosphere. Its disadvantages are several; it is a very complex telescope to operate and astronomers must use it remotely. If something goes wrong, they cannot easily fix it. Because the Hubble orbits close to Earth, half the sky is blocked by Earth. Because it orbits quickly around Earth, objects may be observable for only part of the time; the rest of the time they are blocked by Earth.

5. The CCDs are much more sensitive to light and are linear devices in that twice as much light gives twice as much image. The image is in digital form, which makes data analysis much easier and efficient. The CCDs are much more consistent in their results than are photographs.

6. A 2-m telescope will definitely have its resolution limited by Earth's atmosphere. This size of telescope is diffraction-limited at about 0.05". But the blurring due to the atmosphere is at least 10 times this, at best, and usually closer to 20 times or 1.0".

7. The resolution of a telescope depends on the wavelength of the light observed; the longer the wavelength, the lower the resolution. Radio waves are very long relative to visible light. Because larger telescopes produce higher resolution, radio telescopes must be very large, compared to optical telescopes, in order to have a useful resolving power.

8. Conditions in some objects produce radio waves but little or no visible light. Some objects produce both but by different mechanisms. Radio astronomy allows all these objects to be studied. The radio emissions reveal a great deal of information about the objects that could not be learned by observations in visible light.

9. Even large radio telescopes have poor resolution when compared to optical telescopes. To improve their resolution would require radio telescopes of enormous size, at least kilometers in diameter. The technique of interferometry synthesizes a telescope of this size by separating several radio telescopes by this distance and simultaneously observing the same object. Using some rather complex computer processing, the individual images are combined to synthesize what would have been observed by a telescope the size of the separation between the telescopes. Radio interferometry can now reach resolutions that are far better than optical telescopes.

10. Ground-based optical telescopes have resolutions around 1". The Hubble Space Telescope has a resolution of 0.05". Radio interferometers have reached resolutions of 0.001".

11. Because anything that is warm emits strongly in the infrared, the telescopes and instruments must be cooled to low temperatures to reduce the amount of interference from them. Some infrared observations must be conducted above much of Earth's atmosphere because the atmosphere absorbs certain wavelengths of the infrared radiation coming from space.

12. X-rays will not reflect off a mirror. However, X-rays will reflect off surfaces at low grazing angles. An X-ray telescope is made of sets of nested cylindrical mirrors positioned at the correct angle to both reflect X-rays at grazing angles and focus the X-rays to an image. (See Figure 3.27.)

13. Earth's atmosphere absorbs gamma rays from space and blocks them from reaching Earth's surface. Gamma-ray astronomy must be done from space.

14. Many objects emit their peak amount of radiation at wavelengths other than visible. When the universe is observed at new wavelengths, these different objects suddenly become visible, and astronomers are then able to study them. Generally, observing at many different wavelengths increases the total amount of information available to astronomers.

15. With 1° resolution, the smallest objects visible to the eye would have to be about 60 times bigger than they are now. Reading or any close work would be very difficult or impossible. If we could only see in the infrared, many things would look very different from how they look now. Instead of seeing some objects by reflected light, we would see them by the infrared light that they emitted owing to their warmth. This question is open-ended, and much more could be added to this response.

Conceptual Self-Test

True or False? 1. F 2. F 3. T 4. T 5. F 6. F 7. F

Multiple Choice 8. d 9. d 10. c 11. a 12. d 13. b 14. b 15. c

Problems

1. A 10' angle is equal to 600". But there are 2048 pixels along this angle, so each pixel corresponds to 0.293" or about 0.3". A typical seeing disk of a diameter of 2" would consist of 2" / 0.293" per pixel = 6.8 pixels.

2. If the cage is about 1 m across, then it blocks $(1 \text{ m})^2/(5 \text{ m})^2$ of the light coming in. This is 4%.

3. The amount of light collected by a telescope depends on the area of the mirror, and the area depends on the *square* of the diameter. A 6-m telescope is 3 times bigger in diameter than a 2-m telescope, so it has $3^2 = 9$ times the light-gathering power. The larger telescope will gather light 9 times faster than the smaller telescope, so what the 2-m telescope can accomplish in 1 hour, the 6-m can accomplish in 1/9 hour or 6.7 minutes. A 12-m telescope has 6 times the diameter of a 2-m telescope and therefore 36 times the area. It gathers light 36 times faster. What the 2-m telescope can gather in 1 hour, the 12-m can gather in (60 min)/36 = 1.7 minutes.

4. The angular resolution of a telescope gets poorer as wavelength increases. The angular resolution in arc-seconds is proportional to the wavelength. (a) 3.5 μm = 3,500 nm. 3,500/700 = 5, so the wavelength is 5 times longer. The resolution should be 5 times poorer or 0.05" × 5 = 0.25".
(b) Similarly, for the ultraviolet, 140 nm/700 nm = 0.2 and 0.05" × 0.2 = 0.01".

5. First, find the angular separation of the stars:
$$\frac{\text{angle}}{360°} = \frac{(2 \text{ A.U.})(1.5 \times 10^8 \text{ km/A.U})}{2\pi(200 \text{ lt yrs})(9.5 \times 10^{12} \text{ km/lt yr})}$$
yields an angular separation of 9.05×10^{-6} degrees = 0.033". Use this as the angular resolution:
$$\text{resolution} = 0.25 \frac{\lambda(\mu m)}{\text{diameter(m)}} \quad \text{so diameter} = 0.25(2\mu m)/(0.033") = 15 \text{ m}.$$

6. The Hubble Space Telescope has a mirror diameter of 2.4 m. Observing at 400 nm, it can therefore achieve an angular resolution of 0.25(0.4 μm)/(2.4 m) = 0.042". If the stars in the previous problem

have an angular separation of 0.033" at 200 light-years, then the distance at which their separation will be 0.042" is (0.033/0.042)(200 light-years) = 157 light-years.

7. The CCD records 90/5 = 18 times as much light as a photographic plate. If it took 1 hour to photograph an object, it should take the CCD 1/18 as long or 60 min/18 = 3.3 minutes.

8. Set up a ratio similar to that in problem 5, and solve for the distance.

$$\frac{\text{angle (in arc-seconds)}}{360° \times (3600''/°)} = \frac{(\text{distance})}{2\pi(2.5 \times 10^6 \, \text{lt yr})}$$

An angle of 3.0" leads to a distance of 36 light-years, 0.05" yields a distance of 0.61 light-years. An angle of 0.001" results in a distance of 0.12 light-years.

9. Area is proportional to diameter squared: $2 \times (10 \, \text{m})^2 = 200 \, \text{m}^2$. Taking the square root of this to get the diameter of a single mirror of equivalent area gives 14.1 m. Similarly, $4 \times (8 \, \text{m})^2 = 256 \, \text{m}^2$. Taking the square root of this to get the diameter of a single mirror of equivalent area gives 16 m.

10. (a) First, convert 5 GHz to wavelength: $3\times10^8 \, \text{m} = 5\times10^9 \, \text{Hz} \times \lambda$. $\lambda = 0.06$ m. Converting this to microns gives $\lambda = 60,000 \, \mu\text{m}$. The 5,000-km baseline is 5×10^6 m. Applying the formula for angular resolution:

$$\text{angular resolution} = 0.25\frac{60,000 \, \mu\text{m}}{5\times10^6 \, \text{m}} = 0.003''$$

(b) Applying the formula again for the case of the interferometer gives:

$$\text{angular resolution} = 0.25\frac{1 \, \mu\text{m}}{50 \, \text{m}} = 0.005''.$$

Resource Information

Student CD Media Resources

Interactive Student Tutorials
The Optics of a Simple Lens
Chromatic Aberration
Reflecting Telescopes

Movies/Animations
Hubble Telescope in Orbit
Chandra: Light and Data Paths

Transparencies

42.	Figure 3.1	Reflecting Mirror
	Figure 3.2	Refracting Lens
43.	Figure 3.3	Image Formation
44.	Figure 3.4	Reflectors and Refractors
45.	Figure 3.5	Reflecting Telescopes
46.	Figure 3.6	Keck Telescope
	Figure 3.10	Mauna Kea Observatory
47.	Figure 3.9	Sensitivity

Materials

An assortment of lenses and mirrors can be very helpful in demonstrating the concepts in this chapter. Edmund Optics can be found online at www.edmundoptics.com. It is a great source for lenses, prisms, and other optical components. Meter sticks and clay will allow you to construct very simple models of telescopes.

A laser and pinhole will allow you to demonstrate circular diffraction patterns.

The refracting telescope kit from Project Star (www.starlab.com) provides lenses, tubes, and lens holders for constructing simple telescopes.

A great resource for small telescopes and accessories is Orion Telescopes & Binoculars (www.telescope.com). Although there are many resources for equipment, Orion does a great job explaining how the equipment works. This is where I send students and the general public when they inquire about where to buy their first telescope.

If you want to do extensive demonstrations with optics, the "Blackboard Optics™ Basic Set" from Klinger (item KO4100 or KO4100M) is one example of an assembly of lenses, mirrors, and ray projectors that can attach right to your blackboard. An additional accessory set (KO4100A or KO4100AM) provides components for more demonstrations and experiments in optics.

Suggested Readings

Altschuler, Daniel R. and Eder, Jo Ann. "Bringing the stars to the people: Arecibo Observatory." *Sky & Telescope* (May 1998). p. 70. Provides a summary of the Arecibo radio telescope and a description of its recently opened visitor center.

Andereck, B. and Secrest, S. "The Magic Magnifier." *The Physics Teacher* (May 2001). p. 301. Describes the construction of a simple telescope out of PVC pipe and lenses.

Deans, Paul. "2MASS treasure hunt." *Sky & Telescope* (Dec 2000). p. 54. Showcases results from the near-infrared sky survey conducted by twin 1.3-meter telescopes in Arizona and Chile (2MASS).

di-Cicco, Dennis. "A CCD camera buzzword primer." *Sky & Telescope* (Aug 1997). p. 109. Provides a guide to the terminology associated with CCD cameras.

Elvis, Martin. "NASA's Chandra X-ray Observatory: a revolution through resolution." *Sky & Telescope* (Aug 1999). p. 44. Gives a detailed overview of X-ray astronomy and the characteristics and capabilities of the Chandra X-ray Observatory.

Huebner, J., Gibbs, D., and Ryan, P. "Projecting Chromatic Aberrations." *American Journal of Physics* (September 2000). p. 869. Describes apparatus for demonstrating chromatic aberration to a large class using an overhead projector.

Johnston, Lisa R. "Swift: The Satellite That's Always On Call." *Sky & Telescope* (January 2006). p. 48. A mission update for the Swift observatory that detects gamma-ray bursts and follows their light curve from X-ray into the UV and Visible part of the spectrum.

Kellermann, Kenneth I. "Radio astronomy in the 21st century." *Sky & Telescope* (Feb 1997). p. 26. A brief history and a look toward the future of radio astronomy.

Leonard, Peter J.T. and Wanjek, Christopher. "Compton's legacy." *Sky & Telescope* (July 2000). p. 48. Reviews results of the high energy gamma ray sky obtained during the nine-year mission of the Compton Gamma Ray Observatory.

Miller, D. "Retinal Imaging and Vision at the Frontiers of Adaptive Optics." *Physics Today* (January 2000). p. 31. Good discussion of the potential for adaptive optics to correct for aberrations, diffraction, and the eye's defects.

Milonni, P. "Resource Letter: AOA-1: Adaptive Optics for Astronomy." *American Journal of Physics* (June 1999). p. 476. Provides a guide to the basic concepts and the literature on adaptive optics for astronomy.

Naeye, Robert. "Back to the future." *Astronomy* (Oct 1999). p. 40. A showcase of spectacular images from the Hubble Space Telescope.

Naeye, Robert. "Chandra: Taking the Universe's X-Ray." *Sky & Telescope* (January 2006). p. 36. A mission update for Chandra and its views of the high-energy cosmos.

Parker, Samantha. "The Very Large Telescope." *Sky & Telescope* (August 1998). p. 56. A brief report on the status of the VLT.

Powell, Corey S. "What the Keck? Studies using the world's largest telescope." *Scientific American* (August 1995). p. 20. Describes some of the early results from the Keck Telescope.

Saegusa, Asako. "Celebratory pictures from Subaru." *Nature* (Sept 23 1999). p. 314. Showcases some of the first images from the Subaru Telescope on Mauna Kea.

Roth, Joshua. "GALEX: Seeing Starbirth, Near and Far." *Sky & Telescope* (January 2006). p. 40. A mission update for GALEX and its ultraviolet imaging that traces star formation.

Sincell, Mark. "Making the stars stand still." *Astronomy* (June 2000). p. 42. Describes how adaptive optics work to compensate for atmospheric distortion of astronomical images.

Smith, Robert W. "Ten years and counting: HST in orbit." *Sky & Telescope* (Apr 2000). p. 28. Provides a nice review of the key results from the first ten years of the Hubble Space Telescope.

Stix, Gary. "Shading the twinkle." *Scientific American* (Dec 1998). p. 40. Describes how a null interferometer can be used to detect extrasolar planets.

Talcott, Richard. "Hubble is better than new." *Astronomy* (May 2000). p. 28. A report on the status of the Hubble Space Telescope after the successful December, 1999, repair mission.

Terrance, Gregory. "Exploring the digital darkroom." *Astronomy* (Sept 2000). p. 76. An overview of image-processing techniques for images obtained with CCD cameras.

Tytell, David. "Spitzer: Living Life to the Fullest." *Sky & Telescope* (January 2006). p. 44. A mission update for the Spitzer infrared space telescope and its ability to penetrate obscuring dust.

Wakefield, Julie. "Keck trekking." *Astronomy* (Sept 1998). p. 52. Describes the author's visit to, and some of the projects done at, the Keck Telescope.

Notes and Ideas

Class time spent on material: Estimated:_____   Actual:_____

Demonstration and activity materials:

Notes for next time:

Chapter 4: The Solar System
Interplanetary Matter and the Birth of the Planets

Outline

Summary

Chapter 4 provides an excellent introduction to our solar system as a whole. Inhabitants of the solar system are discussed and compared. Theories for formation of the solar system are given, and then applied to extrasolar systems as well. This chapter lays the foundation for the next several chapters, which look in depth at our Earth, the Moon, the planets, and the Sun.

Major Concepts

- Solar system inhabitants
  - Sun
  - Planets
    - Sizes and distances
    - Properties
    - Classification: terrestrial and jovian
  - Asteroids, comets, and meteoroids
- Formation of the solar system
  - The solar nebula contraction
  - Observations support theory
  - Planet formation
- Extrasolar planets

Teaching Suggestions and Demonstrations

Sizes and distances are important in the study of astronomy. If you haven't already, do a quick review of the metric system to make sure students are familiar with the prefixes and have a fairly good grasp of the different units. Give examples of a broad range of lengths; the book and video *Powers of Ten* is an excellent introduction to the size and scale of the universe and objects within it.

Sections 4.1 and 4.2

Most likely your students will have never seen a **scale model of the solar system** that has the same scale for both sizes and distances. If you choose a scale so that the model can be laid out in a room or even a long hallway, the inner planets are all indistinguishably small dots. If you choose a scale that clearly shows sizes, the planets must be so spread out that it is impossible to see them all at once. It is a great exercise to have students construct scale models. You can divide the students into groups and give them different challenges. For instance, give one group a large collection of spherical objects of different sizes. You could include various balls used in sports (basketball, volleyball, soccer ball, baseball, golf ball, hackysack, Ping-Pong ball) as well as other larger (beachball) and smaller (bead, chickpea, pinhead) objects. The challenge for the group is to use any of the objects they wish (as well as others they can find in the classroom) to create a model showing the *sizes* of the planets to scale. When they are done, ask students to also calculate where a couple of the balls would be placed if the model were to show distances to the same scale.

Meanwhile, give another group a roll of cash register tape and send them out to a hallway to construct a model showing the *distances* of the planets to scale. When they are finished, ask them to calculate the sizes of a few planets to the same scale. A third option is to give a group a road map of your state and ask them to place the Sun at one edge and Pluto as far away as possible. They should then calculate where the other planets would lie and how big they would be.

If your class structure does not allow for group work of this type, you can modify the activities into demonstrations. **(DEMO⚡)** Bring in the collection of balls, hold up the one you have designated to be Earth, and ask students to guess which objects could be used to represent the other planets and the Sun. Or, assign planet roles to various students and ask them to place themselves across the classroom such that their distances are to scale.

These models will help to dispel typical student misconceptions. For instance, many students believe Jupiter is about halfway out to Pluto, when in fact it is closer to halfway to Saturn and only about an eighth the way to Pluto. Students also often enter introductory astronomy classes thinking that Uranus and Neptune are about the same size as Jupiter and Saturn, when in fact they are less than half the size. Emphasize the difficulty encountered in attempting to show sizes and distances of the planets to the same scale. In general it is very difficult to scale planetary orbits and planetary diameters at the same time. For instance, if you use a scale of 12 inches (305 mm) for the diameter of the Sun, the Earth would be only 3mm in diameter and 33 meters away. Pluto would be a mere 0.4mm and 1.3 Km away. So, be sure to plan any scale models of the solar system carefully.

The classification of the planets into **terrestrial** and **jovian**, with Pluto belonging to neither class, will be fairly easy for students to understand. Before showing them Table 4.2, ask them for suggestions of characteristics used to compare and contrast the two types of planets. They will probably be able to generate most of the items in the table, with the exception of the magnetic-field strength and the rotation rate. The formation of either a terrestrial or jovian planet is very dependent on the temperature gradient of the proto-planetary disc of the early solar system. In general at farther distances, there were colder temperatures. At the point where water would solidify, jovian planets could form. Try using the exercise "Temperature and Formation of Our Solar System" from *Lecture Tutorials for Introductory Astronomy* by Adams. This is also a great exercise for students to practice conversions between the various temperature scales.

Some students may confuse **density** with weight. **(DEMO⚡)** Bring in a variety of objects, such as a wooden block, a marble, a rock, and a styrofoam cube and demonstrate finding their densities. The volumes of objects with irregular shapes can be determined by immersing them in water. This demonstration is most effective if at least one high-density object has a lower mass than a low-density object. Try using a small marble and a large wooden block.

The main categories of solar system debris include **asteroids, meteoroids,** and **comets**. Spend some time comparing and contrasting these different types of objects. Calculate the size of a typical asteroid to the same scale as you used in a previous scale model. It is interesting to look not only at the characteristics of the different objects, but also at how we perceive them from our place on Earth and at how they have impacted us. *Discovery 4-1* explains the theory that an asteroid or comet striking Earth may have caused the extinction of the dinosaurs. The possibility of another collision and the potential to find out about it and possibly avoid it ahead of time is a hot topic of debate.

A very common description of asteroids is that they look like potatoes. Bring in a couple of potatoes to use as models. Using a typical asteroid size, calculate the scale of the model. Students often believe that the asteroid belt is very crowded with little room between neighboring asteroids. Hand one of the potatoes to a student and calculate how far away she needs to stand from you, using the same scale you used for the size of the asteroid, to represent a typical distance between asteroids. Students will probably guess that both potatoes should be in the classroom, when in fact they should be perhaps 1000 km apart! Be sure to distinguish among the terms **meteor, meteorite,** and **meteoroid**. Ask your students if any have ever watched a meteor shower, and encourage them to try to view one—given the right conditions, they can be spectacular! (See Table 4.3 for a list of major meteor showers.)

(DEMO冊) Meteorites can be used as a great classroom demonstration. They are widely available from reputable dealers. Try to obtain samples of various types so that students can compare and contrast the samples. A widely available sample is from **Barringer (meteor) Crater** in northern Arizona. During the impact that created this crater, pieces of the original impacting meteorite were scattered over a large area. While passing around the specimen, display Figure 4.17, which shows the crater in all its glory. Samples from this meteorite are sometimes known as "Canyon Diablo" because Diablo Canyon lies very close to the crater. Canyon Diablo are particularly well-suited for handling because they are iron meteorites. If you purchase an uncoated meteorite, you may need to coat it with varnish to keep it from rusting.

Comets can also be quite impressive. Point out that the **comet's tail** is produced by the solar wind, not by the comet's motion through space. Figure 4.10 shows that the comet's tail does not always trail behind it. Comets are often described as "dirty snowballs." A model of a comet can be made by freezing a mixture of water, fine dirt, and soot. Show slides or photos of famous comets. Pick a well-known comet, such as Halley's Comet, and use its period with **Kepler's third law** to calculate the semi-major axis of its orbit.

Section 4.3

Before discussing the formation of the solar system directly, review some of the **major characteristics of the solar system** that must be explained by, or at least be compatible with, a theory of its origin. For instance, all the planets orbit in the same direction around the Sun, and most rotate in this same direction as well. Further, they lie (more or less) in the same plane. Look at the list of nine facts at the beginning of this section and remember to refer back to them as the specifics of the theory of the origin of the solar system are discussed.

Outline the stages in the **formation of the solar system** for students. There are lots of new terms introduced in the text; go over them carefully. Define and discuss **angular momentum**; students will probably not be familiar with it unless they have taken physics. However, they will be familiar with the results of the law of conservation of angular momentum. If any of your students are dancers, ask them to demonstrate a spin in which the arms start far from the body and end up close. Students can try to think of other examples of the conservation of angular momentum as well. One classic demonstration involves a rotating stool and a bicycle wheel. Ask a student to sit on a rotating stool and hold a bicycle wheel vertically. With the stool stationary, give the wheel a spin. Then ask the student to rotate the axis of the wheel so that the plane of the wheel is now horizontal. Because the angular momentum of the system is changing, the student and stool will rotate in such a manner as to conserve angular momentum.

Differentiation can be demonstrated as well. Bring in a jar containing a mixture of water, rocks, sand, and silt. Shake it up and set it in the front of the room. By the end of class, the various particles will have settled out in layers. If you vigorously stir a similar mixture in a bucket, the heavier particles will settle in the center.

In concluding your discussion of the formation of the solar system, return to the nine characteristic facts listed under "Model Requirements" in the beginning of Section 4.3. Ask students how each one can be explained by, or is consistent with, the theory.

Section 4.4

Start this section with a vote: "Who thinks there is life elsewhere in the universe? Who doesn't?" This topic will come up again at the very end of the course, but you can introduce it now as well. Most people would agree that in order to have life elsewhere, there must be other planets. The discovery of **extrasolar planets** has provided exciting developments in astronomy in recent years. Review the Doppler effect briefly to help students understand its importance in detecting planets.

The **Doppler method** makes use of the **stellar wobble** caused by the gravitational effect of the planet on the star. Stars with smaller planets, or planets that are farther away, cause relatively tiny stellar wobbles. **(DEMO!)** This can be demonstrated by using a ball tied to a string and twirling it in a circle. The ball has very little effect on the person. However, if you use a larger ball tied to a rope, such as a softball, or even a bowling ball, this twirling motion causes much more wobble motion for the person doing the demonstration. If you decide to try using a bowling ball, like I use in my class, be sure to take appropriate safety precautions.

Student Writing Questions

1. You have just been given a unique spaceship that takes one-million-kilometer "steps" or jumps each minute. You now have the opportunity to explore the solar system with it. (The ship holds almost unlimited provisions, and fuel is never a problem!) Please do not assume that the planets are all neatly lined up, but rather scattered about on various sides of the Sun. Describe the layout of the solar system you are about to explore and the route of your journey. How long will the trip from one planet to the next take? How long will you be gone from Earth? Would you dare try a trip to the nearest star?

2. You have just come home after an inspiring lecture in astronomy and have just learned how the average density of a planet is determined. Unfortunately, this subject comes up in front of your little sister who, unlike average youngsters who always ask "why," likes to ask instead, "How do you know that?" She is never satisfied with "My professor said so" type of responses. Can you answer her repeated question "How do you know that?" on the topic of the average density of a planet? Just how many "How do you know that?" questions can you answer (assuming no harm comes to your sister) during this episode?

3. You are holding a meteorite in your hand. Trace back all the events that took place, over the past 4.6 billion years, that led to this meteorite being in your possession. Include the times when these events occurred. Be creative and use your imagination!

4. You are standing on the surface of Halley's Comet as it passes perihelion. The year is 2062 and you are wearing a very protective space suit. Describe what it is like to be on the surface of this comet. Include environmental factors such as gravity, temperature, and motion. What do you see when you look up to the sky, away from the Sun?

5.   Asteroid belts have been shown in a variety of science fiction stories such as *The Empire Strikes Back*. In what ways are these visualizations correct and incorrect? Is it possible to actually see a field of asteroids?

Answers to End of Chapter Exercises

Review and Discussion

1.   Three differences between jovian and terrestrial planets include (1) location in the solar system, (2) size, (3) density. The terrestrial planets are in the inner 1.5 A.U. of the solar system; the jovian planets are scattered from 5 to 30 A.U. The jovian planets are much larger than the terrestrial planets. Terrestrial planets have a much higher density than do the jovian planets, which indicates a fundamental difference in composition. Terrestrial planets are rocky; jovian planets are made up of light elements.

2.   Asteroids and meteoroids are important because they often contain material that has undergone little change since the solar system was formed. The surface material of Earth and the Moon, for instance, has changed greatly over time, thus little is known about the original conditions under which they were formed. Comets give us information about conditions in the outer reaches of the solar system.

3.   No, not all asteroids lie in the asteroid belt. There are hundreds of Trojan asteroids that are in the orbit of Jupiter. They orbit 60 degrees ahead of or behind Jupiter. Other asteroids have elliptical orbits that take them closer to the Sun than Earth's orbit. They are the Earth-crossing asteroids.

4.   The consequences of a 10-km meteorite striking the Earth today would be very unpleasant. There would be worldwide effects to the entire environment and likely extinctions of many of the highest-order animals. Earth would likely be shrouded in clouds of dust, water, and even saltwater for years. Huge tidal waves would result from a strike in one of the oceans. Large earthquakes could be triggered. Near the strike, the heat and blast wave would destroy everything for hundreds of kilometers. Debris falling back to Earth from the impact would devastate an even larger region. No part of Earth would go unaffected. Keep in mind that the possibility of such an impact during your lifetime is very low; unfortunately, neither is it zero.

5.   Comets, when they are far from the Sun, are frozen chunks of ice, dust, and rocky particles. They are very cold and dark. When comets approach the Sun, the surface ices start to sublimate, releasing gases and particles of rock and dust. A large cloud of this material surrounds the comet and is called the *coma*. As the comet approaches the Sun, one or more tails are formed.

6.   The Oort Cloud of comets, considered the source of most comets, is like a large, spherical halo around the solar system. Comets enter the inner solar system with a large range of orbital inclinations. Asteroids are mostly confined to the ecliptic. Their position indicates they are the product, perhaps leftovers, of planet formation. The comets, from their distribution and composition, may date from an earlier period in the solar system's formation.

7.   A meteoroid is any particle of material orbiting the Sun that cannot be seen from Earth. (If it could be seen, it would be called an asteroid.) Sizes range from kilometers to microscopic dust particles. If a meteoroid passes through the atmosphere of Earth (or any other atmosphere) the gases are momentarily heated, making them glow, as the meteoroid passes through. This streak of light is known as a *meteor*. The meteoroid likely burns up when passing through the atmosphere. If it does

not, because of its size, composition, or low velocity, and it lands on the surface of a planet or moon, it is known as a *meteorite*.

8. Meteor showers are caused by Earth passing through the orbit of a comet. The orbit of a typical comet is filled with many particles of rock and dust left behind as its ices sublimate. When Earth passes through this swarm of particles, a meteor shower is observed. Many meteors will be seen emanating from one location in the sky.

9. The nebular theory has the solar system forming out of a large, spinning cloud of gas. As it spins, it flattens into a pancake shape and forms a series of concentric rings. Each of these rings eventually forms a planet; the central condensation forms the Sun. The nebular theory has a large rotating cloud collapsing into a disk. The solar system then forms out of the disk. The orbits of the major bodies should therefore be approximately in the same plane and should have the same direction of motion, as is observed. The rotation of the Sun and planets should also be in the same direction. Only two planets have exceptional rotations; otherwise, the observations match the theory's predictions. The theory also predicts the difference in density in the terrestrial and the jovian planets.

10. The key ingredient of the modern condensation theory is interstellar dust. The dust helps to both cool off the solar nebula and provide condensation nuclei upon which particles can grow.

11. In the solar nebula where the jovian planets are now found, the temperatures were sufficiently low for ices of water, ammonia, and methane to form. This provided much more material for the early accretion that occurred, and it proceeded rapidly. The planetesimals that formed could then also attract hydrogen and helium, and the jovian planets grew to a large size. In the region of the inner solar nebula, temperatures were sufficiently high that time had to pass before the first rocky particles could condense and start the accretion process. There was less material to accrete because it was too hot for the icy material to exist. Finally, hydrogen and helium could not be accreted because of the jovian planets' low gravity and high temperatures.

12. In the hot inner solar nebula, only metals and then silicates could condense out. This gave rise to the inner planets, which are quite rocky. It even accounts for Mercury having a higher density than would be expected for a body of its size; it formed from material with a greater abundance of metals. Farther from the Sun, the temperature was low enough for ices to exist.

13. In its initial stage of formation, Earth was in a relatively hot part of the solar nebula. Only rocky silicates could condense at this high a temperature. Earth's water appears to have come later, by the collision of numerous comet-like planetesimals ejected into the inner solar system through interactions with the jovian planets. But this environment was much cooler than before, and the planetary surface of Earth could retain the water and other volatile material that would form its early atmosphere.

14. Astronomers detect extrasolar planets through indirect methods. Radial velocity data showing a wobble in a star's motion can be used to determine the presence of a planet. If the orientation of the orbit of a planet around a star with respect to Earth happens to be edge-on, then observations of the light from the star during the planetary transit will give evidence of the existence of the planet.

15. Most observed extrasolar planetary systems have Jupiter-size planets that orbit in smaller, more eccentric orbits than Jupiter does.

56 Chapter 4

Conceptual Self-Test

True or False? 1. T 2. F 3. F 4. F 5. T 6. T 7. F

Multiple Choice 8. d 9. b 10. d 11. a 12. c 13. b 14. d 15. c

Problems

1. The total mass of all asteroids would be $20,000 \times 10^{17}$ kg $= 2 \times 10^{21}$ kg. The mass of Earth is 6×10^{24} kg. Comparing these, 2×10^{21} kg $/6 \times 10^{24}$ kg $/ = 0.0003$. Thus, the mass of all the asteroids combined is 0.03% of the mass of Earth. As we see them today, the asteroids would not make up much of a planet! A single body would have the following size. Use the formula for density:

$$3000 = \frac{10^{17}}{(4/3)\pi R^3}$$

R = 20,000 m or 20 km, so the diameter would be 40 km.

2. Perihelion distance $= a(1 - e)$. Using the data given for Icarus gives $0.19 = a(1 - 0.83)$, or $a = 1.1$ A.U.
   Aphelion distance $= a(1 + e)$, $= 1.1(1 + 0.83) = 2.0$ A.U.

3. The gravitational acceleration on the surface of a body depends on the mass of that body and inversely on the radius of the body squared. The weight of an object depends directly on this acceleration. Comparing Ceres to Earth: weight is proportional to $(0.0002)/(0.073)^2 = 0.0375$ times the weight on Earth.

   An 80-kg astronaut would weight 80 kg x 9.8 m/s^2 = 784 newtons

   Therefore, the 80-kg astronaut would weigh 0.0375 (784 newtons) = 29.4 newtons

   It is important to distinguish the difference between weight, which is a force and varies from planet to planet, and mass, which is a fundamental measurement of matter and doesn't vary from planet to planet.

4. If Number $= k /$ Diameter^2, then put in the values for Ceres and $k = 10^6$. Notice this works for the other diameters given too. For 1-km asteroids there will be 10^6.

   What is the mass of a 1-km-diameter asteroid? Assume spherical shape and the density given of 3000 kg/m^3. $m = (4/3)\pi \times (500 \text{ m})^3 \times 3000 \text{ kg/m}^3$
   $$m = 1.6 \times 10^{12} \text{ kg}.$$
   Notice that the mass depends on the cube of the radius and therefore also on the cube of the diameter. The following table gives the results for the masses.

Size	Mass Each	Number	Total Mass
1 km	1.6×10^{12} kg	10^6	1.6×10^{18} kg
10 km	1.6×10^{15} kg	10,000	1.6×10^{19} kg
100 km	1.6×10^{18} kg	100	1.6×10^{20} kg
1000 km	1.6×10^{21} kg	1	1.6×10^{21} kg

5. (a) Use Kepler's third law, $P^2 = a^3$:
    $$P = \sqrt{a^3} = \sqrt{50,000^3} = 11 \text{ million years.}$$
    (b) Use Kepler's third law to find the semi-major axis:
    $$a = \sqrt[3]{P^2} = \sqrt[3]{125^2} = 25 \text{ A.U.}$$
    Twice this distance is the major axis, 50 A.U. The maximum aphelion distance cannot be any larger than this.

6. (a) Orbital angular momentum can be expressed as $L = mvr$, where m is the mass of the planet, v is its orbital velocity, and r is the radius of its orbit. Using data from Appendix 3, Table 2A, this gives

    For Jupiter: $L = mvr = (1.90 \times 10^{27} \text{ kg}) (13,100 \text{ m/s})(7.784 \times 10^{11} \text{ m}) = 1.9 \times 10^{43} \text{ kg m}^2/\text{s}$

    For Saturn: $L = mvr = (5.68 \times 10^{26} \text{ kg}) (9650 \text{ m/s})(1.427 \times 10^{12} \text{ m}) = 7.8 \times 10^{42} \text{ kg m}^2/\text{s}$

    For Earth: $L = mvr = (5.97 \times 10^{24} \text{ kg}) (29,800 \text{ m/s})(1.50 \times 10^{11} \text{ m}) = 2.7 \times 10^{40} \text{ kg m}^2/\text{s}.$

    (b) Find the period of the comet so that the speed can be found: $P^2 = a^3 = 50,000^3$, so $P = 11$ million years. The speed of the comet in its orbit is therefore $\dfrac{2\pi(50,000 \times 1.5 \times 10^{11})\text{m}}{3.52 \times 10^{14}\text{ s}} = 134$ m/s.

    $L = mvr = (10^{13} \text{ kg}) (134 \text{m/s})(50,000 \text{ A.U.})(1.5 \times 10^{11} \text{ m/A.U.}) = 1.0 \times 10^{31} \text{ kg m}^2/\text{s}.$

7. F is the force of gravity, M the mass of a planet, and R is its radius. Density, ρ, will be constant.
    $$F \propto M/R^2 \quad \text{and} \quad \rho \propto M/R^3$$

    Substituting R^3 for M in the first equation, and remembering density is constant, gives

    $$F \propto R.$$

    If the radius doubles, then the surface gravity doubles. Thus, as a protoplanet accretes more material, not only does it grow in size, but its gravitational attraction grows in proportion to its radius. It becomes more effective in accreting more matter.

8. First determine the mass of a 100-km planetesimal:

    $$m = 4/3 \ \pi \times (50,000 \text{ m})^3 \times 3000 \text{ kg/m}^3$$
    $$m = 1.6 \times 10^{18} \text{ kg.}$$

    Divide this mass into the mass of Earth to find the number of planetesimals it would take to form Earth.
    $$6 \times 10^{24} \text{ kg} / 1.6 \times 10^{18} \text{ kg} = 3.8 \times 10^6 = 3.8 \text{ million.}$$

9. Take the total mass of water on Earth and divide by the mass of water in one comet:

    $$2 \times 10^{21} \text{ kg} / 10^{13} \text{ kg water per comet} = 2 \times 10^8 \text{ comets (200 million comets).}$$

    200 million comets / 500 million years = 0.4 comets per year or 1 comet every 2.5 years.

10. Using Kepler's third law, find the semi-major axis of the orbit:

$$P^2 = a^3 \text{ so } a = \sqrt[3]{5^2} = 2.92 \text{ A.U.}$$

The maximum speed of the planet is 40,000 m/s. If the semi-major axis of a planet's orbit is a, then its speed v at a point in its orbit a distance r from its parent star is given by:

$$v^2 = GM\left(\frac{2}{r} - \frac{1}{a}\right)$$

The maximum speed occurs at perihelion. Converting a to meters, and using 40,000 m/s for the speed and 2×10^{30} kg for M yields $r = 1.40\times10^{11}$ m = 0.93 A.U. = the distance at perihelion.

Perihelion distance is also given by $r_p = a(1 - e)$. Solve for eccentricity:
$$e = 1 - r_p/a = 1 - 0.93/2.924 = 0.68.$$

Resource Information

Student CD Media Resources

Interactive Student Tutorials
None

Movies/Animations
An Astronomical Ruler
Size and Scale of the Terrestrial Planets
The Gas Giants
Anatomy of a Comet Part I
Anatomy of a Comet Part II
Comet Hale-Bopp Nucleus Animation
Meteor Near Orion
Asteroid/Comet Breakup
Infrared Image of Comet Fragment Impact with Jupiter
Daytime Passage of a Meteor Fireball
Beta Pictoris Warp
Orion Nebula Animation
Solar System Formation

Transparencies

Materials

Supplies needed to create models of the solar system include various-size balls and other round objects and meter sticks.

The National Geographic Video *Asteroids: Deadly Impact* includes fascinating information about the study of impacts and an interview with Eugene Shoemaker.

A bicycle wheel and rotating stool can be used to demonstrate conservation of angular momentum.

A small ball tied to a string and larger ball tied to a rope to demonstrate stellar wobble.

A great source for meteorites is Labenne Meteorites, which offers a wide variety of meteorites at all price ranges. (www.meteorites.tv)

The Astronomical Society of the Pacific has several good resources for teaching about the solar system, including maps, posters, models, and a DVD/Videotape set entitled *The Planets*.

Project Star has a solar system scale model kit (item PS-05).

Suggested Readings

Science (Sept 22, 2000). Issue featuring several articles on the science results from NEAR at Eros.

Aguirre, Edwin L. "Comet Hale-Bopp's memorable performance." *Sky & Telescope* (July 1997). p. 28. Summarizes observations of comet Hale-Bopp.

Aguirre, Edwin L. and Lyster, Timothy. "Walking tours of the solar system: three scale models of the Solar System." *Sky & Telescope* (Mar 1998). p. 80. Describes three exhibits which demonstrate the solar system to scale.

Alpert, Mark. "The fallout from Cassini: plutonium controversy." *Scientific American* (Sept 1999). p. 13. Discusses the controversy surrounding the use of plutonium fuel in the Cassini mission.

Barnes-Svarney, Patricia. "Frozen assets: water ice in the solar system." *Astronomy* (Oct 1997). p. 46. Discusses the presence of water or water ice on bodies in the solar system.

Beres, Samantha. "Home Sweet Spheres." *Astronomy* (March 2001). p. 59. Provides a summary of characteristics and photographs of each of the planets in the solar system.

Binzel, Richard P. "A New Century for Asteroids" *Sky & Telescope* (July 2001). p. 44. A review of what we now know about asteroids since Ceres was discovered 200 years ago.

Chapman, Clark R. "Worlds between worlds." *Astronomy* (June 1996). p. 46. Describes the results from the Galileo mission's observations of the asteroids Ida and Gaspra.

Cowen, Ron. "The day the dinosaurs died." *Astronomy* (Apr 1996). p. 34. Discusses evidence associating the crater Chixulub, the K-T boundary, and the extinction of the dinosaurs, and describes possible scenarios of how the impact actually resulted in the extinctions.

Frank, Adam. "Crack in the clockwork: the solar system may have lost several planets, and Mercury or Mars might be the next to go." *Astronomy* (May 1998). p. 54. Discusses the idea that the solar system may be a chaotic system.

Gehrels, Tom. "Collisions with comets and asteroids." *Scientific American* (Mar 1996). p. 54. Analyzes the risks for a significant impact on Earth from a comet or asteroid and discusses the possible consequences.

Gluck, P. "MBL Experiment in Angular Momentum," *The Physics Teacher* (April 2002). p. 230. Studies the loss and conservation of angular momentum using a small direct current motor as generator.

Graham, Rex. "Making an exceptional impact: Eugene Shoemaker." *Astronomy* (May 1998). p. 36. A biographical article about the life and work of planetary scientist Eugene Shoemaker.

Hartmann, William K. "The great solar system revision." *Astronomy* (Aug 1998). p. 40. Summarizes the highlights of 25 years of planetary exploration.

Henderson, C. "Measuring the Forces Required for Circular Motion." *The Physics Teacher* (February 1998). p. 118. A description of an apparatus that allows students to measure the forces exerted in circular motion.

Jayawardhana, Ray. "Searching for Alien Earths." *Astronomy* (June 2003). p. 48. Discusses a new generation of space-based observatories that will search for Earth-like planets.

Johnson, Torrence V. "The Galileo mission to Jupiter and its moons." *Scientific American* (Feb 2000). p. 40. Summarizes the highlights of the first five years of the Galileo mission.

Kring, David A. "Calamity at Meteor Crater." *Sky & Telescope* (Nov 1999). p. 48. Discusses what we can learn about Earth impacts from studies of Meteor Crater in Arizona.

Pechan, M., O'Brien, A., and Burgei, W. "Conservation of Angular Momentum Apparatus Using Magnetic Bearings." *The Physics Teacher* (January 2001). p. 26. A simple laboratory exercise on angular momentum.

Robinson, Cordula. "Magellan reveals Venus." *Astronomy* (Feb 1995). p. 32. Summarizes the highlights of the Magellan mission to Venus.

Ryan, Jay. "SkyWise: distances." *Sky & Telescope* (Dec 2000). p. 116. A cartoon strip which illustrates relative distances in the solar system.

Stern, S. Alan. "Forging a new solar system: G. P. Kuiper." *Astronomy* (Mar 1999). p. 40. Discusses the life and work of planetary scientist Gerard Peter Kuiper.

Talcott, Richard. "Great Comets." *Astronomy* (May 2004). p. 36. Discusses history's great comets.

Tyson, Neil De-Grasse. "Coming attractions: catastrophic asteroid impact." *Natural History* (Sept 1997). p. 82. An overview of comet and asteroid impacts on Earth.

Yeomans, Don. "Japan Visits an Asteroid." *Astronomy* (Mar 2006). p. 32. Discusses the Japanese Hayabusa probe and its visit to the rubble-strewn asteroid Itokawa.

Notes and Ideas

Class time spent on material: Estimated:_____   Actual:_____

Demonstration and activity materials:

Notes for next time:

Chapter 5: Earth and Its Moon
Our Cosmic Background

Outline

Summary

Chapter 5 discusses Earth and the Moon in detail, including their physical properties, interiors, surfaces, atmospheres, and magnetospheres. Interactions between them, such as tides and tidal locking, are also explored. The chapter ends with a discussion of the formation and evolution of the Moon.

Major Concepts

- Earth and Moon comparisons
  - Mass
  - Density
  - Orbits
  - Structures
- Tides
  - Causes of tides
  - Spring and neap tides
  - Tidal locking
  - Moon's orbit
- Atmosphere of Earth
  - Composition
  - Layers
  - Greenhouse effect
  - Lack of atmosphere on the Moon
- Interiors
  - Seismology
  - Differentiation
  - Layers
- Surfaces
  - Plate tectonics and continental drift on Earth
  - Features of the lunar surface
- Magnetic fields
  - Van Allen Belts
  - Aurorae
- Formation and evolution of the Moon

Teaching Suggestions and Demonstrations

Encourage students to observe the Moon regularly, especially during their study of this chapter. In addition to noticing phases and locations, as discussed earlier, they can pick out large-scale features such as maria and highlands. **(DEMO₅†)** Try using **Starry Night Pro** as a demonstration in class to show students the current phase of the Moon and where to look for it in the sky. Also try to include information about, and video segments of, the Apollo program while covering this section of the text. Views of astronauts bounding across the lunar surface are not only fun to watch, but also emphasize the lower surface gravity of the Moon. The video of an astronaut dropping a hammer and feather together point out that the Moon has no atmosphere and that Galileo really was right about acceleration due to gravity!

Sections 5.1 and 5.2

Before beginning an in-depth presentation of **Earth and the Moon**, ask students to list as many similarities and differences between the two as they can think of. If you'd like to make this pre-assessment a bit more formal, author Paul Green discusses more ideas in his book *Peer Instruction for Astronomy* starting on page 78. As they call out their ideas, you can make a running list on the board or overhead. This exercise provides a nice introduction to the chapter, as it gets students thinking and shows them how much they already know. Students will probably list lots of visual characteristics, like the fact that the Moon has lots of craters and Earth doesn't. You can follow it up by examining Table 5.1 to further investigate similarities and differences that may not be as obvious. Also, extend the responses generated by students; what characteristic of the Moon results in the fact that it is so heavily cratered? (The Moon has no atmosphere.) Continue the comparison with Figure 5.1, which compares the interiors of the two bodies.

A very important point to make to students regarding **tides** is that the significant quantity is the *difference* in gravitational force between the side of Earth facing the celestial body pulling on it and the opposite side, not just the amount of force itself. Ask students to guess which is greater, the gravitational force of the Moon on Earth or that of the Sun on Earth. Then do the calculation to show that the Sun's force is greater. (After all, we orbit the Sun, not the Moon!) Why then, ask students, are the high and low tides mainly determined by the *Moon*? The Moon is closer, and so the ratio of the forces it exerts on the two sides of Earth is greater than the corresponding ratio for the Sun.

The fact that there are two tides a day, instead of just one, can be difficult for students to understand. Because force is proportional to acceleration, use an analogy of three cars accelerating down the highway in the same direction but at different rates. The first car has the greatest acceleration, the middle car a medium acceleration, and the third car has the lowest acceleration. Ask students what they would observe if they were in the middle car. Although all three vehicles are moving in the same direction, an observer in the middle vehicle would see both cars moving *away* from him.

Bring in a tide table or graph to illustrate the cycle of tides. Use Figure 5.3 to discuss **neap and spring tides**.

Students will have heard of the "dark side of the Moon" and so may be familiar with the fact that the Moon always faces the same side toward Earth. (Point out that the "dark side" isn't always dark; during a new Moon it is fully illuminated!) Often, students think that this means that the Moon doesn't rotate, when in fact its period of rotation just exactly equals its period of revolution, because of **tidal locking**. Get two volunteers to help you demonstrate. The "Moon" volunteer should first demonstrate one full rotation in place. Point out to students how her nose points to different walls in the classroom, ending up back where she started. Then, have the "Moon" revolve around the "Earth" volunteer without any rotation; this will look like a one-person do-si-do square dance move. Notice how an observer on Earth sees the whole Moon—front and back of the "Moon's" head—during the course of a month. Finally, conclude with the "Moon" orbiting "Earth" while always facing it. Compare this to the rotation-only motion and watch how the "Moon's" nose faces all four walls, while always facing Earth. Thus, the Moon makes one complete rotation in the same time that it makes one complete revolution.

Sections 5.3 and 5.4

Earth's atmosphere is diagrammed in Figure 5.5. Show students a transparency of this figure and ask them why they think the layers are divided as they are. What, for instance, determines the line between the stratosphere and the mesosphere? The relationship of temperature to altitude is the main characteristic determining the different layers. For instance, in the troposphere, the temperature decreases with increasing altitude, but in the stratosphere it increases. For scale, give students the height of the tallest mountain on Earth and the altitude at which airplanes fly.

The **greenhouse effect** and global warming on Earth are widely debated topics, so they are important and relevant concepts for students to understand. Bring in current journal or newspaper articles to share with students. This is one area in which their study of astronomy will have a direct impact on their understanding of current events. The greenhouse effect will come up again in the chapter discussing Venus.

Remind students of the demonstration showing differentiation when you discuss **Earth's interior**. Compare the amount of information we have about Earth's interior to that of the Moon, as well as the methods used to gain that information. Figure 5.9 shows the layers of Earth as well as the role of seismic waves in determining their characteristics. If you have time, make a model of the interior of Earth showing the different layers to scale.

Sections 5.5 through 5.7

Plate tectonics is actively occurring on Earth but not on the Moon. Ask students if they can figure out which characteristics of Earth are responsible for this fact. If you can find one, show a map of Earth with locations of earthquakes and volcanoes marked, but without the plate boundaries drawn in. Then compare to Figure 5.11 to show the alignment. Discuss areas where plates come together as well as where they spread apart. A great example of how plate tectonics changes the Earth's surface is given in Figure 5.12, which shows the California fault. The Earth's surface has gone through many changes since the initial formation ~4.5 billion years ago. A great example of this change is the most recent super continent "Pangaea" which started breaking apart 200 million years ago and has drifted into the continents that we know today. Pangaea is illustrated in Figure 5.15. **(DEMO⚡)** To demonstrate **convection**, which is responsible for driving the plates, add a couple of drops of food coloring to water in a clear beaker and set it on a hot plate. Try using the exercise "Earth's Changing Surface" from *Lecture Tutorials for Introductory Astronomy* by Adams. This activity covers convection as well, but from a student-centered perspective.

Although the Moon has no continental drift, it does have other interesting **surface features**. Examine Figure 5.16 and identify major areas of the Moon's near side. Project a large picture of the Moon and determine the scale by measuring the diameter of the image and comparing it to the actual diameter of the Moon. Then measure some of the prominent features and use the scale to determine their actual sizes. Challenge students to identify these on the actual full Moon some evening! Figure 5.19 offers a good diagram of how craters are formed. Earth was exposed to the same period of intense cratering that the Moon underwent. Ask students why we do not see as much evidence of bombardment in Earth's past.

Show a photo of the Barringer Meteor Crater in Arizona and discuss estimates of the size of the object that created it.

The Moon also does not have the right conditions for a **magnetic field**, but Earth has a substantial magnetic field owing to its rotating, liquid metal core. Place a bar magnet under a piece of paper and sprinkle iron filings on the paper to illustrate field lines and the shape of the magnetic field. **(DEMO⚡)** You can demonstrate the connection between moving charges and magnetism by making a simple electromagnet out of a nail, a battery, and some wire. If current is running through the wire wrapped around the nail, the nail will pick up paper clips. Disconnect the battery and the paper clips drop. If you keep the nail magnetized too long, you can permanently magnetize it, so be sure to try out this demonstration before doing it in front of a class. The aurora borealis and aurora australis are spectacular light shows visible at high latitudes as a result of our magnetosphere. (See Figures 5.23 and 5.24.) Take a moment to show a video clip of the aurora for students who have never seen them.

Section 5.8

The final section of the chapter deals with the **formation and the evolution of the Moon**. As with the formation of the solar system treated earlier, it is important that the theory explain characteristics about the Earth–Moon system. Go over not only the most widely accepted theory, but also some of the other possibilities to see whether students can find flaws or areas in which these concepts are inconsistent with present observations.

Student Writing Questions

1.   Imagine that a large meteoroid (1 to 10 km across) hits Earth. Describe what you think might happen to humans as a result of this collision. You can let the collision occur wherever you like but do specify this. Think in terms of the worldwide population of humans and not just those that are nearest the impact.

2.   Humans like to work and play. What kinds of things can you do on the surface of the Moon that you cannot do on the surface of Earth? List and describe each.

3.   What arguments can be made in favor of returning to the Moon for more manned exploration? In a sense, what is the Moon "good for" in terms of human development?

4.   In the year 2000, Earth reached a human population of about six billion people. How much larger can this grow? Is there a limit? Human population is doubling approximately every 50 years. How do you think this will affect you by the time you retire?

5.   Although we think of most craters being formed by the impacts of meteorites, some are certainly formed by the impacts of comets. Describe what the after-effects of a comet impact might be on the surface of the Moon. What would happen to all the water ice, other ices, and the organic compounds? Is there any evidence that this has occurred on the Moon?

Answers to End of Chapter Exercises

Review and Discussion

1.   The Moon pulls on the side of Earth facing it with a stronger force than it exerts on the center of Earth. Likewise, the Moon pulls with a weaker force on the far side of Earth than it exerts on the

center of Earth. The result is two high tides raised on Earth's surface, one facing the Moon and one on Earth's opposite side.

2. A synchronous orbit is when the rotational period of an object matches its orbital period. The tidal effect of Earth on the Moon is much stronger than that of the Moon on Earth. Earth's rotation is being slowed by tidal friction. The same happened for the Moon. But the Moon is also much smaller than Earth, so Earth was able to slow the Moon's rotation until it became synchronized with the Moon's orbit.

3. Convection is the rising of hot material through cooler material. (a) In Earth's atmosphere it transports heat from the surface into the atmosphere and is responsible for many of the weather patterns. (b) In Earth's interior it helped form the crust, mantle, and core of the planet. It currently is responsible for volcanism and plate tectonics.

4. The extreme temperature variations of the Moon are, in part, due to the Moon's lack of an atmosphere. An atmosphere helps to insulate the surface from cooling at night. The Moon's very long day (slow rotational period) also plays a role. The Sun is up for a long period, allowing the rock to heat up. With an equally long night, there is ample time to cool down to a low temperature. Earth, in contrast to the Moon, rotates rapidly and has less time to heat up to high temperatures or cool down to low temperatures.

5. The Moon has a low mass and low escape velocity. It experiences high daytime temperatures. All gases, at these temperatures, will exceed the escape velocity. The Moon has been unable to hold an atmosphere.

6. The light from the Sun passes through Earth's atmosphere and heats the surface. This heat, in the form of infrared light, radiates back up through the atmosphere. But greenhouse gases, primarily water vapor and carbon dioxide, in the atmosphere prevent heat from escaping to space by absorbing the infrared. The result is that Earth's surface and atmosphere warm up to a temperature higher than would be expected from simply absorbing sunlight. Possible consequences include a melting of polar ice caps and a corresponding rise in the sea level, and a change in growing seasons, locations of deserts, and other surface features that are temperature dependent.

7. The density of water is 1000 kg/m^3 and the density of rock is typically 3000 kg/ m^3. Because the average density of Earth is 5500 kg/m^3, then the interior of Earth must be made up of high-density material.

8. Certain types of seismic waves cannot travel through liquid rock. It has been known for decades that these waves, produced by earthquakes, do not travel through certain parts of Earth's interior. This region is now mapped out as being the outer core. The inner core appears to be solid.

9. The fact that Earth is differentiated, structured in layers of decreasing density toward the surface, suggests that Earth must have been molten in its past. If it was molten, then high-density material could slowly sink to the interior while lower-density material would float to the surface. This is what is observed today.

10. Plate tectonics is the cause of mountains, trenches, and most other large-scale features on Earth's surface. Mountains are often caused by plates colliding with each other. When plates pull apart, they form trenches that allow new crustal material to rise.

11. The lunar maria are ancient impact basins that were the sites of lava flows. The basins were, at one time, seas of molten lava that have since solidified.

12. The primary source of erosion on the Moon is cratering. There is no water or wind erosion and no erosion due to plate tectonics because none of these exist on the Moon. But they do exist on Earth and therefore the rate of erosion on Earth is much higher than on the Moon.

13. First, it is quite apparent that the lunar highlands are more heavily cratered. The maria were resurfaced by lava flows and all the old craters were covered over, but the highlands remained untouched. Second, samples of highland and maria material were brought back by the Apollo program and age-dated. The highland material was shown to be much older than the material from the maria.

14. The magnetosphere is that region around a planet that is most influenced by the planet's magnetic field. The magnetic field can trap charged particles. Very early satellites detected the fast-moving particles that were trapped in our magnetic field. The regions for Earth in which the particles were found are called the Van Allen Belts. The Moon does not have a magnetosphere because a rapid rotation and a liquid metallic core are necessary for generating a magnetic field. The Moon has neither of these properties.

15. The favored theory for the formation of the Moon is that a large body, maybe Mars-sized, struck Earth a glancing blow. Material thrown off could have then coalesced into the Moon. This theory explains two major features of the Moon. If Earth was young but already differentiated enough to have an iron core and rocky mantle, then the Moon would have formed primarily out of mantle material. This is consistent with the Moon being composed of rock very similar to the Earths mantle and explains why the Moon appears to have no iron core.

Conceptual Self-Test

True or False? 1. T 2. T 3. T 4. F 5. T 6. F 7. F

Multiple Choice 8. b 9. d 10. b 11. b 12. d 13. d 14. a 15. c

Problems

1. Mass is equal to density times the volume:

$$M = 3000 \text{ kg/m}^3 \times 4/3 \times \pi \times (6.378 \times 10^6 \text{ m})^3$$
$$M = 3.26 \times 10^{24} \text{ kg}$$

Surface gravity is the same as the acceleration due to gravity, $g = GM/r^2$. $g = 6.67 \times 10^{-11} \times 3.26 \times 10^{24}$ kg/ $(6.378 \times 10^6 \text{ m})^2$. $g = 5.3 \text{ m/s}^2$.
Escape speed is given in *More Precisely 5-1*. The mass, in Earth masses, is $3.26/5.97 = 0.55$ and the radius is 1.0.

$$v_{escape} = 11.2 \sqrt{\frac{0.55}{1.0}} = 8.3 \text{ km/s.}$$

2. Newton's law of gravity states that the gravitational force is proportional to the product of the masses and inversely proportional to the square of the distance to the center, in this case the radius of the Moon. With 1/4 Earth radius, the Moon's gravity will be $1/(1/4)^2$ times larger, or 16 times. But

the Moon's mass is 80 times less than Earth's. The result is 16/80 = 0.2. The Moon's gravity is one-fifth the gravity of Earth.

The astronaut plus backpack have an equivalent weight of 150 kg.
 The weight on Earth would be 150 kg x 9.8 m/s^2 = 1470 newtons.
 The weight on the Moon would be 1470 newtons x 0.2 = 294 newtons.

It's important to note that although the weight of the astronaut and backpack changes, the mass (150 kg) remains the same.

3. Find the surface area of Earth: Area = $4\pi \times (6.378\times106$ m$)^2 = 5.11\times10^{14}$ m^2. Thus, 0.5% of this is 2.56×10^{12} m^2. The volume of ice in the Antarctic will be this area times the depth, about 3 km or 3000 m. Volume = 7.67×10^{15} m^3.
The oceans cover 71% of the surface area, or $(0.71)(5.11\times10^{14}$ m$^2)= 3.63\times10^{14}$ m^2. Spreading the volume above over this area will give an increase in depth of $(7.67\times10^{15}$ m$^3)/(3.63\times10^{14}$ m$^2)$ = 21 m.

4. If the full Moon is directly overhead, it has to be midnight for the observer, so that Sun is at the nadir. The force of gravity for the Earth and Sun are in the same direction, but the force of gravity from the Moon is opposite these other two forces. The tidal force of the Moon is the difference between the force of the Moon on the person standing on the surface of Earth and the force of the Moon on the person (hypothetically) at the center of Earth. So, the tidal force is $\dfrac{GMm}{(r-R)^2} - \dfrac{GMm}{r^2}$,

where M is the mass of the Moon (7.3×10^{22} kg), m is the mass of the person, r is the distance from Earth to the Moon (380,000,000 m), and R is the radius of Earth (6,400,000 m). For a 70-kg person, the result is a tidal force of 8.16×10^{-5} N.
Repeat for the Sun, using $M = 2\times10^{30}$ kg and $r = 1.5\times10^{11}$ m. For a 70-kg person, this tidal force is 3.54×10^{-5} N.
The weight of the person is $mg = (70$ kg$)(9.8$ m/s$^2) = 686$ N. Find the fractional reduction the tidal forces cause in this weight:
$$1 - [(686 - 8.16\times10^{-5} + 3.54\times10^{-5})/686] = 6.7\times10^{-8}.$$

5. The total volume of Earth is $V = (4/3)\pi r^3$.
The volume of the inner core is $V_{inner} = (4/3)\pi r_{inner}{}^3$, so the ratio of the two is:
$(r_{inner}/r)^3 = (1300/6378)^3 = 8.4\times10^{-3}$.

The outer core has a radius of 3500 km, so its volume is the volume of a sphere of radius 3500 km minus the volume of the inner core: $V = (4/3)\pi(3500)^3 - (4/3)\pi(1300)^3$. The ratio of this to the total volume of Earth is $(3500^3 - 1300^3)/6378^3 = 0.16$, or about 16% of Earth's total volume.

The mantle is about 3000 km thick:
$(6363^3 - 3363^3)/6378^3 = 0.85$, or 85% of the volume of Earth.
The crust is only 15 km thick. Following the reasoning above, the crust comprises only
$(6378^3 - 6363^3)/6378^3 = 0.007$, or 0.7% of the volume of the Earth.

6. The volume of the atmosphere is the surface area of Earth times the thickness of the atmosphere: $4\pi \times (6.378\times10^6$ m$)^2 \times 7500$ m $= 3.83\times10^{18}$ m^3. This volume multiplied by the density will give the total mass of the atmosphere: 3.83×10^{18} m$^3 \times 1.3$ kg/m$^3 = 5.0\times10^{18}$ kg. The mass of Earth is

5.97×10^{24} kg; dividing shows that the mass of the atmosphere is about 8.4×10^{-7} times the mass of Earth.

7. Because the luminosity in Stefan's law is proportional to T^4, compare Earth at 250 K to Earth at 290 K: $(250 / 290)^4 = 0.55$. Subtracting this from 1 gives 0.45, or 45%.

8. Earth's diameter is 2×6378 km = 12,756 km. At 5 km/s, the time it will take is:
    $(12,756$ km$) / (5$ km/s $) = 2551$ s, or about 43 minutes.

9. From the text, a 10-km crater is formed about every 10 million years. Such a crater has an area of : $A = \pi r^2 = 78.5$ km^2. The surface area of the Moon, assuming it is a spherical shape, is $4\pi \times (1738$ km$)^2 = 3.8 \times 10^7$ km^2. Dividing this area by the area of a 10-km crater gives the number of such craters needed to cover the entire surface: 3.8×10^7 km^2 / 78.5 km$^2 = 4.8 \times 10^5$. Multiplying this result by 10 million years gives 4.8 trillion years, about 1000 times longer than the age of the solar system.

    The cratering rate for 10-km craters would have to be approximately 1000 times what it is today in order to have cratered the Moon in the 4.6 billion years since its formation. This would be one 10-km crater every 10,000 years. That's rather often!

10. Set up a ratio: the angle is to 360° as the distance on the Moon is to the circumference of a circle at the Moon's distance. Change degrees to arc seconds.

$$\frac{0.05''}{360° \times 3600''/°} = \frac{d}{2\pi(384,000 \text{ km})}$$

$$d = 0.093 \text{ km or } 93 \text{ m.}$$

Note: The advanced camera for surveys on the Hubble space telescope was used to image the Aristarchus Crater on the Moon in UV/Vis on August 21, 2005. Each pixel covered an estimated 50 to 100 meters, which agrees very well the above estimate.

Resource Information

Student CD Media Resources

Interactive Student Tutorials
Atmospheric Lifetimes
The Greenhouse Effect

Movies/Animations
Seasonal Changes on the Earth
One Small Step
Photographs of Full Rotation of the Moon
Northern and Southern Lights

Transparencies

72.	Table 5.1	Some Properties of Earth and the Moon
	Figure 5.1	Earth and Moon
73.	Figure 5.2	Lunar Tides

Materials

The video *Aurora: Rivers of Light in the Sky,* produced by Skywater Films, Alaska, has some excellent footage of aurora as well as discussion of myth, tradition, and fact surrounding this phenomena.

Simple supplies to demonstrate the connection between electricity and magnetism include a battery, a nail, and wire. To demonstrate magnetic fields, try the Fisher Science "Deluxe Magnetic Field Apparatus" (item S43059-1). It allows students to see iron filings align with the magnetic field in three dimensions.

Suggested Readings

"Looking back at Apollo." *Scientific American* (July 1999). p. 40. A pictorial tribute in recognition of the 30th anniversary of the Apollo 11 lunar landing.

"Origins: special section on the origin and evolution of the Earth." *Earth* (Waukesha, Wis) (Feb 1998). p. 23. A special section devoted to articles about the origin and evolution of Earth.

Anderson, Robert. "Earth from above: Earth photos (from space) on the Internet." *Natural History* (Sept 1997). p. 16. Reviews web sites which contain images of Earth taken from space.

Anderson, Robert. "Plates in motion: plate tectonics Internet sites." *Natural History* (Apr 1999). p. 24. Reviews web sites that feature information about plate tectonics.

Banerjee, S. "When the Compass Stopped Reversing Its Poles." *Science* (2 March 2001), v. 291. p. 1714. An accessible short article on the long-term behavior of Earth's magnetic field.

Beatty, J. Kelly. "Clementine's lunar gold." *Sky & Telescope* (Feb 1997). p. 24. A report on the Clementine mission's possible discovery of water ice on the Moon.

Bell, Jim. "Dome sweet dome: lunar volcanism." *Astronomy* (Oct 1998). p. 94. Describes how to observe lunar volcanic domes with a typical amateur telescope.

Binder, Alan B. "Lunar Prospector: overview." *Science* (Sept 4 1998). p. 1475. A summary and overview of the Lunar Prospector mission.

Culler, Timothy S., Becker, Timothy A., and Muller, Richard A. "Lunar impact history from $^{40}Ar/^{39}Ar$ dating of glass spherules." *Science* (Mar 10 2000). p. 1785. Discusses a recent analysis of the ages of glass spherules found in lunar soil, and relates this to the rate of cratering on the lunar surface.

Dalziel, Ian W. D. "Earth before Pangaea." *Scientific American* (Jan 1995). p. 58. A look at the relative location of the North American continent over geologic time.

Davis, Bill. "The mountains of the Moon." *Sky & Telescope* (Nov 1998). p. 114. Describes an observing project to determine the elevation of lunar features by observing the length of their shadow.

Eicher, David. "Earth is a planet, too: three-dimensional photography." *Astronomy* (Dec 2000).   p. 50. Presents topographic images of Earth.

Foust, Jeffrey A. "NASA's new Moon." *Sky & Telescope* (Sept 1998). p. 48. Describes the results from the Lunar Prospector mission, with particular emphasis on the evidence for water ice on the lunar surface.

Hodge, Paul. "Naming the man in the Moon." *Astronomy* (Feb 1999). p. 82. An interesting discussion on the origin of names for lunar features.

Hoffman, Paul F. and Schrag, Daniel P. "Snowball Earth." *Scientific American* (Jan 2000). p. 68. Discusses the evidence of major climate reversals on Earth.

Karl, Thomas R., Nicholls, Neville, and Gregory, Jonathan. "The coming climate: meteorological records and computer models predict a warmer world." *Scientific American* (May 1997). p. 78. Describes a method of climate modeling based on past meteorological records.

King, Michael D. and Herring, David D. "Monitoring Earth's vital signs." *Scientific American* (Apr 2000). p. 92. Describes how information obtained by the Terra satellite is used to study Earth.

Rubincam, David P., Chao, B. Fong, and Bills, Bruce G. "The incredible shrinking tropics." *Sky & Telescope* (June 1998). p. 36. Describes effects of changes in Earth's obliquity.

Stewart, G. "Measuring Earth's Magnetic Field Simply." *The Physics Teacher* (February 2000) p. 113. An easy and popular activity to measure Earth's magnetic field.

Taylor, S. Ross and McLennan, Scott M. "The evolution of continental crust." *Scientific American* (Jan 1996). p. 76. Discusses the conditions on Earth which allowed the development of our continental crust.

Tyson, Neil De Grasse. "Tide and time." *Natural History* (Nov 1995). p. 18. Discusses the effects of the tidal interaction between Earth and the Moon.

Valley, John W. "A Cool Earth Earth?" *Scientific American* (Oct 2005). p. 58. Discusses the evidence of an early Earth that was much cooler and wetter than once thought.

Wood, Charles A. "Tycho: the metropolitan crater of the moon." *Sky & Telescope* (Aug 1999). p. 120. One of many articles by the author discussing individual features visible on the Moon.

Wright, K. "Seeing the Light." *Discover* (July 2000). p. 51. A very complete discussion of auroras, with great pictures.

Notes and Ideas

Class time spent on material: Estimated: _____   *Actual:* _____

Demonstration and activity materials:

Notes for next time:

Chapter 6: The Terrestrial Planets
A Study in Contrasts

Outline

Summary

Chapter 6 thoroughly investigates the terrestrial planets Mercury, Venus, and Mars, comparing them to Earth and the Moon. Physical characteristics, orbital and rotation properties, atmospheres, surface features, and interiors are discussed. The history and evolution of the planets are outlined and compared to Earth's. Photographs taken by several space probes are included in this chapter. The chapter ends with a brief description of the moons of Mars.

Major Concepts

- Orbits and physical properties
- Appearance from Earth
- Rotations
    - Comparisons
    - Venus's retrograde rotation
    - Mercury's spin-lock orbit
- Atmospheres
    - Current compositions
    - Evolution of atmospheres
    - Greenhouse effect
    - Escape velocity of gases
- Interiors
    - Differentiation
    - Layers
    - Magnetic fields
- Surfaces
    - Unique features
    - Cratering
    - Space probes' investigations

Teaching Suggestions and Demonstrations

Now that the students have studied Earth from an astronomer's perspective, they can investigate the other planets and compare them to our home planet. Throughout this chapter and the next, try to point out unique features and special characteristics of each of the planets. Have students discuss the conditions that led to these individualities. For instance, Venus's distance from the Sun resulted in a runaway greenhouse effect, and Mercury's distance is responsible for its very long solar day.

Sections 6.1 through 6.3

Before showing Table 6.1 of **planetary properties**, sketch a blank table on the board or overhead and have students make some educated guesses about some of the properties. They can estimate sizes, distances from the Sun, densities, orbital periods, and even surface gravities of the other terrestrial planets based on what they know about Earth. (Show Figure 4.3 again so that students can compare sizes.) You can also have them guess periods of rotation, though they will very likely be far off!

A few students can come to the front of the room and create a moving model of the **orbits** of the first few planets to show why Venus has been dubbed "the morning or evening star." Venus's angular distance from the Sun is never more than 47°, and Mercury's is even smaller. We never see these planets if we are star-gazing at midnight! Mars, however, orbits outside the Earth so it is not restricted to positions close to the Sun in the sky.

Both Venus and Mercury have odd **rotations**, and in Mercury's case at least it is due to its proximity to the Sun and the resulting tidal forces. Mercury is in a 3:2 spin-orbit lock, with a period of rotation of 59 days and a period of revolution of 88 days. Go through the diagrams in Figure 6.4 carefully to show why this results in Mercury having a solar day that is two Mercury years long! On Earth, the difference between the solar day and the sidereal day is only four minutes, so we tend to think of them as the same thing. The case of Mercury emphasizes their difference. Venus also has a very slow rotation; furthermore, it is backwards.

Mars, in contrast, has a period of rotation very similar to Earth's. The tilt of its axis is also very similar to Earth's, giving it seasonal variations somewhat like ours. These characteristics have made Mars a prime candidate for science fiction stories about colonizing another planet.

The **atmospheres** of the four terrestrial planets are dramatically different from each other. Go through an escape-velocity calculation to show why Mercury cannot hold onto an atmosphere. Venus has more than enough atmosphere, but it results in a very inhospitable environment. The temperatures of both of these planets are very different from what you might expect based solely on their distances from the Sun. Mercury gets much colder than expected, because its solar day is so long and it has no atmosphere to hold in the heat. Venus is much hotter than expected because of the runaway greenhouse effect.

The atmosphere of Venus is not only responsible for its high temperature but also for a very high **pressure**. Depending on their science backgrounds, your students may not be familiar with the definition of pressure. To demonstrate, bring in a variety of types of footwear. The same person (you, for instance) wearing high heels, tennis shoes, or snowshoes always exerts the same *force* on the ground when standing still, but not the same *pressure*. Atmospheric pressure is due to the weight of all the air pushing down on the surface of Earth. We hardly notice, because we live with atmospheric pressure all the time. Bring a barometer to class and explain how it works. The pressure on the surface of Venus is about 90 atm, about equivalent to the pressure you would feel if you were 1000 meters under the surface of the ocean!

Sections 6.4 through 6.6

Show lots of pictures of the **surfaces** of Mercury, Venus, and Mars. You can even throw in a few of Earth, too. The greens and blues are refreshing after viewing the surfaces of the other planets! Discuss the spacecraft visits to the planets and their importance in providing information. The images of Venus from

Magellan are incredible, as are the *Viking* and *Pathfinder* images of Mars. You can have fun naming features on the surfaces. (For instance, the corona shown in Figure 6.16 has been dubbed "Miss Piggy.") Try to get students to compare conditions on the planets to explain differences in surface features. Why is Mercury the most heavily cratered? It has no erosion. Why are the volcanoes on Mars larger than those on Earth? Mars has a lower surface gravity. Figure 6.13 shows a map of Venus in comparison with a map of Earth. Be sure to look out for false color images of the terrestrial planets showing elevation. Blue is often used to show the lowest elevation. This can foster a misconception that there are currently oceans and seas on Venus and Mars.

Sections 6.7 through 6.9

Figure 6.32 shows an excellent comparison of the **interiors** of Earth, Mars, Mercury, and the Moon. Note especially the large core of Mercury. Ask students why Mercury doesn't therefore have a strong magnetic field. Both a conducting core and a high rate of rotation are needed for the creation of a magnetic field, and Mercury is missing the rotation part. Of all the inner solar system planets, Earth is the only one that appears to be still geologically active.

Section 6.8 returns to the discussion of **atmospheres**. Figure 6.33 directly compares the atmospheres of Venus and Earth. Give examples of infrared radiation being blocked, such as the heating up of the inside of a car sitting in the sun. Go through the greenhouse process and particularly why the greenhouse effect on Venus is characterized as *runaway*. The lack of liquid water on the surface of Venus plays a large role in the process. Discuss these changes on Venus in terms of changes in the CO_2 cycle on Venus. First discuss the CO_2 cycle on Earth which requires volcanism, precipitation, carbonate rock formation, followed again by volcanism. On Venus, precipitation was removed from the cycle, since CO_2 couldn't be removed from the atmosphere of Venus, the runaway greenhouse effect started. Take time to discuss global climate change on Earth and the debate surrounding the greenhouse effect. Venus and the Earth can be somewhat directly compared because they have very similar masses and their cooling rates are about the same. Venus is often referred to as Earth's "sister planet." Mars, on the other hand, went through a different change in the cycle. On Mars, volcanism was removed from the cycle because Mars cooled and became geologically inactive about 3.5 billion years ago. Since CO_2 was not put back up in the atmosphere, it was subsequently locked away in the geology of Mars. You should resist the temptation to directly compare Mars and Earth. Mars has much less mass than Earth and has geologically cooled much faster than the Earth has. Compare the masses of Earth, Venus, and Mars using Table 6.1.

Discuss the polar ice cap on Mars shown in Figure 6.6 and Figure 6.28. **(DEMO!!)** Bring in a sample of solid CO_2 (dry ice) to class to demonstrate how it sublimates from a solid to a gas phase. This is why the polar ice caps of Mars appear to disappear from one pole and reform at the opposite pole as the Martian seasons change.

The chapter ends with a brief look at the two **moons of Mars**. They are aptly named Phobos (fear) and Deimos (terror) to accompany the god of war. Compare the moons to asteroids. Their irregular shapes and low densities make them much more like asteroids than like our Moon. It appears that the Earth–Moon system is unique in the inner solar system.

When it is time to review, show lots of pictures of the planets in random order and have students identify them. Be sure your students can distinguish between images that are taken from Earth-bound telescopes and images from spacecraft. They should be able to justify their answers with physical characteristics or reasoning. You can also list unique characteristics and have students identify the planet described by each. Be sure to discuss various missions to Mars with your class. Mars is currently being explored by many different missions that many countries contribute to. Mars is frequently in the news, so news articles can be used to foster class discussions. Many of these missions are listed in Table 6.2.

Student Writing Questions

1.   One entire side of Mercury has never been imaged; *Mariner 10* always viewed the same side. What do you think the other side might look like? Can an argument be made that it should look vastly different? Or will it be a repeat of the known side, except for details? Could you present a convincing argument for returning to Mercury to study its other side?

2.   We tend to think of Mercury, Venus, and Mars as having inhospitable environments for life. But there might also be some advantages to living on one of these planets. Choose one and make a "sales pitch" with regard to its advantages over Earth or other planets. Think of yourself as a realtor with a big commission at stake.

3.   Get a picture of a Viking image from the surface of Mars. What can be learned from this one image about Mars, its environment, its surface, and its atmosphere?

4.   Bacterial forms of life are known to exist several kilometers deep in Earth's crust. Is it possible that similar life might exist on one of the other terrestrial planets? Argue for and against this idea for Mercury, Venus, and Mars. Include consideration of the requirements for life such as water, appropriate temperature, protective environment, and any others that occur to you.

5.   From what you now know of orbital motion, plan a trip to Mars, from Earth, where Mars is at the aphelion of the trajectory and Earth is at the perihelion. How long will the trip take? How long would you want to have to explore Mars? How many people do you think such a trip should take? What sort of provisions would you have to take along? What would you miss most about Earth and home?

Answers to End of Chapter Exercises

Review and Discussion

1.   The extreme temperature variations of Mercury are, in part, due to its lack of an atmosphere. An atmosphere helps to insulate the surface of a planet from cooling at night. Mercury's very long day (slow rotational period) also plays a role. The Sun is up for a long period, allowing the rock to heat up. With an equally long night, there is ample time to cool down to a low temperature. Earth, in contrast to Mercury, rotates rapidly and has less time to heat up to high temperatures or cool down to low temperatures.

2.   Mercury, for its small size, has a high density. This indicates it has a relatively large metallic core. The fact that Mercury has a magnetic field, though small, lends further evidence that this core, which was differentiated when Mercury was young and molten, is relatively large.

3.   Mercury is composed of higher-density material, on average, than is the Moon. Both differentiated when young; however, the Moon has at best a small core, and Mercury has a large core. The Moon cooled faster than Mercury, which may account for the Moon having visible maria. These impacts had to have occurred when the Moon was rather young, with a thin crust. Both the Moon and Mercury, though, show similar histories of cratering, although Mercury does not appear as heavily cratered. Many of its oldest craters have been covered over by lava flows, more extensive than those that formed the maria on the Moon. It is unclear why this is the case.

4. Schiaparelli, in the mid-nineteenth century, believed he had measured Mercury's rotation to be synchronous with its orbit. In that sense it was similar to our Moon and its orbit around Earth. The smallness of Mercury and its proximity to the Sun helped to further this image of the "Sun's moon." But in 1965, radar observations determined the true rotation of Mercury to be shorter: 59 days, not 88 days.

5. Venus is the third brightest object in the sky, after the Sun and the Moon. It is completely covered by very reflective clouds so that much of the sunlight received by Venus is reflected back into space. Venus also is one of the closest planets to Earth, depending on where it is in its orbit. This also helps make Venus appear bright. Its brightness depends on its phase and distance from Earth.

6. The dynamo model for the production of planetary magnetic fields requires both an iron-rich core and a relatively rapid rate of rotation. Venus lacks the rapid rotation and therefore does not appear to produce a magnetic field. Actually, the fact that it does not have a magnetic field strongly suggests that the dynamo model is correct.

7. At one time, Venus was believed to have a warm, tropical environment. In the 1950s, radio observations of Venus measured its thermal emission. The radiation emitted by Venus has a Planck curve spectrum characteristic of a temperature near 600 K. It was hardly a tropical, habitable planet.

8. The dominant component of the atmosphere of Venus is carbon dioxide. It accounts for 96.5 percent of the atmosphere by volume. Almost all of the remaining 3.5 percent is nitrogen. Trace amounts of other gases, such as water vapor, carbon monoxide, sulfur dioxide, and argon, are also found. The clouds are made of sulfuric acid.

9. The runaway greenhouse effect is a process by which an increased atmospheric temperature increases greenhouse gases, which in turn increase the atmospheric temperature even more. Water and carbon dioxide are both greenhouse gases. When Venus was young, even with some liquid water, its higher temperature, due to its closeness to the Sun, increased atmospheric water and raised its temperature. This did not allow carbon dioxide to remain dissolved in the oceans, forcing it out into the atmosphere and further increasing the greenhouse effect and the temperature.

10. The soil of Mars has a large amount of iron oxide in it (i.e., rust). This gives Mars its red or rust color.

11. River and stream channels are certain evidence that water once flowed on the surface of Mars. The same might be said for similar features in some of Earth's most arid deserts, where water may flow for only a matter of hours during an entire year. But the water flow on Mars is not seasonal as it is on Earth. There is no evidence for liquid water on the surface of Mars today. Liquid water cannot exist on Mars today because the atmospheric pressure is too low; the water would immediately boil into a gas and would be evident in the atmosphere of Mars. But this is not observed; Mars has little water in its atmosphere. Frozen water does exist in the polar ice caps and, potentially, there still may be large amounts of water present in the crust of Mars, below the surface.

12. Gravity on Mars is only 40 percent of what it is on Earth. The height to which a shield volcano grows depends on its ability to support it own weight. With lower gravity, the volcanoes grow correspondingly higher.

13. There is plenty of carbon dioxide to create a greenhouse effect, just no significant atmosphere to be warmed by it. The atmosphere of Mars is less than one percent that of Earth and produces little insulation to keep the surface warm.

14.   A few pros and cons. There is not much to breathe on Mars! Its atmosphere is less than a hundredth that of Earth's atmosphere. Even if you could breathe such a thin atmosphere it would not do you much good; it is composed mostly of carbon dioxide. Note, though, that this is not necessarily true for some simple plants, which absorb carbon dioxide (as all plants do) and might be able to survive in this thin atmosphere.

Water might be obtained from the ice caps of Mars or from subsurface deposits. Air to breathe would be more difficult to come by. Oxygen could be extracted from the oxides in the surface soils, but nitrogen would be rare and have to be imported. Carbon dioxide for growing plants could be collected and concentrated from the atmosphere. Energy would have to come from sunlight, but Mars receives less than half the sunlight Earth receives per square meter. There are many other environmental factors that could be discussed here.

15.   All three planets had their secondary atmospheres produced by outgassing of their volcanoes. Abundant quantities of water and carbon dioxide were likely produced in all three cases. Now, however, the evolution of these atmospheres depends on the planet's distance from the Sun. Really, it is just the story of the three bears: one that was too hot, one that was too cold, and one that was just right. Venus, at the closest distance, was warmer and very likely never had liquid water on its surface. Both water and carbon dioxide are efficient greenhouse gases, so Venus warmed up quickly to a high temperature. Its atmospheric water was subsequently destroyed by solar ultraviolet light.

Mars, being the farthest from the Sun of these three planets, likely had liquid water in which carbon dioxide could dissolve. This allowed the carbon dioxide to become bound into the crustal rocks of Mars. Now, the greenhouse effect, which had kept Mars modestly warm, lessened and the surface temperature of Mars dropped. Water eventually froze out, further reducing the greenhouse effect and making Mars even cooler. The remaining atmosphere has been continually reduced by the effects of solar ultraviolet light.

Earth developed similarly to Mars. Temperatures did not rise, like in the case of Venus, because the carbon dioxide become dissolved in the oceans and subsequently incorporated into Earth's crust. However, being closer to the Sun, Earth's temperature did not drop so low as to freeze out water. The small amount of carbon dioxide and water vapor in Earth's atmosphere has maintained a modest greenhouse effect that has kept the environment at a relatively constant, comfortable temperature. It is just right for life! Of course, life has altered Earth's atmosphere and produced a significant amount of oxygen (from plant life). Animal life continues to exhale carbon dioxide and inhale oxygen. Now a new balance exists. Life on Earth has both created this balance and depends on it for its own existence.

Conceptual Self-Test

True or False? 1. T 2. F 3. T 4. T 5. T 6. F 7. F

Multiple Choice 8. b 9. b 10. d 11. c 12. b 13. b 14. a 15. c

Problems

1.   Mercury's semi-major axis is 57.9 million km and the eccentricity of its orbit is 0.206. It is closest to the Earth when it is farthest from the Sun, at aphelion. This distance is:
$$a(1 + e) = 57.9 \times 10^6 \text{ km } (1 + 0.206) = 6.98 \times 10^7 \text{ km.}$$

Earth is 1.5×10^8 km from the Sun, so the distance between the two planets is (1.5×10^8 km $- 6.98 \times 10^7$ km) $= 8.02 \times 10^7$ km. The time needed for a radar signal to make a round trip is:

$$t = d/v = 2(8.02 \times 10^7 \text{ km})/(3 \times 10^5 \text{ km/s}) = 535 \text{ s} = 8.9 \text{ minutes.}$$

2. Set one-sixth of the escape speed equal to the average molecular speed:

$$\frac{11.2}{6}\sqrt{\frac{M}{R}} = 0.157\sqrt{\frac{T}{(\text{molecular mass})}} \text{ , where } R \text{ is the radius of Mercury in Earth radii (0.38), } T$$

is the daytime temperature on Mercury (around 700 K), and the molecular mass of nitrogen is 28. Solving for M yields:

$$M = (0.157)^2 \times (700/28) \times (6/11.2)^2 \times 0.38 = 0.0671 \text{ Earth masses, about 22\% more than Mercury's}$$

actual mass.

3. The volume of the atmosphere is the surface area of Venus times the thickness of the atmosphere.

$$4/3 \, \pi \, (6.052 \times 10^3 \text{ km} + 50 \text{ km})^3 - 4/3 \, \pi \, (6.052 \times 10^3 \text{ km})^3 = 2.3 \times 10^{10} \text{ km}^3 = 2.3 \times 10^{19} \text{ m}^3.$$

The volume multiplied by the density gives the total mass of the atmosphere:

$$2.3 \times 10^{19} \text{ m}^3 \times 21 \text{kg/m}^3 = 4.9 \times 10^{20} \text{ kg.}$$

This is 98 times the mass of the Earth's atmosphere (see Chapter 5, problem 6.)
It is $(4.9 \times 10^{20}$ kg$)/(4.87 \times 10^{24}$ kg$) = 10^{-4}$ times the mass of Venus.

4. The circumference of Venus is $2\pi \times 6051$ km $= 38,020$ km. The distance covered in 4 days or 96 hours gives 400 km/hr. A kilometer is about 5/8 of a mile, so this is about 250 miles per hour.

5. At closest approach, Venus and Earth are 0.28 A.U. apart.

$$\frac{1'}{360° \times 60'/°} = \frac{x}{2\pi \times (0.28 \times 1.5 \times 10^8 \text{ km})}$$

The smallest feature that can be distinguished is therefore $x = 1.22 \times 10^4$ km.

Change the angle to 0.1" in the above formula for the infrared telescope. The result is then $x =$ about 20 km. This is smaller than the large impact craters, so yes, an infrared telescope could distinguish them.

6. Use Kepler's third law, $P^2 = a^3/M$, with a in A.U. and M, the mass of Venus in this case, in solar masses. First, find the semi-major axis, a. The altitude of the satellite is the distance above the surface of the planet. Therefore, the major axis of the elliptical orbit will be the maximum altitude, plus the minimum altitude, plus the diameter of Venus. The semi-major axis is half this value:
$$a = [294 \text{ km} + 8543 \text{ km} + (2 \times 6053 \text{ km})]/2 = 10,470 \text{ km} = 6.98 \times 10^{-5} \text{ A.U.}$$
In solar masses, the mass of Venus is $(4.87 \times 10^{24}$ kg$)/(2 \times 10^{30}$ kg$) = 2.44 \times 10^{-6}$ solar masses.

The period is therefore $P = \sqrt{\dfrac{(6.98 \times 10^{-5})^3}{2.44 \times 10^{-6}}} = 3.73 \times 10^{-4} \text{ yr} = 197 \text{ min.}$

Using the 1993 orbital data, $a = [180 \text{ km} + 541 \text{ km} + (2 \times 6053 \text{ km})]/2 = 6414 \text{ km} = 4.28 \times 10^{-5}$ A.U. This semi-major axis corresponds to a period of 94 min.

7. Surface gravity is proportional to mass divided by the radius squared. In Earth units, the mass of Mars is 0.11 and the radius is 0.53, so $0.11/(0.53)^2 = 0.39$.
A 70-kg person would have a weight of $70 \text{ kg} \times 9.8 \text{ m/s}^2 = 686$ newtons.
On Mars, the person's weight would be $686 \times 0.39 = 268$ newtons.

It's important to note that, although the weight changes, the mass remains the same.

8. Ten million metric tons of water, with 1000 kg per metric ton, gives 10^{10} kg. The density of water is 1000 kg/m^3. Dividing the mass of water by its density will give its volume, or 10^7 m^3. This is the volume that flows each second. The cross-sectional area of the channel is ($100 \text{ m} \times 10,000 \text{ m} = 10^6$ m^2. Dividing volume/second by area gives a speed of 10 m/s.

9. The volume of the layer of water is the surface area of Mars times the depth of the water:

$$4\pi \, (3.4 \times 10^6 \text{ m})^2 \times 2 \text{ m} = 2.9 \times 10^{14} \text{ m}^3.$$

This volume multiplied by the density of water will give the total mass of water.

$$2.9 \times 10^{14} \text{ m}^3 \times 1000 \text{kg/m}^3 = 2.9 \times 10^{17} \text{ kg}.$$

Comparing this to the mass of Mars gives:

$$2.9 \times 10^{17} \text{ kg} / 6.4 \times 10^{23} \text{ kg} = 4.5 \times 10^{-7}.$$

Comparing this to the mass of the atmosphere of Venus gives:

$$2.9 \times 10^{17} \text{ kg} / 4.9 \times 10^{20} \text{ kg} = 5.9 \times 10^{-4}.$$

10. To find the angular diameter in arc seconds, use the following ratio. Note that the distances are the distances to the moons minus the radius of Mars, since the observer is standing on the surface.

For Phobos: $\dfrac{\text{angle}}{360° \times 60'/°} = \dfrac{(28 \text{ km})}{2\pi(9500 \text{ km} - 3394 \text{ km})} = 16'.$

For Deimos: $\dfrac{\text{angle}}{360° \times 60'/°} = \dfrac{(16 \text{ km})}{2\pi(23,500 \text{ km} - 3394 \text{ km})} = 2.7'.$

The angular diameter of the Sun seen from Mars is 19', so an observer would not see an eclipse.

Resource Information

Student CD Media Resources

Interactive Student Tutorials
None

Movies/Animations
Transit of Mercury
Composite Image of Mars
Mars Polar Cap

Transparencies

Materials

Barometers are helpful in discussing atmospheric pressure. Shoes (from high heels to snowshoes) can be used to discuss the concept of pressure.

The Astronomical Society of the Pacific has Mars and Venus globes (item numbers OA 211 and OA 195) showing major features of these planets.

Earth globes can be purchased from many retail outlets.

Dry ice is available from your local industrial supply company or perhaps a friendly chemist that you might know, since dry ice is often used in chemistry labs.

The video *Mars: Past, Present, Future* (Holiday Space and Science Series) is an excellent description of Mars, including how it has been viewed in the past and our current understanding of this planet.

Suggested Readings

Nature (Feb 18 1999). This issue features four articles on results from the Mars Orbiter Camera.

Science (Mar 13 1998). This issue features several articles on results from Mars Global Surveyor.

Science (Dec 5 1997). This issue features several articles on results from the Mars Pathfinder mission.

Beatty, J. Kelly. "In search of Martian seas." *Sky & Telescope* (Nov 1999). p. 38. Debates the hypothesis that Mars once had large oceans.

Bell, Jim. "Mars Pathfinder: better science?" *Sky & Telescope* (July 1998). p. 36. Discussed the early results from the Mars Pathfinder mission.

Bullock, Mark A. and Grinspoon, David H. "Global climate change on Venus." *Scientific American* (Mar 1999). p. 50. Discusses the hypothesis that volcanism and climate change on Venus are linked.

Carroll, Michael. "Postcards from Mars." *Astronomy* (Aug 2005). p. 40. Gives a good overview of what the Spirit and Opportunity rovers have learned in the first 1.5 years on the Martian surface.

Golombek, M. P., Cook, R. A., and Economou, T. "Overview of the Mars Pathfinder Mission and assessment of landing site predictions." *Science* (Dec 5 1997). p. 1743. An overview of the results from the Mars Pathfinder mission.

Golombek, Matthew P. "The Mars Pathfinder mission." *Scientific American* (July 1998). p. 40. A summary of the Mars Pathfinder mission.

Grinspoon, David H. "Venus unveiled." *Astronomy* (May 1997). p. 44. Describes the observations of impact craters on Venus and discusses the implications about the history of the surface.

Hartmann, William K. "Invading Martian territory." *Astronomy* (Apr 1999). p. 46. Discusses results from all the instruments on Mars Global Surveyor, including the spectrometer, the altimeter, the magnetometer, as well as the imaging camera.

Hartmann, William K. "Red planet renaissance." *Astronomy* (July 2000). p. 36. Traces the evolution of our thought about the age and geologic activity of Mars, including a discussion of the Martian meteorites and recent Mars Global Surveyor results.

Kargel, Jeffrey S. "The rivers of Venus." *Sky & Telescope* (Aug 1997). p. 32. Discusses lava flows on Venus.

Kerr, Richard A. "A wetter, younger Mars emerging." *Science* (Aug 4, 2000). p. 714. Reports on the evidence for geologically recent water seepage on Mars.

Krupp, E. C. "Beyond the pale: the planet Mercury is the go-between from day to night, just as its namesake was the courier for the spirit world." *Sky & Telescope* (Mar 1998). p. 88. An interesting discussion of the mythology associated with Mercury.

Krupp, E. C. "The camera-shy planet: Venus." *Sky & Telescope* (Oct 1999). p. 93. Discusses the history of observing cloud-covered Venus.

Krupp, E. C. "Falling for the evening star." *Sky & Telescope* (May 1996). p. 60. Discusses the mythology associated with Venus.

Krupp, E. C. "War stars." *Sky & Telescope* (July 1997). p. 80. Discusses the mythology associated with Mars.

Lubick, Naomi. "Goldilocks and the three planets." *Astronomy* (July 2003). p. 36. Compares evolution of the atmospheres of Venus, Earth, and Mars and their ability to sustain life.

Malin, Michael C. "Visions of Mars." *Sky & Telescope* (Apr 1999). p. 42. A photo essay featuring the favorite images from the Mars Orbiter Camera by the camera's designer.

Musser, George. "The Spirit of Exploration." *Scientific American* (Mar 2004). p. 52. A summary of the Mars Spirit rover mission a month into the mission.

Naeye, Robert. "Back to Mars: three-dimensional photography." *Astronomy* (Dec 2000). p. 38. Features three-dimensional images from Mars Pathfinder.

Naeye, Robert. "Europe's Eye on Mars." *Sky & Telescope* (Dec 2005). p. 30. The camera on the Mars Express Orbiter is providing a whole new perspective on the red planet.

Nelson, Robert M. "Mercury: the forgotten planet: profile of one of Earth's nearest neighbors." *Scientific American* (Nov 1997). p. 56. A summary of what we know about Mercury, and the possibilities and difficulties in its exploration.

Palucka, Tim. "Living on Mars Time." *Astronomy* (Mar 2006). p. 42. Discusses challenges that controllers of the Spirit and Opportunity Martian rovers face when having to adjust their internal Earth clocks to Martian time.

Panek, Richard. "Venusian testimony." *Natural History* (June 1999). p. 68. Discusses Galileo's observations of the phases of Venus, and how this observation contributed to the heliocentric model of the solar system.

Parker, Samantha. "Images: Venus." *Sky & Telescope* (Aug 1995). p. 54. Features Magellan images of Venus.

Paulson, Murray. "Your guide to observing Mars." *Astronomy* (Mar 1997). p. 88. Although written for the 1997 Mars observing season, this article provides useful general information, especially the use of colored filters, for observing subtle features on Mars.

Peterson, Carolyn Collins. "Welcome to Mars!" *Sky & Telescope* (Oct 1997). p. 34. Summarizes the Mars Pathfinder results, and includes a stunning panoramic view of the Martian surface as seen by Pathfinder.

Robinson, Cordula. "Magellan reveals Venus." *Astronomy* (Feb 1995). p. 32. Summarizes the results of the Magellan mission at Venus.

Rogan, Josh. "Pathfinder's 3-D extravaganza." *Astronomy* (Mar 1998). p. 61. A summary of Mars Pathfinder results with a section of three-dimensional images.

Sheehan, William and Dobbins, Thomas. "Charles Boyer and the clouds of Venus." *Sky & Telescope* (June 1999). p. 56. Discusses the pre-Mariner discovery of the rotation period of cloud tops on Venus.

Sheehan, William and Dobbins, Thomas. "Mesmerized by Mercury." *Sky & Telescope* (June 2000). p. 109. Describes the history of observations of Mercury.

Solomon, Sean C., Bullock, Mark A., and Grinspoon, David H. "Climate change as a regulator of tectonics on Venus." *Science* (Oct 1 1999). p. 87. Discusses the relation between tectonics, volcanism, and climate change on Venus.

Tytell, David. "Martian mudflows." *Sky & Telescope* (Sept 2000). p. 56. A short report on the observation of young water outflow features on Mars.

Zuber, Maria T. "Snapshots of an ancient cover-up." *Nature* (Feb 18, 1999). p. 560. An overview of four other articles in the same issue which summarize results from the Mars Orbiter Camera.

Notes and Ideas

Class time spent on material: Estimated:_____   *Actual:_____*

Demonstration and activity materials:

Notes for next time:

Chapter 7: The Jovian Planets
Giants of the Solar System

Outline

Summary

Chapter 7 explores the planets Jupiter, Saturn, Uranus, and Neptune in detail. Their general properties, atmospheres, and interiors are discussed. Spacecraft visits to these planets are briefly outlined.

Major Concepts

- The view of the jovian planets from Earth
- Spacecraft visits to the jovian planets
- Discoveries of Uranus and Neptune
- General properties
    - Size, mass, density, surface gravity
    - Rotation
- Atmospheres
    - Compositions
    - Appearance
    - Bands, spots, and weather
- Interiors
    - Layers
    - Magnetospheres
    - Internal heating

Teaching Suggestions and Demonstrations

Before starting your lecture, take a **"concept inventory"** of your class to see what they might already know about the jovian planets. Discovering prior knowledge that your students may have is very important to the teaching process. Author Paul Green discusses this in his book *Peer Instruction for Astronomy* starting on page 11. He also includes **"concept tests"** for the planets that can be used throughout the lecture. These can be used in conjunction with additional **"clicker questions"** that are provided with the instructor materials.

At the beginning of the chapter, review with students the list of comparisons between the terrestrial and the jovian planets that was generated in Chapter 4. You can use Jupiter as the prototype jovian planet, and compare the others to it. Remember to compare them to Earth as well. On the other hand, one could compare Jupiter to our Sun due to its composition, since all the jovian planets have compositions more like our Sun than our Earth. Continue to emphasize a special characteristic of each planet. Jupiter and

Saturn are easy; Jupiter is the largest and the home of the **Great Red Spot**, and Saturn has the most spectacular ring system. A unique characteristic of Uranus is its rotation axis, which is tilted so that it is nearly parallel to the planet's orbital plane, instead of nearly perpendicular as with the other planets. **Neptune's Great Dark Spot** and the fact that its orbit is crossed by Pluto's orbit can be highlighted. You might consider using *Lecture Tutorials for Introductory Astronomy* by Adams. On page 61 of the Adams work, there is a very useful activity entitled, "Temperature and Formation of Our Solar System." This activity shows the importance of temperature along the early proto-planetary disk and how it determined the various types of planets that formed. The position of Jupiter is particularly important, because it is approximately where water freezes into a solid and thus making formation of the jovian planets possible. In practice, these lecture tutorials may take longer than what you had anticipated. So, be flexible and patient when including these "learner-centered" activities during your lecture.

Sections 7.1 and 7.2

During class try using **Starry Night Pro** software to show the locations of Jupiter and Saturn in the Night Sky, because they are both naked-eye planets. This software can also show the positions of **Uranus** and **Neptune**, but they aren't naked-eye planets and won't be as interesting if you are limited to making only naked-eye observation with your class. Using Starry Night as a demo during class takes some practice to become familiar with the operation of the software and it's something you should definitely try out before class. By using Starry Night during class, you'll encourage your students to install and try the software on their own. If you'd like to pass out pre-made customized sky charts to your class, try using **SkyChart** because it can offer a wider field of view than Starry Night does.

If **Jupiter and Saturn** are up during the night while you are teaching this course, try to arrange observing sessions for your students. Students will appreciate seeing these planets with their own eyes since it gives them "ownership" of the night sky that we all share. Even with a small telescope, Jupiter's bands and the Great Red Spot are visible, and Saturn's rings are beautiful. If you do not have access to a telescope, you can at least point out the locations of the planets and have students follow their motions through the background stars over the course of the semester. Encourage students to view Jupiter through binoculars as well. Although little or no detail will be visible, they will be able to see that Jupiter is a disk (unlike stars, which appear as points). Even better, the four Galilean moons are visible through binoculars.

Briefly discuss the **spacecrafts** that have visited the jovian planets, and try to give students a feel for the complexity of the missions. One obvious point is that the spacecrafts are aiming for moving targets! The *More Precisely* box (page 199) that covers gravitational slingshots is very interesting. Also have students consider what happens to the spacecrafts after their missions are complete. *Galileo* was directed into the planet Jupiter at the end of its lifetime. However, the *Voyager* spacecraft wandered out of our solar system. The book *Murmurs of Earth: The Voyager Interstellar Record*, by Carl Sagan and others, details the record of pictures and sounds constructed to send along with the craft should it ever be found by extraterrestrials. The idea of other intelligent beings possibly finding a spacecraft from Earth is very interesting to students. Impress upon them that the process of deciding what to include in the record is fascinating by itself. If you have time, divide students into small groups and charge each team with deciding upon a list of pictures and sounds they would choose to represent Earth. You could also assign this as a group project to be completed outside of class.

Emphasize to students the excitement surrounding the **discovery of Uranus**. This event was, after all, the first time a new planet had been *discovered* rather than just known from ancient times. The **discovery of Neptune** is also an important event in the history of science, because it was actually predicted after astronomers observed Uranus's orbit and determined something was influencing it. The discovery of Neptune is considered historically as a crowning achievement of **Newton's universal law of gravitation**. Contrast the two types of discoveries and ask students if they can think of other examples of each.

Section 7.3

Begin your discussion of the **bulk properties and characteristics of the jovian planets** by reminding students of the sizes of these planets compared to each other and to Earth and the Sun. Bring back the various spheres you used in Chapter 4 or create a new scale model. **Figure 7.5** also shows the planets to scale. Display figures of the individual planets as well, and ask students how they differ. The colored bands and spots on Jupiter are even more remarkable when compared to the duller Saturn and the nearly nondescript Uranus. Ask students to keep these differences in mind and see how they can be explained as you discuss the planets further. **Table 7.1** compares less obvious characteristics as well. Using the surface-gravity values, students can calculate how much they would weigh on each of the jovian planets. As students examine the table, ask them what stands out. Jupiter has a very large magnetic field, unlike the other jovian or terrestrial planets, and Saturn's density is lower than the density of water. The general tendency is that the density of the planets decreases as their distance from the Sun increases. There are some "glitches" in this trend though, namely Earth, Uranus, and Neptune. Discussing these glitches could serve as a great advanced topic for group discussions.

A third characteristic that is unique is the **tilt of Uranus's rotation axis. (DEMO⚡)** Demonstrate this using a globe for Uranus and another sphere for the Sun. When discussing Earth, students should have noticed that the tilt of the axis does not change as Earth orbits the Sun; the same applies to Uranus, although it seems very strange in this case. Ask students to imagine seasonal variations on this planet and also to hypothesize about what could be the cause of such a dramatic tilt. Uranus's moons orbit equatorially, so a collision event that knocked Uranus "sideways" seems somewhat unlikely. While discussing rotation, also be sure students understand differential rotation.

Saturn is the most oblate of the planets. Its rapid rotation has the effect of "pulling" the equator away from the planet. **(DEMO⚡)** Demonstrate this by taking a simple spring (typical spring constant of 20 N/m) with closed loops on both ends. Attach a small mass (e.g., 100 g) to one end and insert a small rod through the other loop. Twirl the mass and spring, showing that as the period of rotation increases, the mass moves outward.

Sections 7.4 through 7.6

Figure 7.9 and **Figure 7.14** can be used to compare the **atmospheres** of Jupiter and Saturn, respectively. They are very similar in structure but different in size. Saturn is smaller than Jupiter, but has a cloud layer about three times as thick. See if students can figure out that the reason for this is Saturn's smaller gravity. The thickness of the clouds results in a less colorful appearance, because the higher clouds block our view of the lower layers. Spend some time looking in detail at Jupiter's beautifully colored belts, zones, and spots. The Great Red Spot is about two Earth diameters in length. Cut out an oval to scale and paste it on the sphere representing Jupiter; this can be compared to the Earth model to convince students of the relative sizes. The longevity of the Great Red Spot on Jupiter also surprises students. Contrast it with the Great Dark Spot on Neptune, which has already disappeared. A great analogy of the Great Red Spot on the Earth is a hurricane. Take an informal student concept inventory about what makes a hurricane weaken and what makes a hurricane strengthen. There is enough coverage of hurricanes in the media that many students will already know that hurricanes weaken over land and strengthen when they travel over warm water. This need for a heat source under the storm can be likened to the internal heat given off by Jupiter that has kept the Great Red Spot active for at least 340 years and probably longer.

Try using the **animation** "Galileo's Mission to Jupiter" to give students insight into planetary exploration. You might consider not using the narration provided, but you can easily narrate the animation yourself. The narration provided is best for students who are reviewing the material on their own. Similarly, the animation of "Saturn's Storm" can be used the same way.

Use **Figure 7.20** to compare the **interiors** of the four jovian planets. Liquid hydrogen is a difficult concept for students; they are familiar with hydrogen only as a gas. A liquid metal is also an unfamiliar concept. (**DEMO‼**) Bring some mercury to class to show students. Remember that mercury is a hazardous material, so handle it appropriately. Discuss the tremendous pressure inside Jupiter and Saturn (due to their large gravities) and contrast with Uranus and Neptune, which do not have enough mass to compress hydrogen to its metallic form. Try using the animation entitled "Gas Giants II" to show differences in the jovian interiors. Again, using the narration provided will be up to each instructor.

Jupiter's **magnetic field** is strikingly large compared to all other planets in the solar system. As discussed previously, a rapid rotation and metallic interior are necessary for a strong magnetic field. Jupiter has both. Uranus and Neptune are missing the metallic hydrogen and so have weak magnetic fields. The relatively weak magnetic fields of Uranus and Neptune are likely produced by dissolved ammonia in the "slushy" water layers of these two planets. **Figure 7.23** summarizes the magnetic and rotational properties of the four jovian planets.

As with the terrestrial planets, review by showing lots of photos of the jovian planets and ask students to identify each image and explain their reasoning. Then have students list characteristics held in common by all the jovian planets, as well as a couple of unique properties of each.

Student Writing Questions

1. You are in a spacecraft descending through the planet Jupiter. First you move slowly through the atmosphere and then more quickly through the interior. The spacecraft, being indestructible, protects you completely but allows you to observe the environment. Describe what you see and feel.

2. Imagine you have discovered life in the atmosphere of Jupiter. Describe what it is like and how it has adapted to its environment. Please, use your imagination, but remember that the environment must be consistent with what we know about Jupiter.

3. Discuss how you believe Uranus became tilted into its present position. Choose whether it happened while being formed or at a later date. Which of these is more likely?

Answers to End of Chapter Exercises

Review and Discussion

1. Uranus was discovered by the British amateur astronomer William Herschel in March 1781. Herschel was engaged in charting the faint stars when he came across an odd-looking object that he described as "a curious either nebulous star or perhaps a comet." It appeared as a disk in Herschel's telescope and moved relative to the stars, but too slowly to be a comet. Herschel had found the solar system's seventh planet.

2. As astronomers observed Uranus, they realized its positions were different from what was predicted. Using perturbation theory, an eighth planet was predicted to be affecting the orbit of Uranus due to its gravitational influence. The predictions were refined, and in time Neptune was discovered close to the predicted position. The discovery of Neptune championed Newton's universal law of gravitation.

3. The jovian planets have retained most or all of their original atmospheres for two reasons. They are all fairly massive planets and, as such, have sufficiently strong gravity to hold an atmosphere of hydrogen and helium. Second, they are located in the outer part of the solar system where temperatures are lower. The atoms and molecules of gas cannot attain a high enough velocity to escape the jovian planets' gravity.

4. The equatorial regions of Jupiter appear to rotate faster than the polar regions. This is known as *differential rotation*. It is the first indication that Jupiter is not solid. The faster motion of the atmosphere at the equator gives rise to a wind moving at about 300 km/h relative to the overall rotation of Jupiter's interior.

5. Because Saturn has weaker gravity than Jupiter owing to its lower mass, its cloud layers are thicker, not as compressed as on Jupiter. Saturn is farther from the Sun and has a cooler temperature than does Jupiter. This produces a thicker layer of ammonia clouds on top, which hides the more colorful cloud layers that occur deeper in the atmosphere.

6. Saturn's atmosphere is cooler than Jupiter's because of its greater distance from the Sun. Because of Saturn's weaker gravity, its atmosphere is 2.5 times deeper than Jupiter's. The cloud layers are similar to Jupiter's but thicker; the top layer of ammonia ice hides much of the cloud features below it. Saturn's atmosphere is underabundant in helium because it has precipitated out. Each cloud layer on Saturn is about three times the thickness of the corresponding layer on Jupiter.

7. The Great Red Spot is a reddish-colored area in Jupiter's atmosphere that has been seen for over 300 years. It is a region of swirling, circulating winds like a whirlpool or a terrestrial hurricane. It is about twice Earth's diameter in length. The source of its energy appears to come from the zonal atmospheric flows to its north and south. However, there are still some uncertainties as to how it continues to be maintained.

8. The nature of Jupiter's coloration isn't fully understood. The "zonal" clouds are white and composed of ammonia ice. The yellows and browns are found in lower clouds, which contain ammonium hydrosulfide ice. It is possible that sulfur, phosphorus, or their compounds contribute to these clouds. One reason for the differences in coloration is thought to be the temperature differences between the belts (relatively warm) and the zones (relatively cooler). Since the cloud chemistry involving sulfur and phosphorus are very dependent on temperature of the clouds, the colors can vary dramatically. Below these clouds are bluish clouds of water ice. Saturn is described in answer 6.

    Methane gas efficiently absorbs red light. Uranus and Neptune have increasing abundance of methane compared to Jupiter or Saturn. Reflected sunlight from Uranus and Neptune thus has less red light and is mostly blue. Because Uranus has less methane than Neptune, it appears more blue-green; Neptune appears quite blue.

9. See answers to questions 5 and 8 above. Jupiter has the most colorful appearance, because its topmost layer of clouds is thinner and has more gaps than the corresponding layer on Saturn; thus the colorful lower layers can be seen. The blue color of Uranus and Neptune is due to the higher percentage of methane in their atmospheres which absorb red light and reflect blue light.

10. When Jupiter formed, gravity compressed its gases, causing the temperature to rise. The atmosphere has allowed this energy to slowly leak out of Jupiter, causing it to continue to emit more energy than it receives from the Sun.

11. Saturn radiates about three times as much energy as it receives from the Sun. It is also observed to have helium in a lower abundance in its atmosphere than would be expected. A model suggests that helium condenses out in the cool atmosphere of Saturn and rains into the interior. The result of this helium precipitation depletes the outer layers of helium. But as the helium moves inward, it becomes compressed and heated. This energy must then be radiated away and can account for Saturn's excess emissions.

12. It is the rotational axis of Uranus that is so unusual. It has a tilt of 98° relative to its orbit. At times during its orbit around the Sun, the north or south poles can actually point toward the Sun.

13. Magnetic fields, in general, are produced by rapid rotation and some sort of electrically conducting material in the interior of the object. Jupiter has a rotation rate of just under 10 hours and a large amount of liquid metallic hydrogen in its interior.

14. Because they have lower masses than Jupiter or Saturn, both Uranus and Neptune do not have liquid metallic hydrogen in their interiors. They may also have thick layers of slushy water with ammonia dissolved in it. This ionic layer could produce the magnetic fields of these planets.

15. Jupiter's clouds were known, but details of their motions were sketchy. Its smallest moons were discovered by *Voyager* but even its largest moons were nothing but points of light. No one knew what these moons looked like. *Voyager* also discovered Jupiter's ring and magnetosphere. Saturn was known to have some moons, seen as nondescript points of light, and three major rings. Generally, Saturn was seen as almost featureless. Uranus and Neptune were difficult to image, although color differences were known ever since their discoveries. Uranus had only five known moons, and Neptune had only two. Uranus was discovered to have a ring system using stellar occultation measurements. There was similar information suggesting a ring system around Neptune, but it was rather uncertain. Nothing was known about any features on any of the moons.

Conceptual Self-Test

True or False? 1. F 2. T 3. F 4. T 5. T 6. F 7. T 8. T

Multiple Choice 9. a 10. d 11. d 12. b 13. c 14. a 15. b

Problems

1. Since this problem deals with small angles, you can find the length that corresponds to 0.05" at the certain distance by setting up a ratio:
$$(\text{angle}/360°) = (\text{length}/\text{circumference}).$$

   So the smallest size that the *Hubble Space Telescope* can resolve is:
   $$\text{length} = \text{angle}/(360° \times 3600 \text{ "}/°) \times (2\pi r).$$

   For Jupiter: length = $[.05"/(360° \times 3600 \text{ "}/°)] \times (2\pi \times 4.2 \text{ A.U.} \times 1.50 \times 10^8 \text{ km/A.U.}) = 150$ km.
   For Neptune: length = $[.05"/(360° \times 3600 \text{ "}/°)] \times (2\pi \times 29 \text{ A.U.} \times 1.50 \times 10^8 \text{ km/A.U.}) = 1100$ km.

2. At closest approach, Neptune and Uranus are (4498 million km) − (2871 million km) = 1627 million km apart. The gravitational force between them will be $F = G\, m_1 m_2/r^2$:

   $$F = (6.67 \times 10^{-11} \text{Nm}^2/\text{s}^2) (8.68 \times 10^{25} \text{ kg})(1.02 \times 10^{26} \text{ kg})/(1.63 \times 10^{12} \text{ m})^2 = 2.2 \times 10^{17} \text{ N}.$$

The gravitational force between Uranus and the Sun is:

$F = (6.67 \times 10^{-11} \text{Nm}^2/\text{s}^2) (8.68 \times 10^{25} \text{kg})(1.99 \times 10^{30} \text{kg})/(2.87 \times 10^{12} \text{ m})^2 = 1.4 \times 10^{21}$ N.

This is 6400 times larger than the force on Uranus from Neptune at closest approach.

3. Distance = speed × time, so the time for the light to travel to Jupiter and back would be
    $t = d/v = 2(4.2 \text{ A.U.} \times 1.50 \times 10^8 \text{ km/A.U.})/(3 \times 10^5 \text{ km/s}) = 4200$ s = 1.17 hours.
    A spacecraft orbiting Jupiter would travel $d = (20 \text{ km/s})(4200\text{s}) = 84,000$ km.

4. You must assume that the diameter is to remain constant. In this case, the density is proportional to the mass. If the density is proposed to be 0.08 kg/m^3 and Jupiter's true density is 1330 kg/m^3, this is a reduction of 16,600, so the mass is reduced by this same factor.
    (1/16,600) Jupiter masses = 6×10^{-5} Jupiter masses.

5. Use the law of gravity from *More Precisely 1-2* to compare the force of gravity for Jupiter to Earth's gravity. Jupiter is 318 times more massive and 11.2 times larger than Earth:
    $$\frac{318}{11.2^2} = 2.54$$
    Thus, Jupiter's gravity is 2.54 times that of Earth's gravity. Doing the same for Saturn gives
    $$\frac{95}{9.5^2} = 1.05.$$
    Comparing Jupiter to Saturn gives 2.54 / 1.05 = 2.4.

6. From Table 7.1, the surface temperature of Jupiter is 120 K. The average molecular speed can be calculated from the formula given in *More Precisely 5-1*:
    $$\text{avg. molecular speed} = 0.157\sqrt{(120/2)} = 1.22 \text{ km/s}.$$
    Using the rule of thumb discussed in *More Precisely 5-1*, a body that has an escape speed equal to six times this average molecular speed will be able to hold its atmosphere. Find the corresponding mass using the equation given:

    $m = v^2 r/11.2^2 = (6 \times 1.22)^2 \times (11 \text{ Earth radii})/11.2^2 = 4.7$ Earth masses.
    This mass is 1.5% of Jupiter's actual mass.

7. Saturn's equatorial radius is 60,000 km. Its circumference is $2\pi R$ or 377,000 km. At 1500 km/h, it should take 377,000/1500 = 251 hours = 10.5 days for the flow to encircle the planet.

8. (Energy emitted from Saturn/ Energy from Sun at Saturn) = 3
    (Energy from Saturn/3) = Energy from Sun at Saturn
    Using Stefan's law,
    $(97)^4 / 3 = T^4$. T = 74 K.

9. First, calculate the mass of Uranus inside the core. Use the definition of density:
    $m = \rho V = (8,000 \text{ kg/m}^3) [(4/3)\pi(2 \times 6.4 \times 10^6 \text{ m})^3] = 7.03 \times 10^{25}$ kg.

    The entire mass of Uranus is given as 8.7×10^{25} kg, so the mass outside the core is
    $(8.7 \times 10^{25} \text{ kg} - 7.03 \times 10^{25} \text{ kg}) = 1.7 \times 10^{25}$ kg.

    The fraction of the planet's mass that is core is therefore 7.03/8.7 = 0.81 or 81%.

10. Neptune's surface temperature is 59 K. Using Wien's law gives:

λ_{max} = (0.29 cm)/T = (0.29 cm)/59 = 0.0049 cm = 49 μm, which is in the infrared.

Resource Information

Student CD Media Resources

Interactive Student Tutorials
Jupiter- Differential Rotation

Movies/Animations
Galileo Mission to Jupiter
Saturn Storm
The Gas Giants Part II
Strange X-ray Pulses from Jupiter

Transparencies

97.	Figure 7.1	Jupiter
98.	Figure 7.2	Saturn
99.	Figure 7.3	Uranus
100.	Figure 7.4	Neptune
101.	Table 7.1	Planetary Properties
	Figure 7.6	Jovian Planets
102.	Figure 7.7	Seasons on Uranus
103.	Figure 7.8	Jupiter's Convection
	Figure 7.11	Jupiter's Red Spot
104.	Figure 7.9	Jupiter's Atmosphere
	Figure 7.14	Saturn's Atmosphere
105.	Figure 7.20	Jovian Interiors
106.	Figure 7.21	(Pioneer 10) Mission
107.	Figure 7.23	Jovian Magnetic Fields

Materials

Slide sets of NASA images of the jovian planets obtained by spacecraft flybys are available from the Public Information Office, Jet Propulsion Laboratory, California Institute of Technology. Order online at www.finley-holiday.com.

NASA keeps many images available for download at www.NASA.gov. This is an extensive website, but is organized by specific missions. It might take some time to find what you're looking for, but it is well worth it.

Items useful for demonstrations in this chapter include a mass on a spring and a sample of mercury.

Suggested Readings

"Galileo probes Jupiter's atmosphere." *Science* (May 10 1996). p. 837. This issue contains a special section devoted to the Galileo mission results.

Beatty, J. Kelly and Levy, David H. "Crashes to ashes: a comet's demise." *Sky & Telescope* (Oct 1995). p. 18. A detailed summary of the analysis of observations from the 1994 impact of comet Shoemaker-Levy 9 on Jupiter.

Beatty, J. Kelly. "Galileo: an image gallery III." *Sky & Telescope* (July 1999). p. 40. Showcases images from the Galileo mission.

Burnham, Robert. "Into the maelstrom." *Astronomy* (Apr 1996). p. 42. Describes the results from Galileo's atmospheric probe.

Carroll, M. "The Long Goodbye." *Astronomy* (October 2003). p. 37. A retrospective of the entire Galileo Mission to Jupiter, from Galileo's arrival to Jupiter system to the controlled entry of Galileo into Jupiter's atmosphere.

Dobbins, Thomas and Sheehan, William. "Jupiter's deep mystery: South Equatorial Belt." *Sky & Telescope* (Dec 1999). p. 118. Describes observations of Jupiter's South Equatorial Belt.

Gould, Stephen Jay. "The sharp-eyed lynx, outfoxed by nature. Part one: Galileo Galilei and the three globes of Saturn." *Natural History* (May 1998). p. 16. Discusses Galileo's and other historic observations of Saturn.

Johnson, Torrence V. "The Galileo mission to Jupiter and its moons." *Scientific American* (Feb 2000). p. 40. Summarizes Galileo mission results about each of the Galilean moons and the Jupiter atmospheric probe.

Kenyon, S. "Cosmic Snowstorm." *Astronomy* (March 2004). p. 43. Discusses computer models of planet formation. Specifically the importance of ice crystals in the formation of objects in the outer solar system.

Krupp, E. C. "Managing expectations." *Sky & Telescope* (Aug 2000). p. 83. Discusses the discovery of Uranus.

Krupp, E. C. "The fountains of Neptune." *Sky & Telescope* (Sept 1996). p. 66. Discusses mythology associated with Neptune and its moons.

Levy, David H., Shoemaker, Eugene M., and Shoemaker, Carolyn S. "Comet Shoemaker-Levy 9 meets Jupiter." *Scientific American* (Aug 1995). p. 84. A summary of observations from the impact of comet Shoemaker-Levy 9 on Jupiter written by the discoverers of the comet.

Lunine, Jonathan I. "Neptune at 150." *Sky & Telescope* (Sept 1996). p. 38. Provides a summary of our knowledge of Neptune.

McAnally, John W. "A Jupiter observing guide." *Sky & Telescope* (Oct 2000). p. 124. Offers advice on observing the features on Jupiter.

Moore, Patrick. "The hunt for Neptune." *Sky & Telescope* (Sept 1996). p. 42. Describes the discovery of Neptune.

Oberg, James. "The spacecraft's got swing: the Cassini probe's gravity assist from Earth." *Astronomy* (Aug 1999). p. 48. Discusses the gravity assist maneuver used by the Cassini spacecraft to direct it towards Saturn.

Rogan, Josh. "Bound for the ringed planet: Cassini mission to Saturn." *Astronomy* (Nov 1997). p. 36. An overview of Saturn, its moons and rings, and the Cassini mission.

Sagan, Carl. "The first new planet: William Herschel discovers Uranus in 1781." *Astronomy* (Mar 1995). p. 34. Details the discovery of Uranus.

Sagan, Carl, et al. *Murmurs of Earth: The Voyager Interstellar Record.* Random House, New York, 1978.

Talcott, Richard. "Jumping Jupiter." *Astronomy* (June 1998). p. 40. Reports on results from Galileo shortly after the start of the Galileo Extended Mission.

Ward, William R. and Hahn, Joseph M. "Neptune's eccentricity and the nature of the Kuiper belt." *Science* (June 26 1998). p. 2104. Discusses the relations between the orbit of Neptune and the structure of the Kuiper belt.

Weissman, Paul. "Making sense of Shoemaker-Levy 9." *Astronomy* (May 1995). p. 48. Discusses the analysis of observations made during the impact of comet Shoemaker-Levy 9 on Jupiter.

Notes and Ideas

Class time spent on material: Estimated:_____   *Actual:_____*

Demonstration and activity materials:

Notes for next time:

Chapter 8: Moons, Rings, and Pluto
Small Worlds Among Giants

Outline

Summary

Chapter 8 is broken into three sections. First, the large and medium-sized moons of the solar system are discussed. Their properties and characteristics are presented and they are compared to each other and to our Moon. Next, the ring systems of the jovian planets are explored. The third main topic is the Pluto–Charon system. The chapter ends with a discussion of the current question in astronomy regarding the classification of Pluto as a planet.

Major Concepts

- Moons of the solar system
  - Galilean moons, Titan, and Triton
  - Medium-sized moons
- Ring systems
  - Saturn's rings
  - Ring systems of the other jovian planets
  - Formation and evolution of ring systems
- Pluto
  - Discovery
  - Moon: Charon
  - Classification
- Kuiper-Belt objects

Teaching Suggestions and Demonstrations

Often, students believe that there is not much to the solar system beyond the nine planets, the Sun, and perhaps asteroids. In fact, there are over 90 moons, with widely varying sizes, compositions, and special characteristics. As with the planets, try to emphasize unique properties of these objects. Students are more likely to remember the moons as individual bodies if they can relate special characteristics to them. Also, continue to compare and contrast the different objects. When students point out a difference, ask them what property could account for it.

Sections 8.1 through 8.3

The first two sections discuss the **largest moons** in the solar system. Table 8.1 lists several of their characteristics. It is interesting to point out that although the jovian planets have the vast majority of the moons (all except four, one each for Earth and Pluto, and two for Mars), our own Moon is among the largest. Spend some time having students pick out interesting points from Table 8.1. For instance, notice that the Moon's orbital period is much longer than that of any other large moon. Why? Use the modified form of Kepler's third law and discuss how Jupiter's mass affects the orbital periods of its moons. Also, compare the distances of the various moons in terms of parent planet radii.

(DEMO) **Starry Night Pro** can be used to follow the orbits of the **Galilean moons** around Jupiter. Zoom in and identify one of the moons to follow. Measurements of the orbital distance can be made in order to measure the distance in terms of Jupiter diameters. This distance can be converted to meters. The period can be determined by visually watching the moon to return to the same position relative to Jupiter. Using the period of the moon as well as the distance, the mass of Jupiter can be determined by using **Newton's form of Kepler's third law**. I have tried this in class before, and I'm always amazed how accurate the results can be.

Remind students of the discovery of the **Galilean moons**. (Galileo actually called them the "Medicean stars," in honor of Prince Cosimo II and his brothers of the Medici family, which helped to secure Galileo the position of mathematician to the grand duke.) These moons are visible in a telescope or even with a good pair of binoculars. If Jupiter is up at night during the time you are teaching this course, you can have your students try to track the moons in their orbits around Jupiter as Galileo did. Tracking them is difficult, but your students will at least be able to tell that the positions of the moons are changing.

Each of the large moons has at least one **unique property** that makes it particularly interesting or memorable. Io has active volcanoes, Europa has an ocean of liquid water, and Ganymede is the largest moon in the solar system. Callisto, the fourth Galilean moon, has a large pattern of concentric cracks on its surface. Titan, the largest moon of Saturn, has an atmosphere that is thicker and denser than Earth's. Neptune's large moon, Triton, has nitrogen geysers and an odd orbit; its orbit is tilted 20° and is retrograde, indicating that either something cataclysmic occurred to Triton or it was captured after the formation of the planet. The presence of an atmosphere on one moon and substantial quantities of water on another are particularly intriguing to scientists interested in the possibility of life elsewhere in the solar system.

Io's orange color makes it a unique object in the solar system. The color is attributed to sulfur and sulfur compounds. Sulfur usually appears yellow or pale yellow. **(DEMO)** A very impressive demonstration can be easily done to show how sulfur can appear orange. In a test tube or beaker place some powered sulfur. Heat it slowly over a Bunsen burner or on a hot plate. Be careful not to ignite it! Because its melting point is about 113°C it can safely be heated in boiling water and then "finished" over the flame. When melted, the sulfur will turn an orange or orange/brown color. The color compares nicely to the usual pictures of Io.

Cover that the concept of tidal forces isn't just associated with raising the oceans on the Earth. Tidal heating causes the interiors of Io and Europa, as well as other moons, to be warm inside. This heating, as caused by the flexing on the interior, causes Io to be molten inside and makes Io the most volcanically active object in the solar system.

Consider calculating for students the **angular diameters** of the parent planets as seen from the surfaces of some of their moons. For example, if you were standing on Io, Jupiter would subtend an angle of 20° in the sky. This is 40 times the angle subtended by the Sun from Earth!

The 12 **medium-sized moons** are more uniform than the large moons. They are shown in Figures 8.13 and 8.14 to scale with Earth's Moon. All are locked into synchronous orbits by the gravities of their parent planets. It appears that all contain some water ice as well.

The moons **Europa,** and perhaps **Enceladus**, are thought to be places where the conditions might exist for life namely because there is thought to be subsurface liquid water on both worlds due to tidal heating. Titan is also of interest in terms of life because the conditions there are thought to be similar to the conditions of the early Earth. Each of these worlds is a high priority for space exploration and this spirit of discovery should be conveyed to your students by discussing mission details of the **Galileo, Cassini, Huygens Probe**, as well as future missions.

The **names** of most of the moons in the solar system refer to mythological characters. Often, a connection exists between the names of the moon and its parent planet. For instance, Jupiter is the ruler of the gods, and Ganymede is a cupbearer to the gods. Neptune is the god of the sea, and Triton is his son. Have students look up the names and briefly report on them in class. (See Resource Information for a good Web site, or do your own Web search.)

Section 8.4

Saturn's **rings** are truly spectacular, and even more so when compared in size to Earth as shown in Figure 8.19. (DEMO斤) Pull out your models of the planets and add a scale model of the rings to Saturn to emphasize. Include some detail. Note that although the rings are wide and extend far from the planet, they are also very thin and so are not very apparent when seen edge on. Discuss the Roche limit and the critical role of gravity in the formation and evolution of ring systems. The **shepherd satellites** are one example of the influence of gravity on maintaining a ring system. The fact that Triton is spiraling into the planet and will break up and become a ring someday illustrates the role of gravity in creating rings. Calculate the **Roche limit** for planet Earth and for the Sun.

The rings of Saturn are influenced by Saturn's moon by resonance points of the moon's orbits. This can cause gaps, such as the **Cassini gap**. These gravitational resonance points are also responsible for the fine detail within the ring systems. The moons can also act as shepherd moons, and make a ring thin and distinct. Examples of this effect are the moons **Prometheus** and **Pandora** that cause the **F-ring** of Saturn.

Figure 8.19 compares the **ring systems of the four jovian planets**. Saturn's rings were first noted by Galileo, though he didn't know what they were and reported that the planet looked like it had "ears." The others were discovered fairly recently, either by stellar occultations or spacecraft flybys.

Sections 8.5 and 8.6

Pluto has long been considered the "oddball" in the solar system. Compared to the other planets, it really is strange. Its orbit is more elliptical and more tilted than any other, and its path crosses the path of Neptune. It does not belong with either the terrestrial planets, which are close to the Sun, or the jovian planets, which are gaseous. Its moon, Charon, is more like a smaller twin than a satellite. However, when compared to the moons in the outer solar system or to the more recently discovered **Kuiper-Belt objects (KBOs)**, Pluto does not seem so far out of place at all! Take a vote in your class to see how many students would reclassify Pluto and how many would retain its planet status. Discuss the discovery of KBO 2003U$_{313}$ this question has grown even more interesting. Have a class discussion about whether there should be 8, 9, or 10 (or even more) planets. I've often wondered why asteroids were never considered planets when they were discovred. This could make for an interesting class discussion.

Conclude Chapter 8 with a review slide show of all the inhabitants of the solar system, including planets, moons, rings, asteroids, comets, meteoroids, and the Sun. The next chapter in the text discusses the Sun, so the slide show can serve as a review as well as a bridge to the next material the students will encounter.

Student Writing Questions

1.   You have been given your choice of any moon in the outer solar system to be your own, to do with as you choose. Which one would it be? Why? What natural resources or properties does it have that attracted you to it? What will you do with it?

2.   You are a news reporter 100 million years from now. Describe the series of events that are taking place as Triton approaches Neptune's Roche limit. What is happening to Neptune's smaller moons? How is Neptune being affected?

3.   Explore the issue of the abundance of water throughout the solar system. Where is it most commonly found? Why is this? How does the quantity of water (or ice) compare to the quantity of water on Earth? How did Earth get all its water?

4.   Make the case for the possibility of life existing *inside* of Europa. Discuss the requirements for life and how Europa might provide for all of these. Now, how will we ever determine whether life does exist inside Europa? Speculate on the type of mission that would be needed to settle this question once and for all.

5.   Miranda has just been purchased by the Planetary Holding of Uranus and Neptune (PHUN) Co. for development as an amusement center. With its low surface gravity (calculate this) and shear cliffs up to 5 km high, what sort of unique rides, games, and sporting events could you develop on the surface of Miranda?

Answers to End of Chapter Exercises

Review and Discussion

1.   The densities of the Galilean moons decline with distance from Jupiter, just as the density of terrestrial planets decline with distance from the Sun. Their densities, however, are lower than the terrestrial planets. Water ice is found on three of them; Io is mostly made up of denser material, having lost most of its volatile material. The density decline is likely due to the increased abundance of water and ice.

2.   Io is the most volcanically active object in the solar system. Its surface has no impact craters owing to the constant resurfacing by volcanism. Its colorful surface is the result of sulfur, sodium salts, and other material deposited by eruptions.

3.   Europa appears to be covered by an ocean of water that is frozen on top. If this is true, its ocean might be suitable for supporting life.

4.   Ganymede is internally differentiated, has a small magnetic field, and its surface has evidence of an ice tectonic activity. All of these attributes are consistent with a recent episode of internal heating.

5.   Titan has a thick atmosphere! Although the atmosphere is composed of nitrogen, the *Voyager* probes could not see the surface of Titan because it has a thick layer of haze in its upper atmosphere. The primary layer is from 100 to 200 km above the surface, with two thinner layers at 300 and 400 km elevation.

6. Over the next 100 million years Triton will spiral closer and closer to Neptune. This is caused by its tidal interaction with Neptune and its retrograde orbit. As it reaches the Roche limit of Neptune it will be torn apart, forming a very large ring.

7. Miranda displays a wide range of surface terrains that seems exaggerated for its small size. There are ridges, valleys, and large faults. Apparently, Miranda has been disrupted by forces from within or from without.

8. Saturn has a tilt of 27°. Because its rings are equatorial, we sometimes see them tilted by this amount; at other times we see them edge-on. During Saturn's 30-year orbit around the Sun this orientation changes about every 7 to 8 years. First we see the rings from the north, then edge-on, then from the south, then edge-on again, and finally back to a north view. The thickness of the rings is very small compared to their width, so they nearly disappear when seen edge-on.

9. Collisions between ring particles are predicted to destroy the ring system in a relatively short time compared to the age of the solar system. If this is the case then either the rings were recently formed or they are replenished by new material.

10. Mimas is the cause of the Cassini Division. Ring particles in the Cassini Division have an orbital period twice that of Mimas. They feel a gravitational pull from Mimas at the same place in their orbit every time they are the closest to Mimas. These particles are therefore pulled out of the orbit of the Cassini Division.

11. Shepherd satellites are small moons with orbits on either side of a ring. They gravitationally confine the material to a very narrow ring by pushing on the particles when they orbit. Saturn's F ring has two shepherd satellites.

12. Uranus has nine distinct rings. They are dark, narrow, and widely spaced. Saturn's rings are bright, wide, and close together. Both systems of rings, however, are very thin. Neptune has four dark rings, two quite narrow and two quite broad and diffuse. One of the rings is apparently "clumped" in places for unknown reasons, producing the appearance of partial ring arcs from Earth.

13. Irregularities in the orbits of Uranus and Neptune suggested a ninth planet. Percival Lowell predicted the location of this planet but could not find it. Finally, Clyde Tombaugh, in 1930, discovered this planet and it was named Pluto. However, this discovery turned out to be purely serendipitous because the irregularities in the orbits of Uranus and Neptune were not real.

14. Pluto's size and density are more similar to the moon Triton than they are to any other object in the solar system. It is neither rocky like the terrestrial planets nor gaseous and liquid like the jovian planets. Pluto also has an icy surface like Triton.

15. In the 1980s, eclipses of Charon and Pluto were observed. Timing of the eclipses gives the diameters, as both the size of the orbit and its circular nature are known. Kepler's third law allows the combined mass of Pluto and Charon to be determined. If their densities are assumed to be the same, then their individual masses may be determined from their volumes.

Conceptual Self-Test

True or False? 1. T 2. T 3. T 4. T 5. F 6. T 7. T 8. F

Multiple Choice 9. a 10. c 11. c 12. b 13. d 14. c 15. b

Problems

1. The inner edge of Saturn's B ring has a radius of 92,000 km. The orbital speed of particles there is:

$$v = \sqrt{GM/R} = \sqrt{(6.67 \times 10^{-11} \, \text{Nm}^2/\text{kg}^2)(5.7 \times 10^{26} \, \text{kg}) \Big/ (9.2 \times 10^7 \, \text{m})} = 20.3 \, \text{km/s.}$$

By comparison, the speed of the Earth satellite would be:

$$v = \sqrt{(6.67 \times 10^{-11} \, \text{Nm}^2/\text{kg}^2)(6.0 \times 10^{24} \, \text{kg}) \Big/ (6.4 \times 10^6 \, \text{m} + 500,000 \, \text{m})} = 7.6 \, \text{km/s.}$$

This is less because Saturn's mass is much greater than Earth's.

2. According to Kepler's third law, the ratio of P^2/a^3 is the same for Io and the other satellite:
$$\frac{42^2}{6^3} = \frac{10^2}{x^3} \; ; \; x = 2.3 \text{ Jupiter radii.}$$

3. The acceleration due to gravity from Jupiter at Io's center is:

$$g = GM/R^2 = (6.67 \times 10^{-11} \, \text{N m}^2/\text{kg}^2) \times (1.9 \times 10^{27} \, \text{kg})/(4.22 \times 10^8 \, \text{m})^2 = 0.7116 \, \text{m/s}^2.$$

At the surface of Io closest to the planet, the acceleration due to Jupiter is different because the distance is the distance between Io and Jupiter minus the radius of Io:

$$g = (6.67 \times 10^{-11} \, \text{N m}^2/\text{kg}^2) \times (1.9 \times 10^{27} \, \text{kg})/(4.22 \times 10^8 \, \text{m} - 1.82 \times 10^6 \, \text{m})^2 = 0.7178 \, \text{m/s}^2.$$

The difference in these two accelerations is 0.0062 m/s^2.

Io's mass is 1.22 times the mass of the Moon, or 8.9×10^{22} kg. Therefore, its surface gravity is:
$$g = (6.67 \times 10^{-11} \, \text{N m}^2/\text{kg}^2) (8.9 \times 10^{22} \, \text{kg})/(1.82 \times 10^6 \, \text{m})^2 = 1.8 \, \text{m/s}^2.$$

The tidal acceleration is $(0.0062/1.8) = 0.0034$ or 0.34% of the surface gravity.

Repeating the calculation for the Moon and Earth yields a tidal acceleration of 2.4×10^{-5} m/s^2 and a surface gravity of 1.6 m/s^2. The ratio is 1.5×10^{-5}.

4. Titan has a mass of 1.83 Moon masses = 1.35×10^{23} kg and a radius of 2.58×10^6 m. Its surface gravity is: $g = (6.67 \times 10^{-11} \, \text{N m}^2/\text{kg}^2) \times (1.35 \times 10^{23} \, \text{kg})/(2.58 \times 10^6 \, \text{m})^2 = 1.35 \, \text{m/s}^2$. This is close to 1/7 of Earth's surface gravity, which is 9.81 m/s^2.

For the escape speed, find the mass and radius of Titan in terms of Earth's mass and radius.

Mass = (1.83 Moon masses)(0.012 Earth masses per Moon mass) = 0.022 Earth masses.
Radius = 2580 km/6400 km = 0.403 Earth radii.

$$\text{Escape speed} = 11.2\sqrt{\frac{0.022}{0.403}} = 2.6 \text{ km/s}.$$

5. In each case the angular diameter can be found by setting up a ratio of (angular diameter to 360°) = (diameter of object to 2π times distance to object from Jupiter's cloudtops).

$$\frac{\theta}{360°} = \frac{diameter}{2\pi(dist)}.$$

In calculating the angular diameter of the Sun, the radius of Jupiter is negligible compared to the distance to the Sun. However, for the moons, the radius of Jupiter must be subtracted from the Jupiter–moon distance.

The angular diameter of the Sun: $\theta = (360°)(2 \times 7\times10^5 \text{ km})/(2\pi \times 7.8\times10^8 \text{ km}) = 0.10° = 6'$.

For Io: $\theta = (360°)(2 \times 1820 \text{ km})/[2\pi \times (4.2\times10^5 \text{ km} - 7.1\times10^4 \text{ km})] = 0.60° = 36'$.

For Europa: $\theta = (360°)(2 \times 1570 \text{ km})/[2\pi \times (6.7\times10^5 \text{ km} - 7.1\times10^4 \text{ km})] = 0.30° = 18'$.

For Ganymede: $\theta = (360°)(2 \times 2630 \text{ km})/[2\pi \times (1.07\times10^6 \text{ km} - 7.1\times10^4 \text{ km})] = 0.30° = 18'$.

For Callisto: $\theta = (360°)(2 \times 2400 \text{ km})/[2\pi \times (1.88\times10^6 \text{ km} - 7.1\times10^4 \text{ km})] = 0.15° = 9'$.

Yes, it would be possible to see a solar eclipse from Jupiter's cloudtops.

6. Escape speed is given by: $v_{esc} = \sqrt{(2GM/r)}$, and density = $\rho = M/V$. Rearranging, $M = \rho V = \rho(4/3)\pi r^3$. Substitute this expression for mass into the equation for escape speed and then solve for r, the radius of the moon:

$$r = \frac{v}{\sqrt{(2G\rho\frac{4}{3}\pi)}} = \frac{40 \text{ m/s}}{\sqrt{(2\times6.67\times10^{-11}\text{Nm}^2/\text{kg}^2)(2000 \text{ kg/m}^3 \times \frac{4}{3}\pi)}} = 38,000 \text{ m} = 38 \text{ km}.$$

7. Determine first the mass of a typical ring particle of 6-cm radius = 0.06 m. The mass will be the volume times the density:
$$\text{mass} = [(4/3)\pi(0.06\text{m})^3] \times 1000 \text{ kg/m}^3 = 0.905 \text{ kg}.$$

The number of ring particles is the total mass divided by the mass of one ring snowball:
$$(10^{18} \text{ kg})/(0.905 \text{ kg}) = 1.1 \times 10^{18}.$$

8. The Roche limit is 2.5 times the planet's radius. For Pluto this is 1137 × 2.5 = 2843 km. Charon's distance is 19,600 km, which is (19,600/2843) = 6.9 times farther out.

9. Because Pluto's mass is 0.0021 Earth masses, your weight will be reduced by this amount. However, because Pluto is smaller than Earth, 0.18 Earth radii, your weight will be multiplied by the square of (1/0.18). The result is 0.065.
    weight = 70 kg x 9.8 m/s² = 686 newtons (on Earth) x 0.065 = 45 newtons (on Pluto)

The mass of Charon is 0.12 times that of Pluto, so your mass will be further reduced by this factor. But its radius is smaller too, by 0.522, so your mass will be multiplied by the square of (1/0.522). The result is 0.44.

weight = 70 kg x 9.8 m/s^2 = 686 newtons (on Earth) x 0.0286 = 20 newtons (on Charon)

It's important to note that, although the weight changes, the mass remains the same.

10. The round-trip distance is 2 × 40 A.U. × 150,000,000 km/A.U. = 1.2 × 10^{10} km. Dividing this by the speed of light, 300,000 km/s, gives 40,000 s or 11.1 hours.

A satellite orbiting Pluto in a circular orbit would travel at a speed of

$$v = \sqrt{GM/R} = \sqrt{(6.67\times10^{-11}\,\text{Nm}^2/\text{kg}^2)(1.27\times10^{22}\,\text{kg}) \Big/ (1,150,000\,\text{m} + 500,000\,\text{m})} = 717\,\text{km/s}.$$

The distance traveled = 717 km/s × 40,000 s = 28,700 km. This corresponds to:
(28,700 km)/ (2π ×1650 km) = 2.8 orbits.

Resource Information

Student CD Media Resources

Interactive Student Tutorials
None

Movies/Animations
Galileo Flyby of Io
Io Cutaway
Jupiter's Moon Europa
Jupiter's Moon Ganymede
Voyager Ring Spokes Animation
Pluto Viewed by HST
Historical Observations of Pluto
Orbits of Neptune and Pluto

Transparencies

108.	Table 8.1	The Large Moons of the Solar System
	Table 8.2	The Medium-Sized Moons of the Solar System
109.	Figure 8.2	Galilean Moons
	Figure 8.3	Galilean Moon Interiors
110.	Figure 8.4	Io
111.	Figure 8.5	Europa
112.	Figure 8.6	Ganymede
113.	Figure 8.7	Callisto
114.	Figure 8.8	Titan
	Figure 8.9	Titan Revealed
115.	Figure 8.10	Titan's Surface
	Figure 8.11	Titan's Atmosphere
116.	Figure 8.12	Triton
117.	Figure 8.13	Saturnian Moons

© 2007 Pearson Prentice Hall, Upper Saddle River, NJ. All rights reserved. This material is protected under all copyright laws as they currently exist. No portion of this material may be reproduced, in any form or by any means, without permission in writing from the publisher.

Materials

The Web site http://www.r-clarke.org.uk/planets/ contains a page for each planet that includes the mythology surrounding the names of the planet and of its moons.

Suggested Readings

Davies, Paul. "New Hope for Life Beyond Earth." *Sky & Telescope* (June 2004). p. 40. Discusses new discoveries on Earth of life in extreme conditions. The possibility of life existing on Europa is highlighted.

Dobbins, Thomas and Sheehan, William. "Beyond the Dawes limit: observing Saturn's ring divisions." *Sky & Telescope* (Nov 2000). p. 117. Discusses the history of observations of Saturn's rings.

Dobbins, Thomas and Sheehan, William. "Saturn's enigmatic crepe ring." *Sky & Telescope* (Sept 1998). p. 116. Describes the discovery of Saturn's C ring.

Elliot, James L. "The warming wisps of Triton." *Sky & Telescope* (Feb 1999). p. 42. Discusses Triton and how we study it with Earth–based observations.

Kerr, Richard A. "Neptune's icy cold satellite comes to life." *Science* (Oct 15 1999). p. 383. A report on observations of Triton which suggest its surface may be younger than previously thought.

Luu, Jane X. and Jewitt, David C. "The Kuiper Belt." *Scientific American* (May 1996). p. 46. Discusses our knowledge of the Kuiper belt.

McEwen, A. S., Belton, M. J. S., and Breneman, H. H. "Galileo at Io: results from high-resolution imaging." *Science* (May 19 2000). p. 1193. Presents high resolution images of Io taken by the Galileo spacecraft in late 1999 and early 2000.

Pappalardo, Robert T., Head, James W., and Greeley, Ronald. "The hidden ocean of Europa." *Scientific American* (Oct 1999). p. 54. A nice summary of the Galileo results on Europa.

Pappalardo, Robert. "Jupiter's Water Worlds." *Astronomy* (July 2004). p. 34. Discusses the evidence for liquid water beneath Europa, Ganymede, and Callisto. The implications for possible life on Europa is also presented.

Reddy, Francis. "The Tenth Planet." *Astronomy* (Nov 2005). p. 48. Discusses the debate about if the newly discovered Kuiper Belt object 2003 UB_{313} should be dubbed the tenth planet. The question is not straightforward.

Showman, Adam P. and Malhotra, Renu. "The Galilean satellites." *Science* (Oct 1 1999). p. 77. Provides a detailed summary of our understanding of each of the Galilean moons.

Tytell, David. "The New Kings of the Kuiper Belt." *Sky & Telescope* (Oct 2005). p. 28. Discusses three new Kuiper Belt discoveries, including $2003UB_{313}$, and how they have transformed the landscape of the outer solar system.

Tytell, David. "Frosting Saturn's Moons." *Sky & Telescope* (March 2006). p. 38. Discusses exciting new results from the Cassini spacecraft about the icy moons of Saturn.

Weissman, Paul R. "The Oort Cloud." *Scientific American* (Sept 1998). p. 84. Summarizes our current state of knowledge of the Oort Cloud.

Notes and Ideas

Class time spent on material: Estimated:_____   Actual:_____

Demonstration and activity materials:

Notes for next time:

Chapter 9: The Sun
Our Parent Star

Outline

Summary

Chapter 9 begins Part 3 of the text: The Stars. The Sun is the first star considered in the text, and this chapter is devoted to it. The Sun's overall properties, layers, structure, and surface activity are all discussed. The generation of energy by the proton–proton chain and the transport of that energy are also included.

Major Concepts

- Solar properties
- Structure of the Sun
    - Interior – core, radiation zone, convection zone
    - Surface – photosphere
    - Atmosphere – chromosphere, transition zone, corona
    - Solar wind
- Energy
    - Production: proton–proton chain
    - Transport
- Activity and magnetic fields
    - Sunspots and the solar cycle
    - Flares
    - Prominences

Teaching Suggestions and Demonstrations

At the beginning of class, set a timer for 8 minutes. When it goes off, briefly stop what you are doing and announce to the class that the light that left the Sun as they were entering class has just arrived. Students are familiar with kilometers and astronomical units. This exercise gives them an idea of another way to characterize distances; the Sun is about 8 light-minutes from Earth. (You can also point out that light from the Sun won't have reached Pluto for another 5 hours, or the nearest star for over 4 years!)

Section 9.1

For the rest of the text, many characteristics of astronomical objects will be given in terms of how they compare to the Sun. For instance, the masses, radii, and luminosities of stars and clusters of stars are usually given in "solar masses," "solar radii," and "solar luminosities." Thus it is important that students have a good feel for the basic **properties of the Sun**. Go over the solar properties in Table 9.1 in some detail. Have students calculate how these compare to the corresponding properties of Earth. For instance, the Sun's mass is about 330,000 times the mass of Earth.

It is a good idea to compare the sizes of the Sun, Earth, and Moon at the same time. A good class activity to use is the exercise "Sun Size" from *Lecture Tutorials for Introductory Astronomy* by Adams. Be sure to consider how much time to devote to this exercise, since it normally takes more class time than you'd estimate. Students often have the misconception that the three are closer together and are closer to each other in size. You should specifically address these misconceptions.

Project a cross section of the Sun, such as Figure 9.2, and give an overview of the **structure** before discussing each layer in detail. Planets are described in terms of "interior," "surface," and "atmosphere." So is the Sun, although the meaning of these terms is slightly modified. The "surface" is the photosphere, which is the layer we see. Those layers above (chromosphere, transition zone, and corona) comprise the atmosphere, and those below (convection zone, radiation zone, and core) make up the interior.

(DEMO⚡) Bring a light meter or solar cell to class to demonstrate how light can be measured. Hold it near a bulb radiating in all directions and then move it farther away to show how a lower light level is measured at greater distances. Convince students that from the reading at a known distance and a little geometry, the **total energy output of the Sun** can be calculated. Then go through the calculation of the Sun's luminosity as shown in the end of Section 9.1.

Sections 9.2 and 9.3

Figure 9.6 shows the **temperature and density** as a function of radius for the solar interior. There are no sharp edges on the graphs; ask students what determines the boundaries between the different layers. The **core** is the area where temperatures are high enough for the energy production to occur. In the **radiation zone**, the temperatures are lower, but still high enough that all the atoms are ionized and the radiation travels freely. In the **convection zone**, the temperatures are even lower, and electrons are now bound to nuclei; atoms absorb the photons so the energy can no longer be transported through radiation. Remind students of the convection demonstration from a previous chapter. Contrast energy transport by radiation and by convection.

The **photosphere** ("sphere of light") is the visible surface of the Sun and is actually very thin. Make a scale drawing or model of the layers of the Sun to emphasize the comparative thicknesses. (Remind your students to never stare directly at the Sun and never look at the Sun through a telescope without proper filters.)

The **chromosphere** ("sphere of color") is only visible during a solar eclipse, as it is dimmer than the photosphere. The "color" is produced by the Hα line, and the layer looks slightly pink. Show the solar spectrum (Figure 9.9 or Figure 2.15) and marvel at the complexity of it! It is also fun to bring in a prism and go outside or use sunlight coming in a window to look at the solar spectrum, minus the details.

The **corona** ("crown") is the wide layer that extends out into space, eventually turning into the **solar wind**. It is also only visible during a total solar eclipse. One reason astronomers get so excited about solar eclipses is that they provide a rare opportunity to view and study these layers of the Sun.

Section 9.4

From our view on Earth, the Sun seems like a fairly stable, uneventful place. Section 9.4 details several active events that take place on the Sun. **Flares, prominences,** and **sunspots** are all related somehow to magnetic fields. **(DEMO⚡)** Repeat the earlier demonstration of magnetic fields by placing a bar magnet under a piece of paper and sprinkling iron filings on top. Show students how the filings align with the magnetic field lines. Emphasize the loop structure of the magnetic field lines, and compare to the shapes of prominences.

(**DEMO**⚡) If you have a telescope and appropriate filters, students can observe **sunspots**. It is particularly interesting to watch the spots move over the course of several days and to try to estimate the rotational period of the Sun. An easy way to observe sunspots is to use a "Sunspotter®" which is a compact project solar telescope that makes observing the Sun safe for everyone. The mounting of the Sunspotter makes pointing very easy and can be used by students with no prior telescope training. The **chromosphere** can be safely observed using **H-alpha** solar telescopes that observe at a very narrow band pass centered at 656 nm. H-alpha telescopes have become more affordable over the past few years. An alternative is to find a Web site with daily pictures of the Sun and compare the positions of the sunspots on the images from day to day. The site SpaceWeather.com has daily images for both sunspots and **coronal holes**, as well as predictions of **solar flares**.

Section 9.5

The **proton–proton chain** is ultimately the source of most of the energy we receive to keep life going on Earth, so it is worth spending some time discussing it. If you wish, you can discuss conservation of charge and show how it applies at each step. You can also point out that the total number of nucleons (protons and neutrons) is the same before and after each reaction. Refer to a periodic table of the elements when discussing the fusion of hydrogen to helium. Go through the calculation of the amount of energy produced in the sequence of reactions and the corresponding rate at which hydrogen is being fused. The numbers are impressive!

Neutrinos are both fascinating and important to our overall understanding of the processes that take place in the core of the Sun. Describe some of the neutrino detection experiments that have been attempted. One of the earliest involved a huge tank of cleaning fluid buried deep in a mine!

Student Writing Questions

1. Throughout human history, the Sun has been recognized as the "giver of life." Humans have feared losing the Sun, whether during an eclipse, at night, or as it moves southerly during the fall season. From what you have learned of the Sun and the processes that occur in it, describe why it is that we should no longer have these fears. On human time scales, the Sun will always shine; it cannot suddenly, and permanently, disappear.

2. When they occur, solar flares put out only a fraction of the total energy of the Sun. For some types of stars, this is not the case. What if the Sun suddenly had a flare that emitted energy equal to the entire output of the Sun? Considering the lifetime of a typical flare and the radiation emitted (electromagnetic and particulate), what would be the effects on life and the general environment of Earth? How would different parts of Earth be affected?

3. Controlled nuclear (hydrogen) fusion has been attempted for years with very little success. It still may be feasible, and if so, it would give humans an enormous supply of energy. But this is the same process the Sun does every second and on a huge scale. Discuss the pros and cons of developing a fusion program versus developing solar energy use. What are the difficulties and the advantages of each? Which might be more economical for developing countries?

4. During the Maunder minimum of the sunspot cycle (see Figure 9.19), weather in Europe was severe, below average in temperature. It has been referred to as a mini ice age. What if solar astronomers were able to predict such an occurrence again: a 70-year period of time during which Earth would experience very cold temperatures that would affect crop yields and energy use? How would we react to this? How should preparations be made? Who would be most affected? Can humans really prepare for such a lengthy event?

5. Although Question 1 has you consider the fact that the Sun will last a very long time, you also are now aware that the Sun cannot last forever. Knowing what you now know about the energy source of the Sun and the fact that it will run out of hydrogen in its core in another 5 billion years, what do you think will happen to the Sun? How will it die out? Predict what it will look like as it goes through this process. Save what you have written until you have completed Chapter 12. Then compare what you predicted would happen to what actually will happen. Are there differences? What most surprises you about how the Sun will die out?

Answers to End of Chapter Exercises

Review and Discussion

1. Refer to Figure 9.2 for help in answering this question. The regions are: core, radiation zone, convection zone, photosphere, chromosphere, transition zone, and corona. You may also want to include the solar wind, although it is really not a part of the Sun because it is material being lost. The radius of the core is 200,000 km, the radiation zone is 300,000 km thick, the convection zone is 200,000 km thick, and the photosphere, chromosphere, and transition zone are 500 km, 1500 km, and 8500 km, respectively. The corona extends about a few million kilometers above the chromosphere and transition zone. Energy is produced in the core. It is transported through the radiation and convection zones. The photosphere is the layer we see, or the visible "surface" of the Sun. The chromosphere, transition zone, and corona are considered the Sun's atmosphere.

2. The Sun has 330,000 times the mass of Earth.

3. The solar surface is 5800 K, and the interior is about 15 million K.

4. Knowing basic facts about the Sun, such as its mass, composition, and physical processes, allows astronomers to predict the entire structure of the Sun. This is known as a *model*. The model is correct if it successfully predicts observed properties of the Sun, such as its luminosity, radius, and temperature. Some of the input information to the model is uncertain, but the results suggest how correct this input data is. By making slight adjustments in the input parameters, the model is adjusted until its predictions are in agreement with all the observed properties. Once the model "works," astronomers are then able to learn from the model about the properties in the interior of the Sun. Models are used as a test to see whether we fully understand the structure and processes of objects. They are also then used to predict properties that may not be directly observable. Models also make predictions of observables that help us further test the validity of the model.

5. The solar radiation is first produced in the core of the Sun. Because the gas is totally ionized, it is transparent to radiation and so the radiation passes through it freely. But farther out the temperature drops, and more and more of the gas is not ionized or only partially ionized. Such a gas is opaque to radiation. At the outer edge of the radiation zone, all of the radiation has been absorbed by the gas. This heats the gas, and it physically rises, while cooler gas from the surface falls. This is the region

of convection. The energy is transported by convection to the photosphere. Here, the density of the gas is so low that radiation can freely escape into space.

6. Virtually all the visible radiation we receive from the Sun comes from a thin layer called the *photosphere*. It is only 500 km thick, a small fraction of the Sun's radius. So what we see is a sharply defined region of the Sun, below which radiation cannot escape and above which the gas is too thin to emit significant quantities of light.

7. The most obvious evidence of solar convection is solar granulation. The granules are the tops of the convection cells as they rise and fall. The motions of the cells can be measured directly.

8. Because the corona of the Sun is extremely hot, some of the gas can escape into space; it escapes the gravity of the Sun. The gas is mostly composed of ionized hydrogen, that is, protons and electrons. The rush of particles away from the Sun is known as the *solar wind*.

9. All of these objects are caused by the Sun's magnetic fields. Sunspots are caused by kinks or loops of magnetic field extending through the lower atmosphere. Flares are not well understood but are the result of magnetic instabilities. They produce large quantities of energy in just a matter of minutes. Prominences are caused by very large loops of magnetic field that carry luminous gas far above the solar surface.

10. The number of sunspots varies considerably over an 11-year cycle. At the peak of the cycle there may be hundreds of spots; at the minimum there may be virtually none. Although this cycle appears to be rather stable, between 1645 and 1715 there were almost no sunspots observed, and the cycle had stopped. Maunder was a British astronomer who first noticed this hiatus in sunspot activity.

11. The Sun's energy output is fueled by the fusion of hydrogen into helium. In this process, which takes place in the core of the Sun, four hydrogen atoms (really just protons) come together and fuse to form a heavier element, helium. In the process, a small amount of matter is lost; it has been converted into energy.

12. The law of conservation of mass and energy states that the sum of all the mass and energy of a system must always remain constant. But mass and energy are interchangeable. From Einstein's famous equation $E = mc^2$ we see how mass and energy are equivalent. The constant c is the speed of light, and when squared, is a very large number. Thus, small amounts of mass are equivalent to large quantities of energy.

13. Only hydrogen goes into the proton–proton chain. What comes out is helium, two neutrinos, and energy in the form of gamma rays. The mass of helium produced is 0.7% less than the mass of the hydrogen that was fused to make it. This small amount of mass was converted into energy. The amount of energy is easily calculated from $E = mc^2$.

14. The detection of solar neutrinos is very important to the complete understanding of the Sun's interior. Neutrinos are produced in the proton–proton chain, which occurs in the Sun's core. The neutrinos pass unimpeded through the Sun. So neutrinos, in a sense, allow astronomers to directly observe the core of the Sun and the processes that occur there. Finding the predicted number of neutrinos would help scientists verify that the model for the energy production in the Sun's core is correct.

15. If the Sun's internal energy source suddenly shut down, nothing immediately would be observed from Earth other than a stop in the emission of neutrinos. The Sun would continue to shine for possibly millions of years before it would noticeably dim.

Conceptual Self-Test

True or False? 1. T 2. F 3. F 4. F 5. T 6. F 7. F

Multiple Choice 8. c 9. c 10. a 11. b 12. c 13. a 14. b 15. c

Problems

1. (a) First, find the distance from the Sun to Mercury at perihelion:
$$\text{perihelion distance} = a(1 - e) = 0.39\text{A.U.} (1 - 0.206) = 0.31 \text{ A.U.}$$
Because light varies by the inverse square law, the solar constant on Mercury will be $(1/0.31)^2$ times the solar constant on Earth: $1400 \text{ W/m}^2 (1/0.31)^2 = 14,600 \text{ W/m}^2$.

   (b) Jupiter's distance from the Sun is 5.20 A.U.; on Jupiter the solar constant will be:
$$1400 \text{ W/m}^2 (1/5.2)^2 = 52 \text{ W/m}^2.$$

2. (a) Convert minutes to seconds: 5 minutes = 300 s. At a speed of 10 km/s, the wave will travel (10 km/s)(300 s) = 3000 km.

   (b) The circumference of the Sun divided by the wavelength is $(2\pi \times 7.0 \times 10^5 \text{ km})/(3000 \text{ km}) =$ approximately 1500 wavelengths.

   (c) The period of an object orbiting just above the photosphere is $T = d/v = 2\pi r/(GM/r)^{1/2}$:
$T = (2\pi \times 7.0 \times 10^8 \text{ m})/[(6.67 \times 10^{-11} \text{ N m}^2/\text{kg}^2)(2.00 \times 10^{30} \text{ kg})/(7.0 \times 10^8 \text{ m})]^{1/2} = 1.00 \times 10^4 \text{ s} =$ 167 min. The wave period is therefore about 1/33 of the orbital period.

3. From Wien's law, λ_{max} is proportional to $1/T$.

   Comparing two areas of the Sun gives the ratio $\lambda_1/\lambda_2 = T_2/T_1$, so $\lambda_2 = T_1/T_2 \times \lambda_1$.

   (a) In the core, $\lambda_{max} = (5800\text{K}/10^7\text{K}) (500 \text{ nm}) = 0.29 \text{ nm}$ (hard X-ray).

   (b) In the convection zone, $\lambda_{max} = (5800\text{K}/10^5\text{K}) (500 \text{ nm}) = 29 \text{ nm}$ (far UV).

   (c) Just below the photosphere, $\lambda_{max} = (5800\text{K}/10^4\text{K}) (500 \text{ nm}) = 290 \text{ nm}$ (near UV).

4. The granule material will move 1000 km in 1000 s, which is about 17 minutes. This is comparable to a granule lifetime.

5. Because energy emitted is proportional to the 4th power of the temperature, the ratio of the energies will be $\dfrac{4500^4}{5800^4} = 0.36$. This means that the sunspot emits 36% of the energy of the surrounding photosphere, or 64% less.

6. (a) Convert the solar luminosity into mass using $E = mc^2$: $(3.86 \times 10^{26} \text{ J/s}) = m \times (3 \times 10^8 \text{ m/s})^2$.

Therefore $m = 4.3 \times 10^9$ kg/s = 4.3 million tons of mass lost due to radiation per second. This is a little over twice the mass lost from the solar wind.

(b) The Sun's total mass is about 2×10^{30} kg, so it would take $(2 \times 10^{30}$ kg$)/ (2 \times 10^9$ kg/s$) = 10^{21}$ s = about 30 trillion years for all of the Sun's mass to escape.

7. Let n equal the number of rotations made by the material at the poles when it has been "lapped" by the material at the equator. Then $n +1$ is the number of rotations made by the material at the equator in this same time. Set the times equal:

$$n(36 \text{ days}) = (n +1)(25.1 \text{ days})$$

Solving for n gives $n = 2.30$ rotations. Since this is the number of rotations made by the polar material and the period of rotation at the poles is 36 days, this time corresponds to $(2.30 \times 36 \text{ days}) = 83$ days.

8. The text notes that 600 million tons of hydrogen are needed each second to fuel the Sun's luminosity. This mass is 6×10^{11} kg/s. Divide this into Earth's mass to find how long an Earth's mass of hydrogen will last the Sun: 5.98×10^{24} kg $/ 6 \times 10^{11}$ kg/s $= 9.97 \times 10^{12}$ s. This is about 300,000 years.

9. The Sun is 71% hydrogen by mass, so the mass of hydrogen available is $0.71 \times 1.99 \times 10^{30}$ kg $= 1.41 \times 10^{30}$ kg. As noted in Problem 8., the Sun uses 6×10^{11} kg/s of hydrogen to maintain its luminosity. Dividing the first number by the second gives 1.41×10^{30} kg $/ 6 \times 10^{11}$ kg/s $= 2.35 \times 10^{18}$ s. Converting this into years gives about 75 billion years.

10. Dividing the energy per reaction into the solar luminosity will show how many reactions occur each second: $3.86 \times 10^{26} / 4.3 \times 10^{-12} = 9.0 \times 10^{37}$ reactions per second. Two neutrinos are produced but only one gets to Earth. The cross-sectional area of Earth is $\pi(6.4 \times 10^6 \text{ m})^2 = 1.3 \times 10^{14}$ m^2. The area of a sphere with radius of 1 A.U. is given in the text to be 2.8×10^{23} m^2. Dividing Earth's cross-sectional area by the total area of this sphere at 1 A.U. and multiplying by the number of reactions per second will give the number of neutrinos passing through Earth each second.

$$(1.3 \times 10^{14} \text{ m}^2 / 2.8 \times 10^{23} \text{ m}^2) \times 9.0 \times 10^{37} \text{ reactions per second} =$$
$$\text{about } 4 \times 10^{28} \text{ neutrinos per second.}$$

Resource Information

Student CD Media Resources

Interactive Student Tutorials
Super Spaceship—Voyage to the Sun

Movies/Animations
May 12, 1997 Solar Flare Event
Eruption of a Solar Active Region
Tritium-Helium Fusion

Transparencies

122.	Figure 9.1	The Sun
123.	Figure 9.2	Solar Structure

Materials

A "Sunspotter®" from Learning Technologies, Inc. www.starlab.com.

A "Personal Solar (H-alpha) Telescope" or PST from Coronado, Inc. www.coronadofilters.com.

A bar magnet and iron filings can be used to demonstrate magnetic field lines.

The website http://www.sunspotcycle.com/ has daily images of the Sun showing sunspots and coronal holes.

A light meter and a solar spectrum chart suitable for hanging on a wall are available from Edmund Scientific.

It is helpful to have a large periodic chart available when discussing the proton–proton chain.

The Astronomical Society of the Pacific sells solar eclipse glasses, and various other daytime astronomy materials.

Suggested Readings

Baliunas, Sallie and Soon, Willie. "The sun-climate connection." *Sky & Telescope* (Dec 1996). p. 38. Discusses the relationship between climate on Earth and solar activity.

Bartusiak, Marcia. "Underground astronomer." *Astronomy* (Jan 2000). p. 64. Talks about the life and work of Raymond Davis, the inventor of neutrino astronomy.

Boyle, Alison and Grimes, Ken. "Ghostbusting the Universe." *Astronomy* (Dec 2003). p. 44. A brief overview of neutrino astronomy and its implications for cosmology.

Burtnyk, Kimberly. "Anatomy of an aurora." *Sky & Telescope* (Mar 2000). p. 34. Describes the formation of the aurora.

Di-Cicco, Dennis. "Photographing the analemma." *Sky & Telescope* (Mar 2000). p. 135. Discusses methods and techniques used to photograph the analemma.

Eather, Robert H. "An aurora watcher's guide." *Sky & Telescope* (Mar 2000). p. 42. Offers advice on how to observe the aurora.

Frank, Adam. "Blowin' in the solar wind." *Astronomy* (Oct 1998). p. 60. Discusses the solar wind and its interaction with the Earth's magnetic field.

Franklin, A. "The Road to the Neutrino." *Physics Today* (February 2000). p. 22. Historical description of the discovery and subsequent study of the neutrino.

Harrington, Phil. "The sunny side of stargazing." *Astronomy* (Jan 2000). p. 100. Offers advice on how to observe the Sun.

Hayden, Thomas. "Curtain call." *Astronomy* (Jan 2000). p. 44. Describes the distant future of the Earth and Sun.

Haxton, W. and Holstein, B. "Neutrino Physics." *American Journal of Physics* (January 2000). p. 15. Technical and thorough treatment of the basic concepts of neutrino physics.

Lang, Kenneth R. "SOHO reveals the secrets of the sun." *Scientific American* (Mar 1997). p. 40. Reports on the results of the SOHO mission.

Lang, Kenneth R. "Unsolved mysteries of the Sun - part 1." *Sky & Telescope* (Aug 1996). p. 38. Discusses solar neutrinos, the corona, and the solar wind.

Lang, Kenneth R. "Unsolved mysteries of the Sun - part 2." *Sky & Telescope* (Sept 1996). p. 24. Discusses helioseismology (the study of solar oscillations) and the results of the SOHO mission.

Medkeff, Jeff. "A beginner's guide to solar observing." *Sky & Telescope* (June 1999). p. 122. A guide to observing sunspots and other features on the Sun.

Odenwald, Sten. "Solar storms: the silent menace." *Sky & Telescope* (Mar 2000). p. 50. Discusses effects felt on Earth from solar storms.

Schaefer, Bradley E. "Sunspots that changed the world." *Sky & Telescope* (Apr 1997). p. 34. An interesting account of sunspots throughout history.

Semeniuk, Ivan. "Catching cosmic ghosts." *Astronomy* (June 1999). p. 38. Discusses neutrinos and neutrino astronomy.

Semeniuk, Ivan. "Astronomy and the New Neutrino." *Sky & Telescope* (Sept 2004). p. 42. Gives a general overview of all the neutrino detectors around the world and the astronomy they aim to accomplish.

Tyson, Neil De Grasse. "Journey from the center of the Sun." *Natural History* (Apr 1996). p. 68. Describes how a photon of light travels from its place of origin in the core to the surface of the Sun.

Notes and Ideas

Class time spent on material: Estimated:_____   *Actual:_____*

Demonstration and activity materials:

Notes for next time:

Chapter 10: Measuring the Stars
Giants, Dwarfs, and the Main Sequence

Outline

Summary

Chapter 10 discusses determinations of the major stellar characteristics, including spectral type, temperature, mass, size, luminosity, and apparent brightness. The H–R (Hertzsprung–Russell) diagram and regions within it are covered. Binary stars are introduced. The first two main methods of distance determination (which cover distances out to about 10,000 pc) are explained.

Major Concepts

- Measuring nearby stars
  - Parallax and distance
  - Proper motion and transverse velocity
  - Radial velocity
- Stellar characteristics
  - Apparent magnitude
  - Absolute magnitude and luminosity
  - Temperature
  - Spectral classification
  - Size
  - Mass
- The H–R diagram
  - Axes
  - Star groups: main sequence, red giants, white dwarfs
  - Lines of equal radius
- Distance determination using the H–R diagram
- Binary stars
  - Visual
  - Spectroscopic
  - Eclipsing
  - Mass determination

Teaching Suggestions and Demonstrations

This chapter is packed with fascinating and fundamental information! Make sure you budget enough time for it. Lots of stellar characteristics are introduced. Emphasize not only *what* we know about stars but also *how* we know it. The challenge faced by astronomers in studying distant objects is enormous; present the techniques used as creative and innovative ways people have come up with to meet that challenge. Spend plenty of time on the H–R diagram. It is arguably one of the most powerful tools astronomers have; it also provides a wealth of information about stars.

There are several good class activities from *Lecture Tutorials for Introductory Astronomy* by Adams for this chapter. These include: Apparent and Absolute Magnitudes, The Parsec, Parallax and Distance, H-R Diagram, as well as Spectroscopic Parallax. Be sure to consider how much time to devote to these exercises, since they normally take more class time than you'd estimate. These activities can easily take up all the time that you've devoted to Chapter 10. You might consider having your class do these lecture tutorials in lieu of a normal lecture approach.

Section 10.1

Perform a **concept inventory** by asking students to generate of list of **stellar characteristics** that they believe are of interest to astronomers. Alternatively, you can use the **concept tests** covering stellar properties starting on page 94 of Paul Green's *Peer Instruction for Astronomy*. Make sure the final list contains all the major properties to be discussed in this chapter as well as those already discussed, including mass, temperature, color, brightness or luminosity, size, chemical composition, distance, and motion. Point out that some of these characteristics (like mass, size, temperature, and composition) are intrinsic properties of the star, whereas others (such as distance) depend upon the viewpoint of the observer. Also remind students of methods of determining these characteristics already discussed. Stellar spectra are used to help determine composition; the Doppler effect provides information about one component of a star's velocity.

Determining **distance** is clearly a challenge in astronomy. We have no depth perception when we look up at the night sky; all the stars appear as points of light on the celestial sphere. This chapter begins with a review of parallax and presents it as a rung on the "cosmic distance ladder" (see Figure 10.16). Later chapters add more rungs to the ladder, until the final rung is discussed in Chapter 15 (see Figure 15.11 for the complete distance ladder). Point out to students now that different methods are necessary for measuring different distances, just as different methods and tools are used to find the thickness of a piece of paper, the length of a table, the height of a building, the distance across town, and the distance across the country.

(DEMO⚡) Have students try the demonstration of **parallax** discussed in the Prologue again, in which they hold a finger out and sight beyond it to the far wall, first with one eye closed and then the other. Then show Figure 10.1 and use it to define the related unit of distance, the **parsec** (pc), and to derive the formula relating distance and parallactic angle. Using geometry (arc length/radius equals central angle in radians) or trigonometry (for small angles, $\sin \theta \approx \theta$) derive the distance to an imaginary object with a parallax of 1 arc second in kilometers and compare to the conversion given in Appendix 3. Student should also try to remember the relationship between parsecs and light-years, as these two units are often used with the same objects. Parallax is useful for finding the distances to nearby stars; show Figure 10.2 to give some examples of stars in our neighborhood.

Stellar motion turns out to be more complicated than many students would think at first glance. First of all, the observed motion of a star with respect to the background stars has to be divided into parallax (a result of Earth's motion) and **proper motion** (actual motion of the star perpendicular to our line of sight). Observing the same star at the same time of year over the course of many years will help to eliminate the parallax contribution. Then, proper motion (which is measured in arc seconds per year) has to be translated into speed. (DEMO⚡) Ask students to imagine two stars, one twice as far from us as the other, with identical velocities perpendicular to the line of sight. Will the two stars have the same proper motion, and if not, which one will be greater? To demonstrate, line up three students in the front of the classroom, one on each side and one in the middle. One "end" student represents Earth. She holds an arm out straight so that the other two students are lined up with it. Then, the other students each walk the same number of paces perpendicular to the line of students. With her other arm, Earth student points to the near student and then to the far student. The angle between her arms clearly gets smaller when she points to the farther student. If the distance to a star is known, then proper motion can be converted into **transverse velocity**.

The story still is not complete, however. Remind students of the discussion of the Doppler effect from Section 2.7. The change in wavelength (or frequency) can be used to determine a star's **radial velocity**. The star's total velocity can be found from these two perpendicular components, radial velocity and transverse velocity. Finally, consider the fact that Earth itself is moving, carrying its observers with it. If the star's motion with respect to, say, the center of the galaxy is desired, then the motion of our planet must also be taken into consideration.

Sections 10.2 through 10.4

The next three sections deal with the intrinsic stellar properties of **luminosity, temperature,** and **size**. The connection among these three quantities is presented at the end of Section 10.4: Luminosity is proportional to the square of the radius times the 4th power of the temperature. You may wish to go ahead and present this relationship at the beginning of your discussion so that students can keep it in mind as you examine each property individually.

Ask students if they can name any bright stars. Then, look them up in Appendix 3, Table 3, and compare their distances. Sirius, in the constellation Canis Major, is only 2.7 pc away, but Rigel, in Orion, is 240 pc away. Given this information, ask them to make a guess as to how the two stars would compare if they were the same distance from us. This exercise will help students understand the importance of distance in determining the **absolute brightness** of a star when the **apparent brightness** is the observed quantity. If you can darken the room sufficiently, hold identical light sources at different distances and have students qualitatively compare apparent brightnesses. Bring back the light meter and source you used in Chapter 9 and try to quantitatively demonstrate the inverse-square law. Use a laser to show that light from a laser does not diminish according to the inverse-square law.

The **magnitude scale** is very useful and also often difficult for students to understand. First, it is confusing because brighter stars have lower numbers for their magnitudes. Second, it is not linear; a difference of 5 magnitudes represents a factor of 100 times in brightness. (Briefly discuss the history of the magnitude scale and the nature of our "light-detectors," otherwise known as eyes.) Distinguish between **apparent magnitude** and **absolute magnitude**, and compare to the apparent and absolute brightnesses discussed above. Before introducing the equation in *More Precisely 10-1*, work through some examples that can be done with the "5 magnitudes corresponds to 100 times in brightness" rule. For example, find the absolute magnitude of a star that is 100 pc away (10 times the distance of the standard 10 pc) and has an apparent magnitude of +6. Point out that 10 times farther away means an object is 100 times dimmer (inverse-square law) and 100 times dimmer in brightness corresponds to 5 magnitudes. So, the star has an absolute magnitude of $+6 - 5 = +1$. (Note that the 5 is subtracted because the star's absolute magnitude is brighter than its apparent magnitude because it is farther away than 10 pc.) Once you have done some examples like this one, check them with the equation in *More Precisely 10-1*. For the example just given, the equation reads

$$\text{apparent magnitude} - \text{absolute magnitude} = 6 - 1 = 5 \log_{10} (\text{distance}/10 \text{ pc}),$$

which is indeed correct for a distance of 100 pc. Reasoning through simple examples first can often help students understand formulas that may otherwise be intimidating. Having convinced students of the validity of the equation, apply it to problems that are harder to do in one's head to demonstrate the equation's usefulness.

Finally, before leaving the discussion of magnitudes, return to Appendix 3, Tables 3 and 4, and examine the data for some stars. For instance, students can compare apparent magnitude to absolute magnitude for a star closer than 10 pc and for another farther than 10 pc. While you are there, ask students to explain the difference in proper motions in the two tables: The proper motions of the brightest stars are mostly all less than 1 arc second/year, but the proper motions of the nearest stars are mostly all greater than 1 arc second/year. For practice, you can even have students use the distance and proper motion to calculate the transverse velocity and compare to the value given in Table 3 or Table 4 of Appendix 3.

One of the most important concepts regarding **stellar temperature** is that surface temperature determines a star's **color**. Review the blackbody curves introduced in Chapter 2 and discuss Table 10.1. Contrary to the everyday phrase "red-hot," red stars are a lot *cooler* than blue stars. (Remind students of a match or candle flame.) Figure 10.8 shows how a star's temperature can be determined by intensity measurements through just two different filters, B and V.

Stellar spectra are also related to temperature. Touch on the history of the classification scheme in order to explain the odd order of the letters. Be sure to include Annie Jump Cannon (1863–1941), who became the supervisor of a team of women working in astronomy at Harvard University and known as "computers." Her version of the classification scheme is the one we use today, and she is responsible for the classification of some 250,000 stellar spectra!

Examine Figure 10.9, which shows **stellar spectra** for each spectral class. Point out the hydrogen Balmer lines and address some of the other differences among spectral classes. Spectral lines from molecules are only apparent at the lower temperatures; molecules would not be able to stay together at the higher temperatures! Have a contest in your class to come up with a mnemonic to remember the order of the classes. An example other than the one given in the text is Oh Bother, Astronomers Frequently Give Killer Midterms!"

Finally, consider the **sizes** of stars. Figure 10.11 is an excellent one to use to illustrate sizes. The range of sizes is quite impressive. Preview coming attractions by asking students to guess what factors might account for the variety of sizes of stars.

Sections 10.5 and 10.6

So far you have been discussing individual properties of stars. Now it is time to look at relationships between properties. Before introducing the **Hertzsprung–Russell (H–R) diagram**, give an example of how a relationship between two properties of a population could be examined. For instance, ask students to consider all the children in an elementary school and to imagine finding the height and age of each one and then plotting each one as a dot on a height vs. age diagram. Call a student to the board to sketch his predication of what the diagram might look like. Briefly discuss the exercise and the outcome, and note that the collection of dots may follow a general trend (older is taller), but the dots probably won't fall exactly on a line. Are there exceptions to the general trend?

Next, present students with the axes of the **H–R diagram** and ask them to make a guess at the outcome if a large number of stars were plotted. Be sure to emphasize that on the temperature (horizontal) axis, hotter is on the left and cooler is on the right. This will probably seem backwards to them, but it is important to emphasize so that they can compare their guesses with an actual H–R diagram. On the luminosity (vertical) axis, brighter is at the top and dimmer is at the bottom. Once students have sketched a guess, show an actual diagram. Try overlaying the transparences of Figures 10.13 and 10.14, which show H–R diagrams of the nearest and the brightest stars, respectively. (You can return to these later and discuss why these two selected populations have different diagrams.) Your students will very likely have predicted the trend of the **main sequence**, though they may not have the shape right. The relationship shown is that hotter stars are brighter. Next, introduce the other two main regions, the white dwarfs and the red giants, and discuss how they are exceptions to the "brighter = hotter" trend. Engage your students in speculation about why this might be. What could make a cool star appear bright, or a hot star appear dim? The answer is size.

(DEMO₁ℑ) Use **Starry Night Pro** to produce an H–R diagram of various areas of the sky. The H–R diagram function gives an overall diagram for the current field of view. The H–R diagrams produced by Starry Night Pro are biased toward brighter visible stars, but work well as a demonstration. The database doesn't allow for very specific H–R diagrams, such as for globular clusters.

Adding a third characteristic, **stellar size**, to a two-dimensional plot is very confusing, so begin with an example. Ask students to consider, for instance, an A or a B star that is the *same size* as the Sun. Each square meter of A star surface would be brighter than a corresponding square meter of Sun surface. So, if the two were the same size, the A or B star would clearly be brighter. (Compare the luminosities of the Sun and Procyon A or Altair on Figure 10.13.) Next, imagine two stars with the same luminosities but different colors, such as Sirius A and Arcturus on Figure 10.14. Arcturus is cooler, and therefore each square meter of its surface is dimmer than a square meter of the surface of Sirius A. Therefore, if it has the same luminosity, it must have many more square meters of surface to make up for each one being dimmer. Indeed, it lies above the 10 solar-mass line on the H–R diagram and Sirius A is just above the 1 solar-mass line. Compare an H–R diagram (*luminosity* vs. *temperature*) with the lines of constant *radius* drawn in to the *radius-luminosity-temperature relationship* given in Section 10.4.

As an example of the complexities of determining stellar evolution, have your students imagine taking a snapshot of crowd of people, perhaps at a sports stadium. With only a snapshot, you can't actually watch a person develop and grow, then spend most of their lives as a fully grown adult, then to decline in stature as they age. With only a snapshot, one must make assumptions and build models of how a person might age and develop. These are the challenges of classifying stars as well as working out their evolution since we'll never be able to watch individual stars make their way along the H–R diagram.

The H–R diagram forms the next rung in the cosmic distance ladder with a method called **spectroscopic parallax**. Project an H–R diagram and demonstrate how knowing a star's spectral class leads to a determination of its luminosity or absolute magnitude, which, combined with its apparent brightness or magnitude, yields the distance. Ask students if they can pick out the difficulty with this method. What about a K star? Its luminosity will be very different if is determined to be a main sequence star or a red giant. If you have access to a set of standard stellar spectra, show students the spectra of stars with the same spectral type (for instance, K2) but different luminosity classifications (such as V vs. I). They will be able to tell a difference in line widths.

Section 10.7

The final section of this chapter discusses **stellar masses**. Because **binary star systems** are so useful in determining stellar masses, binaries are also introduced in this section. Mass determinations from binary star systems provide an excellent opportunity to review and practice Kepler's third law. In discussing the types of binaries (visual, spectroscopic, and eclipsing), be sure to emphasize that the different classifications refer to how we perceive the stars, not to any differences in intrinsic characteristics.

Binaries are **eclipsing** if their orbital plane happens to lie edge-on to our line of sight. Examine the binary light curve in Figure 10.18 and discuss each dip in the light intensity. Then, draw some different examples and see whether students can figure out why the curves are different. For instance, if the eclipse is not total, the dips will be pointed rather than flat at the bottom. If a main sequence star is orbiting a larger red giant, the dip corresponding to the smaller star being in front will be greater than that corresponding to the smaller star in back, unlike Figure 10.18.

Because **lifetime** is related to mass, this property is also considered. The connections among mass, luminosity, and lifetime will become more apparent in chapters on stellar evolution.

As you wrap up this chapter, return to the list of stellar properties generated by students in the beginning. Briefly touch on each one. Can each property be determined for at least some stars? How? Many of these properties are given in terms of the Sun. For instance, mass is often given as a certain number of solar masses instead of in kilograms. Conclude the chapter by listing all the properties of the Sun, as they are the basis of measurements of other stars as well.

Student Writing Questions

1.   Imagine what it would be like for Earth to orbit one of the typical stars found near the Sun, say the star named Ross 154. Refer to information provided in this chapter and in the tables at the back of the text to find the properties of this star. Pay close attention to its luminosity and spectral type. Describe what the environment of Earth would be like orbiting this star.

2.   About half of all stars in the sky are binary. Imagine Earth orbiting a binary star, say the star named 61 Cygni. Refer to information provided in this chapter and in the tables at the back of the text to find the properties of this star. Pay close attention to its luminosity and spectral type. Describe what the environment of Earth would be like orbiting this star. In particular, give details about the day-night cycle and how the two "suns" would appear.

3.   If you had the choice of visiting any type of star or star system studied in this chapter, which would it be? What is it about this object that fascinates you? Do you think you would have to travel far to find one of these?

4.   Astronomers used to measure stellar brightnesses one at a time at the telescope using a photometer. Now, CCDs allow this to be done for whole fields of stars in about the same amount of time. Discuss how these changes have increased the amount of data astronomers now deal with. How many stars might there be on one CCD image? The CCDs are also more sensitive to light. How many more stars can astronomers now observe? What will be possible with the new and larger telescopes being built?

5.   Give all the observations necessary to plot just one star in the H–R diagram. Give the details of the observations as they would be made from a traditional observatory on Earth. How much time would it take to make all these observations? How much longer would it have taken 80 years ago when Hertzsprung and Russell first did this work?

Answers to End of Chapter Exercises

Review and Discussion

1.   Parallax is the apparent motion of a nearby object due to the change in the viewing position of the observer. Astronomers view a nearby star from opposite sides of Earth's orbit. The position of this star appears to change, relative to distant background stars. The amount of this motion is inversely

proportional to the distance. The inverse of this motion measured in arc seconds is equal to the distance measured in parsecs.

2. A parsec (pc) is the distance at which an object would have a parallax of 1 arc second. Conversely, one astronomical unit (A.U.) will subtend an angle of 1 arc second at a distance of 1 parsec. The parsec is equal to 206,265 A.U.

3. A star's real space motion is observed as two components: the radial velocity and the proper motion. The radial velocity is just the star's motion toward or away from us. The proper motion is an angular motion measured in arc seconds per year. If the distance to the star is known, it can be converted into the true transverse velocity. The transverse velocity and radial velocity can be combined to obtain the true space motion.

4. In terms of stellar radii, giant stars can be tens of times, up to about 100 times, larger than the Sun. Main sequence dwarfs are about 10 times smaller than the Sun. White dwarfs are 100 times smaller than the Sun. Giants are brighter than the Sun. Main sequence dwarf stars are fainter and less massive than the Sun. White dwarfs may have a mass about the same as the Sun or a little more or less, but they are much fainter than the Sun.

5. The apparent magnitude of a star depends on its intrinsic brightness and its distance; it is what the astronomer always measures. The absolute magnitude is a measure of the star's intrinsic brightness. Using the magnitude system, the absolute magnitude is the magnitude of the star if it were at a distance of 10 pc. For the absolute magnitude to be calculated, the apparent magnitude and distance to the star must be known.

6. Temperatures of stars are measured photometrically by using the B and V filters. Brightnesses are compared and matched to a blackbody curve of a specific temperature. The temperature can also be measured using the spectral types.

7. The absorption spectra of stars depend strongly on temperature. The temperature determines which elements produce absorption lines in the visible spectrum. Spectra are classified as either O, B, A, F, G, K, or M. The O-type is the hottest and the M-type is the coolest. Within each of these types is a numerical subclassification ranging from 0 to 9 (e.g., F0, F1, F2, ... F8, F9, G0, G1, ...). For a specific spectral type, the number 0 is the hottest and 9 is the coolest. To classify a star's spectrum, the absorption lines have to be identified. They are then matched to the corresponding spectral type. A spectrum with strong ionized helium lines is type O; one with strong hydrogen lines is type A, etc.

8. The Hertzsprung–Russell (H–R) diagram is a plot of stars' absolute magnitudes against their spectral types. Each star to be plotted must have its spectral type determined. The apparent magnitude must be observed and the distance determined by some method such as parallax so that the absolute magnitude can be calculated. Absolute magnitude is on the vertical scale, with the brightest end of the scale at the top. Spectral types are on the horizontal scale, with O-type on the left and M-type on the right. Note that the corresponding temperature scale goes from hottest to coolest, from left to right. See Figures 10.13 and 10.14 for examples.

9. About 90% of all stars plotted in the H–R diagram are found along a narrow S-shaped band running diagonally from upper left to lower right. This is the main sequence. Stars along the main sequence all have a common source of energy, namely the fusion of hydrogen into helium. A star's mass will determine where it lies on the main sequence. The most massive stars are in the upper left end; the lowest-mass stars are in the lower right end. The Sun is about in the middle of the main sequence. See Figures 10.13, 10.14, and 10.21 for examples.

10. Observation of a star's spectrum can place it in the H–R diagram *without* the distance being known. Then the star's absolute magnitude can be compared to its apparent magnitude and its distance calculated. For instance, the spectrum of a star will determine the spectral type (e.g., K5). Then closer examination of the absorption lines will allow astronomers to determine the luminosity class, that is, if the star is a main sequence star, giant, or supergiant. This information places the star on the H–R diagram so that its absolute magnitude can be read. Absolute magnitude compared to apparent magnitude yields distance.

11. The most commonly occurring stars in the H–R diagram are main sequence dwarfs, or M-type main sequence stars. About three-quarters of all stars are of this type. However, these are not the stars that we commonly see with our eyes or even with telescopes. The most commonly seen stars are those with high intrinsic brightness, which can be seen over large distances. The M-type main sequence stars are intrinsically faint and are difficult to detect. Compare Figure 10.13, an H–R diagram of nearby stars, to Figure 10.14, an H–R diagram of the brightest stars.

12. The masses of stars in binary systems can be determined using Kepler's third law. If the period of the orbit and the semi-major axis can be observed, then the sum of the two stellar masses can be directly calculated. If the center of mass of the system can also be determined, then the individual masses can be calculated. Generally, the complete solution can be done with visual and eclipsing binaries. Spectroscopic binaries provide only partial information on the masses.

13. The lifetime of a star does not depend only on the amount of fuel available to it; it also depends on how fast it uses that fuel, given its luminosity. One star may have 10 times as much mass (fuel) as another star, but it also uses that fuel 1000 times faster. The net result is that the more massive star has a lifetime 100 times shorter than the low-mass star. More massive stars need to use fuel at a greater rate, because their gravity is much greater.

14. The bright, hot, massive stars of the main sequence have short lifetimes; there is no such thing as an old O- or B-type star. But fainter, cooler, and less massive stars have long lifetimes, in many cases much longer than the age of the universe. In this case there is a mixture of ages in the main sequence (assuming the main sequence is not that of a star cluster, where all the stars formed at the same time and have the same age). A K- or M-type main sequence star may be recently formed or may be billions of years old; they all look pretty much the same in the H–R diagram. For A-, F-, and G-type stars, the ages will not be extremely old but could be rather young. Again, there can be a mixture of ages but not as extreme as for the K- and M-type stars. So, the life span of a star can be determined by noting its position on the H–R diagram, but the age of a particular star cannot necessarily be determined.

15. The three different types of binary star systems mentioned—visual, eclipsing, and spectroscopic— are not intrinsically different; they are only different in that we observe them differently. Visual binaries require that the two stars be seen as separate stars. This can only occur if the stars are relatively near to us and widely separated from each other. Most stars are too distant from us to be seen as a visual binary. Eclipsing binaries must be aligned almost exactly edge-on with respect to us in order for the eclipse to be seen. Any other orientation prevents the eclipse from being seen. This makes them relatively rare. Spectroscopic binaries can be seen at almost any distance and through a wide range of orientations. They are therefore much more common.

Conceptual Self-Test

True or False? 1. F 2. F 3. F 4. F 5. T 6. F 7. F

Multiple Choice 8. d 9. b 10. b 11. c 12. d 13. c 14. b 15. b

Problems

1. The distance in parsecs is 1/parallax. For Spica, the distance is 1/ 0.013 = 77 pc. Neptune orbits the Sun at 30.1 A.U., so the parallax would be 30.1 times larger, or 0.39".

2. At a distance of 20 pc, the angle 0.5" corresponds to:
    $$(0.5")/(360\times60\times60) \times (2\pi \times 20 \text{ pc}) \times (3.09\times10^{13} \text{ km/pc}) = 1.5 \times10^{9} \text{ km}.$$

    If this is the distance traveled per year, then the speed per second is:
    $$1.5 \times10^{9} \text{ km/yr} \div 3.15\times10^{7} \text{ s/yr} = 47 \text{ km/s}.$$

    A redshift of 0.01% corresponds to a radial velocity of $(0.01/100) \times (3\times10^{5} \text{ km/s}) = 30 \text{ km/s}$.

    The magnitude of the three-dimensional velocity is therefore
    $$\sqrt{(30^2 + 47^2)} = 56 \text{ km/s}.$$

3. (a) In <u>solar units,</u> the radius-luminosity-temperature relationship is $L = R^2T^4$. Using the values provided, $L = 3^2 (10,000 / 5,800)^4$. $L = 80$ solar luminosities.

    b) Using the values provided, $64 = R^2 2^4$. $R = 2$ solar radii.

4. The first question to ask is, "How much brighter is star B than star A?" This is easy; it is 4.5 / 0.5 = nine times brighter. This is how they would appear if at the same distance from us. But both stars appear to be the same brightness. Obviously, star B, being intrinsically brighter than star A, must be farther away than star A. But how much farther away must it be? It must be dimmed by a factor of nine. Using the inverse-square law, making a star three times farther away makes it nine times fainter, so star B must be three times farther away than star A.

5. Star B is intrinsically fainter by five magnitudes. By definition of magnitudes, this is a factor of 100 in luminosity. Yet they both have the same apparent magnitude. So star A must be more distant than star B. By the inverse-square law, star A must be 10 times farther away if its 100-times-greater luminosity appears the same as star B.

6. The luminosity of the Sun is 3.90×10^{26} W. The energy received per unit area per unit time at a distance of 10 pc time will be this luminosity divided by the surface area of a sphere of 10 pc:
    $$\frac{3.90\times10^{26} \text{ W}}{4\pi \times (10 \text{ pc} \times 3.09 \times 10^{16} \text{ m/pc})^2} = 3.3 \times 10^{-10} \text{ W/m}^2.$$
    This is $(3.3\times10^{-10})/(1400) = 2.3\times10^{-13}$ times the solar constant.

7. The difference in magnitudes is $(+6) - (-27) = 33$ magnitudes. Therefore, the brightnesses range by a factor of $(2.512)^{33} = 16$ trillion times.

8.   Rearranging the formula given in *More Precisely 10-1* gives:

$$d = 10^{(m-M+5)/5} = 10^{(10.0-2.5+5)/5} = 320 \text{ pc.}$$

9.   Using Kepler's third law, $P^2 = a^3 / (m_1 + m_2)$. Substituting the values given:

$$(25 / 365)^2 = (0.3)^3 / (m_1 + m_2)$$

$$m_1 + m_2 = 5.8 \text{ solar masses.}$$

But $m_2 = 1.5 \, m_1$ so $2.5 \, m_1 = 5.8$; $m_1 = 2.3$, and $m_2 = 3.5$ solar masses.

10.   Stellar lifetime is proportional to mass divided by luminosity. If solar units are used, then the lifetime will be in solar lifetimes.

(a) For the red dwarf: Lifetime = (0.2/0.01) × 10 billion years = 200 billion years.
(b) For the 3 solar mass star: Lifetime = (3.0/30) × 10 billion years = 1 billion years.
(c) For the blue giant: Lifetime = (10/1000) × 10 billion years = 100 million years.

Resource Information

Student CD Media Resources

Interactive Student Tutorials
Hertzsprung–Russell Diagram
Binary Stars—Radial Velocity
Eclipsing Binary Stars—Light Curves

Movies/Animations
None

Transparencies

138.	Figure 10.1	Stellar Parallax
139.	Figure 10.2	Sun's Neighborhood
140.	Figure 10.3	Real Space Motion
141.	Figure 10.4	Inverse-square Law
142.	Figure 10.5	Luminosity
	Figure 10.6	Apparent Magnitude
143.	Figure 10.7	Star Colors
	Table 10.1	Stellar Colors and Temperatures
144.	Figure 10.8	Blackbody Curves
145.	Figure 10.9	Stellar Spectra
146.	Table 10.2	Spectral Classes
147.	Figure 10.11	Stellar Sizes
148.	Figure 10.12	H–R Diagram of Well-Known Stars
	Figure 10.13	H–R Diagram of Nearby Stars
149.	Figure 10.14	H–R Diagram of Brightest Stars
	Figure 10.4	Hipparcos H–R Diagram
150.	Figure 10.16	Stellar Distances
151.	Table 10.3	Luminosity Classes
	Table 10.4	Variation in Stellar Properties within a Spectral Class

Materials

Light sources, a light meter, and lasers are available from Edmund Scientific.

A Second Atlas of Objective-Prism Spectra, by Nancy Houk and Michael Newberry, provides standard spectra for the different spectral and luminosity classes.

Suggested Readings

Berman, Bob. "Magnitude cum laude." *Astronomy* (Dec 1998). p. 92. Describes the stellar magnitude system.

Boss, Alan P. "The birth of binary stars." *Sky & Telescope* (June 1999). p. 32. Describes our knowledge of the formation of binary star systems.

Clark, Roger N. "What magnitude is it?" *Sky & Telescope* (Jan 1997). p. 118. A detailed discussion of magnitudes and how they depend on the object and the wavelength band used for observing.

Kaler, James B. "Stars in the cellar: classes lost and found." *Sky & Telescope* (Sept 2000). p. 38. Discusses the development of stellar spectral classes, including the recently added classes L and T.

MacRobert, Alan M. "The spectral types of stars." *Sky & Telescope* (Oct 1996). p. 48. Discusses stellar spectra, including spectral class, luminosity class, and peculiar spectra.

MacRobert, Alan M. "The stellar magnitude system." *Sky & Telescope* (Jan 1996). p. 42. Explains the stellar magnitude scale.

McAlister, Harold A. "Twenty years of seeing double." *Sky & Telescope* (Nov 1996). p. 28. Describes the physical information that can be obtained from studies of binary stars.

Perryman, Michael. "*Hipparcos:* the stars in three dimensions." *Sky & Telescope* (June 1999). p. 40. A summary of findings from the *Hipparcos* mission about a variety of topics including the bending of starlight, stellar oscillations, dark matter searches, distances to the Hyades and Pleiades, and cosmology.

Schilling, Govert. "A hundred million points of light: Sloan Digital Sky Survey." *Nature* (Oct 5 2000). p. 557. Describes the goals of the Sloan Digital Sky Survey.

Ringwald, Fred. "OBAFGKMLT." *Mercury* (Jan/Feb 2005). p. 22. A very good discussion of the historic development of the stellar spectral sequence, plus some helpful hints in remembering the spectral sequence.

Tanguay, Ronald Charles. "Observing double stars for fun and science." *Sky & Telescope* (Feb 1999). p. 116. Describes projects for observing binary stars.

Tomkin, Jocelyn. "Once and future celestial kings: calculating a star's past and future brightness." *Sky & Telescope* (Apr 1998). p. 59. Discusses the connection between distance, proper motion, and the apparent brightness of stars, including results from the *Hipparcos* mission.

Trefil, James. "Putting stars in their place." *Astronomy* (Nov 2000). p. 62. Discusses the development of the Hertzsprung–Russell diagram.

Trefil, James. "Puzzling out parallax." *Astronomy* (Sept 1998). p. 46. Discusses how parallax is used to measure stellar distances.

Turon, Catherine. "From Hipparchus to Hipparcos." *Sky & Telescope* (July 1997). p. 28. Gives an overview of significant results from the *Hipparcos* mission.

Notes and Ideas

Class time spent on material: Estimated:_____   Actual:_____

Demonstration and activity materials:

Notes for next time:

Chapter 11: The Interstellar Medium
Star Formation in the Milky Way

Outline

11.1 Interstellar Matter
11.2 Star-Forming Regions
11.3 Dark Dust Clouds
11.4 Formation of Stars Like the Sun
11.5 Stars of Other Masses
11.6 Star Clusters

Summary

The characteristics and properties of the interstellar medium as well as the different types of nebulae and clouds that comprise it are discussed in Chapter 11. Methods of probing the interstellar medium are also addressed. The formation of stars from interstellar clouds is described in detail. The chapter ends with a discussion of star clusters.

Major Concepts

- The interstellar medium
  - Gas and dust
  - Reddening
  - Composition
  - Density
- Star-forming regions
  - Emission nebulae
  - Reflection nebulae
  - Dark dust clouds
  - Molecular clouds
- Probing the interstellar medium
  - 21-cm radiation
  - Molecular gas
  - Radio observations
- Star formation
  - Interstellar clouds
  - Protostars
  - Main sequence stars
  - Brown dwarfs
- Star clusters
  - Globular clusters
  - Open clusters
  - Associations

Teaching Suggestions and Demonstrations

The interstellar medium is often an overlooked component of the universe for beginning astronomy students. It is not nearly as obvious as planets, stars, and galaxies are. Moreover, it is often seen by the introductory student as a collection of wispy clouds of gas and dust, not as a substantial or significant contributor. At the beginning of this chapter, point out to students that not only is the interstellar medium fascinating in its own right, but it also is the birthplace of stars, giving it a rather important role in the universe as a whole.

Sections 11.1, 11.2, and 11.3

The first three sections of Chapter 11 discuss the **interstellar medium** itself. It should come as no surprise to students by this point in the course that most of the interstellar medium is hydrogen. Discuss the other components (formaldehyde probably *will* be surprising) and distinguish between **gas** and **dust**.

Densities in interstellar space are very low; however, the distances between stars are so vast that it turns out there really is a lot of gas and dust between stars. A density of only 10 hydrogen atoms per cm^3 is not unusual, although regions can be found with densities 100 times higher or lower than this. This density is better expressed as 1.7×10^{-20} kg/m^3. A volume of space one parsec in radius (a typical distance between stars) contains 1.3×10^{50} m^3. As density is mass divided by volume, it is simple to calculate the total amount of mass in this typical volume of space due to interstellar gas. The result is 2×10^{30} kg, which is one solar mass.

Reddening of starlight as it passes through the interstellar medium is due to the same processes that result in red sunsets and sunrises. To demonstrate, put a few drops of milk in a jar of water and shine a light through it. To the side of the light beam, the milky water looks bluish, because the milk particles have preferentially scattered out the blue light. The effect of interstellar gas and dust on our ability to observe in visible wavelengths is dramatic. Have students imagine being in a dense forest. Even if they are not in the center, the view in every direction is about the same. Probing the forest in more than visible light would give students more information. For instance, they could yell or blow a whistle to see whether anyone responded. In a similar matter, radio and infrared wavelengths allow astronomers to "see" farther than visible light. (Be careful with this analogy. Sound waves are obviously not electromagnetic radiation; radio waves are.)

If possible, show lots of color photographs while discussing the interstellar medium. Emission nebulae in particular are often stunning. You can also show reflection nebulae, dust clouds, star-forming regions, and a picture of the Milky Way. Darken the room so that students get the full effect of the photos.

Blue colors in **reflection nebulae** are often due to the scattering of the shorter visible light wavelengths, as in the above milky-water demonstration. Red colors in **emission nebulae** are mostly due to the Balmer line, Hα. You can bring the hydrogen spectral source and diffraction grating glasses back to class to remind students about this emission line. Using a star chart, show your students how to find M42, the Orion Nebula, which is a good example of an emission nebula.

For examples of **dust clouds** and **dust lanes**, show the Horsehead Nebula (Figure 11.13) and the Trifid Nebula (Figure 11.7). Dust clouds are not always dark. Reflection nebulae are caused by starlight reflecting off dust particles, and dust clouds themselves often radiate in the infrared part of the spectrum. **(DEMO⚡)** Use **Starry Night Pro** to show students how to find naked-eye emission nebulae. During the winter months you can show **M-42 (the Orion Nebula)**, which is the middle star in the sword of Orion. If you've covering this chapter closer to the summer months, you can show **M-8 (the Lagoon Nebula)** which is located just above the spout of the "teapot" of Sagittarius. It's interesting to note that the location of M-8 in the sky isn't too far from the galactic center. Showing these naked-eye star forming regions can foster a real connection with the sky for your students. Another related activity is to have your students prepare finder charts for both M-42 and M-8 using **Sky Chart III**.

An extremely important source of information about our Galaxy is **21-cm radiation**. Determine whether your students can come up with some of the advantages of using it. For one, it results from a spin-flip transition in atomic hydrogen, and because hydrogen is (by far) the most abundant element in the interstellar medium, we should be able to find plenty of it to study. Second, because the energy difference in the two states of the hydrogen is so low, the frequency of the emitted radiation is low and the wavelength is long. (Now would be a good time to do a brief review of emission spectra and the relationships among energy, frequency, and wavelength.) The long wavelength means it is in the radio frequency range, and, as was seen earlier, radio waves travel unimpeded through the interstellar medium.

Sections 11.4 and 11.5

Stages in the **formation of a star like the Sun** are summarized in Table 11.2. The dividing lines between most adjacent stages are not rigid; there is not an exact moment that a cloud fragment becomes a protostar, for instance. The evolution from protostar to actual star is more clearly defined: When hydrogen begins fusing into helium, a star is born. The times given in Table 11.2 may be hard for students to relate to. You can create a timeline to compare the lengths of time the star spends at each stage. It should be obvious that the evolutionary process slows down as the star nears the main sequence portion of its life. Using a scale of 10^5 years equals one centimeter, the time for a star to evolve from stage 6 to stage 7 is three meters, whereas the time it takes to evolve all the way from the beginning to stage 5 is less than a third of a meter. To put star birth in the context of a star's life, point out that, using the same scale, the main sequence lifetime of our Sun would be represented by a kilometer!

The numbers in Table 11.2 can also be used with the radius-luminosity-temperature relationship from Chapter 10 to calculate the **luminosity** of the object at each stage. You can do this for stages 4, 5, and 6 and compare to the **evolutionary track** shown on the H–R diagram. Spend some time discussing the evolutionary tracks. Make sure students understand that the H–R diagrams shown in Chapter 10 represent data about temperature and luminosity for lots of different stars. Each star on a diagram is represented by one point. Furthermore, the main sequence shows a general relationship between a star's temperature and its luminosity but is *not* an evolutionary track. (A star does not move up or down the main sequence.) In the current chapter, the temperatures and luminosities of a single star at different points in its evolution are shown as a path or track "followed" by the evolving object.

All the numerical data in Section 11.4 refers to a 1 solar-mass star. Figure 11.25 shows evolutionary tracks for a solar-mass star plus one more massive and one less massive star. Although details of evolution vary, as a general rule the more massive protostars evolve more quickly into more massive stars.

Section 11.6

Show some pictures of **open clusters** and **globular clusters** to begin this final section of the chapter. Figure 11.28 (the Pleiades) and Figure 11.29 (Omega Centauri) provide excellent examples. Compare the two types of clusters with a chart that includes different characteristics. Let students suggest the first few entries by looking at the photos and pointing out obvious differences. Number of stars and general shape of cluster will probably be the first two entries. The presence or lack of gas and dust is another important distinction. Point out the reddish tint to the globular cluster (indicating old stars) as compared to the blue reflection nebula surrounding the young, hot stars of the Pleiades. A comparison of the H–R diagrams of the two clusters is also very informative. Because stellar evolution beyond the main sequence has not yet been discussed, ask students to hypothesize explanations for the truncated appearance of the main sequence of Omega Centauri.

Student Writing Questions

1. Choose a color photograph of a region of interstellar matter that is rich in detail. It might be one from your text, one shown in class, or one that you have found in an article. Describe it! Use an artistic approach, rather than a scientific one. Remember, one picture is worth (at least) a thousand words!

2. It is likely that the Sun, like other stars, formed as part of a cluster of stars. In what way might that environment have affected the formation of the solar system? For better or worse? Imagine the solar system forming in a very dense star cluster as opposed to a very loose star cluster. What might result from these two different situations that would eventually affect the structure of our solar system?

3. In this chapter, we see lots of stars forming throughout the Milky Way Galaxy. Is it possible for this process to be stopped such that a cloud that might have formed a star is disrupted? What might cause such a disruption? Which stages of star formation might be most vulnerable to disruption? What will happen to the material in the cloud?

4. Along with star formation, planetary formation is presumably occurring too. And it is upon planetary surfaces that life might eventually form. Trace the events experienced by an organic molecule from its origin in the molecular cloud to its eventual destiny on the surface of a terrestrial-type planet. Are the chances good or poor for its survival? Is the planetary surface more protective or more deadly to this molecule than interstellar space?

5. What would it be like to live inside either an emission nebula, a dark dust cloud, or molecular cloud? Suppose the solar system moved into such a region. What would the sky look like at night? Consider both the gas, dust, and stars that you would see. Would this region be dangerous to life on Earth? How often might this actually occur?

Answers to End of Chapter Exercises

Review and Discussion

1. Interstellar gas is composed of 90% hydrogen, in atomic and molecular forms, 9% helium, and 1% heavier elements. Some of the heavy elements are underabundant compared to stars and our solar system. Presumably these elements have gone into making up interstellar dust. The dust is believed to be composed of silicates, graphite (a form of carbon), and iron.

2. Interstellar matter is not spread uniformly through space. By examining Figure 11.4, it is obvious that the clouds of interstellar dust vary greatly over the galaxy. Our view of the stars in some directions is severely limited; in other directions there is virtually no dust. Gas is also unevenly distributed. On average there may be only one atom per cubic centimeter, but in large molecular clouds the density can be hundreds or thousands of times greater.

3. Astronomers can study a dust cloud by examining how it both dims and reddens starlight that passes through it. Spectra of the starlight can indicate the composition and temperature of the gas that is mixed in with the dust. Starlight can also reflect off dust particles, and this light informs astronomers about the size and possible composition of the particles. Finally, dust particles emit infrared light

from their own warmth. The infrared spectrum gives added information about the composition of the dust.

4. An emission nebula is a region of hot and glowing interstellar gas. Such a region surrounds a newly formed star or stars. It absorbs ultraviolet light emitted by the bright young stars and, in return, emits a variety of emission lines characteristic of the gases of which it is composed.

5. The 21-cm radio radiation observations are sensitive only to *atomic* hydrogen, not *molecular* hydrogen, so this technique cannot be used to probe molecular clouds.

6. Our Sun would not produce much of an emission nebula because it emits very little ultraviolet light. What little it emits would be quickly absorbed by the gas in its immediate vicinity; an emission nebula would not be seen because of the glare of sunlight.

7. The temperature of the gas must be initially low enough so that the gas can gravitationally collapse. As it does so it radiates away its gravitational energy and does not heat up much. Then, as the cloud gets denser, radiation cannot escape so easily, and the interior of the cloud starts to heat up. Slowly at first, and then ever increasingly, heat pushes against gravity and slows the collapse of the protostar. Gravity continues to compress the gas and heat it until finally the core temperature reaches 10 million K, which is sufficient to initiate hydrogen fusion. The object is now a star.

8. An evolutionary track is the "path" taken on the H–R diagram of the changes in a star. In this chapter the evolution is traced from birth to main sequence star. The track is simply a plot of the luminosity against the surface temperature and how it changes with time. Tracks are predicted by computer models, and stars are observed at various stages along the track.

9. The large interstellar clouds in which stars form are very massive. They fragment into small clouds, each of which eventually forms a star. Therefore, a cluster of stars is formed rather than just a single star.

10. A protostar becomes a full-fledged star when it first begins to fuse hydrogen into helium.

11. Brown dwarfs occur when a cloud fragment has insufficient mass to form a star. As the gas collapses and the core temperature increases, there is not enough gas to compress and heat the core to 10 million K. Hydrogen fusion never occurs, and the object just radiates off its excess energy from formation. This is a brown dwarf.

12. Star formation takes place too slowly for astronomers to watch and follow over time. But astronomers have two other methods. First, they make computer models, which can be changed rapidly with time. Second, there are very many stars in the sky, and astronomers can try to locate stars at the various stages of formation and evolution. The observations are then used to further refine the computer models.

13. Radio and infrared observations are used in the study of star formation because the entire process occurs deep inside a molecular cloud, which, itself, is deep inside a dark, dense dust cloud. Visible light cannot escape from this environment, but long wavelength radio and infrared radiation can.

14. The H–R diagram plots the changes in luminosity and surface temperature that occur during the various stages of star formation. This can then be compared to observations. Stages 1 to 3 cannot be plotted easily because the cloud is generally too cool to fall within the normal boundaries of the diagram.

15. The difference between open and globular clusters was, at first, one of appearance. Open clusters have stars that are widely separated; globular clusters have stars that appear densely packed together. Upon closer examination there are other equally important differences. Open clusters tend to have few stars (a few hundred to a few thousand), whereas globular clusters have about 100,000 stars. Globular clusters are much older, in the range of 10 billion to 15 billion years old. Open clusters are normally under a billion years old. Finally, open clusters are only found in the disk of the galaxy. Globular clusters are found in the spherical halo of the galaxy, concentrated toward the center of the galaxy.

Conceptual Self-Test

True or False? 1. F 2. F 3. F 4. T 5. F 6. T 7. T

Multiple Choice 8. d 9. b 10. c 11. d 12. b 13. b 14. c 15. b

Problems

1. Each cubic meter will have a density of 10^3 atoms/m^3 × $1.7×10^{-27}$ kg/atom = $1.7×10^{-24}$ kg/m^3. Earth is a sphere with a radius of $6.378×10^6$ m, which has a volume of $V = 4/3\ \pi\ r^3 = 1.09×10^{21}$ m^3. Mass = density × volume = $1.7×10^{-24}$ kg/m^3 ×$1.09×10^6$ m^3 = $1.9×10^{-3}$ kg = 1.9 g.

2. $f = c/\lambda$. Substituting values and solving for the frequency gives $f = (3×10^{10}$ cm/s$) / 21$ cm. $f = 1.429×10^9$ Hz or 1428.57 MHz.
   [Although the accepted standard values are $\lambda = 21.1$ cm and $f = 1420.4058$ MHz.]

   The change in wavelength will be $\Delta\lambda = \lambda v/c$.
   For the receding clouds: $\Delta\lambda = (21$ cm$)(75$ km/s$)/(3×10^5$ km/s$) = 0.0053$ cm.
   For the approaching clouds: $\Delta\lambda = (21$ cm$)(50$ km/s$)/(3×10^5$ km/s$) = 0.0035$ cm.
   The range in wavelengths is 20.9965 cm to 21.0053 cm, and the corresponding range in frequencies is 1428.8 MHz to 1428.21 MHz.

3. A cloud density of 10^{12} hydrogen molecules/m^3 multiplied by the mass of a hydrogen molecule will then give the mass density of the molecular cloud. The mass of a hydrogen molecule (H_2) is twice the mass of a proton, or $2 × 1.67×10^{-27}$ kg. So the mass density of the cloud is:
   $(10^{12}$ hydrogen molecules/m$^3) × (2 × 1.67×10^{-27}$ kg/molecule$) = 3.34×10^{-15}$ kg/ m^3.

   The volume of the cloud is mass divided by density, where mass is the same as the mass of the Sun:
   $V = 1.99×10^{30}$ kg$/3.34×10^{-15}$ kg/m$^3 = 5.96×10^{44}$ m^3.

   This volume equals $(4/3)\pi R^3$. Solving for R gives a radius of $5.22×10^{14}$ m = 3500 A.U.

4. The light diminishes by a factor of 2 for every 5 pc it travels. A distance of 60 pc is 12 times 5, so there are 12 factors of 2. It will therefore be diminished by a total factor of $2^{12} = 4096$, or about 4100.

   To find out how many magnitudes this corresponds to, remember that a difference of 5 magnitudes corresponds to a factor of 100. The fifth root of 100 is 2.512. If x represents the number of magnitudes, then $(2.512)^x = 4096$ and $x = 9$ magnitudes.

5. $v_{esc} = 11.2\sqrt{\dfrac{M}{R}}$ with mass and radius in Earth units.

Earth's radius is 6378 km, so 1 pc = 3.09×10^{13} km/6378 km = 4.84×10^9 Earth radii. Earth's mass is 6×10^{24} kg, and the mass of the Sun is 2×10^{30} kg, so one solar mass is 3.3×10^5 Earth masses. The escape speed for each nebula can be calculated using the information from Table 11.1 by the following:

$$v_{esc} = 11.2\sqrt{\frac{M \text{ (in solar masses)} \times 3.3 \times 10^5}{R \text{ (in pc)} \times 4.84 \times 10^9}}.$$

For the first nebula, M8, $v_{esc} = 11.2\sqrt{\dfrac{2600 \times 3.3 \times 10^5}{7 \times 4.84 \times 10^9}} = 1.8\,\text{km/s}.$

Repeating with data for the other nebulae gives:
   M16: 1.1 km/s
   M17: 1.1 km/s
   M20: 0.80 km/s.

The average speed of a hydrogen nucleus in a cloud is given by

$$v_{avg} = 0.157\sqrt{\frac{\text{average temp (in K)}}{\text{mass (in proton masses)}}}.$$

For M8, the result is

$$v_{avg} = 0.157\sqrt{\frac{7500}{1}} = 13.6\,\text{km/s}.$$

Repeating with temperatures of the other nebula results in:
   M16: 14.0 km/s
   M17: 14.6 km/s
   M20: 14.2 km/s.

Because the average speeds are higher than the escape speeds, the clouds are not held together by their own gravity.

6. Find the escape speed and the average speed using the formulas from problem 5.

$$v_{esc} = 11.2\sqrt{\frac{1000 \times 3.33 \times 10^5}{10 \times 4.84 \times 10^9}} = 0.93\,\text{km/s}$$

$$v_{avg} = 0.157\sqrt{\frac{10}{2}} = 0.35\,\text{km/s}.$$

The average molecular speed is less than half the escape speed, so the cloud will begin to collapse.

7. $L = R^2 T^4$, so $R = \dfrac{\sqrt{L}}{T^2}$, with quantities in solar units.

(a) The protostar's initial radius is $R = \dfrac{\sqrt{5000}}{(3500/5800)^2} = 200$ solar radii.

b) The protostar's final radius is $R = \dfrac{\sqrt{3}}{(5000/5800)^2} = 2.3$ solar radii.

8. Refer to Figure 11.22. A three-solar mass star drops from about 10,000 solar luminosities to about 10 solar luminosities as it evolves from stage 4 to stage 6. This is a factor of 1000, which corresponds to about 7.5 magnitudes. (See problem 4.) Answers will vary depending on the reading of the graph.

9. $L = R^2 T^4 = (0.1)^2 \times (0.1)^4 = 10^{-6}$ solar luminosities.

10. Let the tidal radius equal "r". The force of gravity on a mass m at this radius is given by $\dfrac{GM_c m}{r^2}$.

The tidal force at the same point is $\dfrac{2GM_g mr}{D^3}$.

In these equations, D is the distance of the cluster, = 8000 pc. M_c = the cluster mass and M_g = the galaxy mass. Setting the two expressions equal and solving for r yields

$$r = \sqrt[3]{\frac{(D^3 \times M_c)}{(2 \times M_g)}} = \sqrt[3]{\frac{(8000^3 \times 20,000)}{(2 \times 10^{11})}} = 37 \text{ pc.}$$

Resource Information

Student CD Media Resources

Interactive Student Tutorials
None

Movies/Animations
M16 The Eagle Nebula
Gaseous Pillars of Star Birth
Orion Nebula Mosaic
Bi-Polar Outflow

Transparencies

Materials

See Chapter 2 for information on spectral tubes and diffraction grating glasses.

Beautiful posters of nebulae are available from the Astronomical Society of the Pacific.

Suggested Readings

Anonymous. "Hubble observes the violent birth of stars" *Astronomy* (Oct 1995). p. 22. Features HST images of jets from newly forming stars.

Anonymous. "Young star clusters found by HST in the 'Antennae': NGC 4038 and 4039." *Sky & Telescope* (June 1995). p. 12. Features images of star clusters formed in the colliding galaxies known as "the Antennae."

Benningfield, Damond. "Galaxies colliding in the night." *Astronomy* (Nov 1996). p. 36. Describes collisions of galaxies and the associated star formation.

Boss, Alan P. "Companions to young stars." *Scientific American* (Oct 1995). p. 134. Discusses the formation of binary stars.

Croswell, Ken. "Lone star infants." *Astronomy* (Feb 1996). p. 36. Describes observations of the nearby protostellar system HD 98800.

Croswell, Ken. "Probing our local cloud." *Astronomy* (Mar 1997). p. 38. Describes the low density interstellar cloud in which the Sun is located.

Djorgovski, S. George. "The dynamic lives of globular clusters." *Sky & Telescope* (Oct 1998).   p. 38. Describes the dynamics and evolution of globular clusters.

Eicher, David J. "Plunge into the Lagoon: the Lagoon Nebula (M8, NGC 6523)." *Astronomy* (July 1996). p. 82. An observer's guide to the Lagoon Nebula in Sagittarius.

Fortier, Edmund A. "Dusty infant stars: a fine sight." *Astronomy* (July 1997). p. 78. Gives directions for observing five nearby (within 500 light years) star clusters.

Frank, Adam. "Starmaker." *Astronomy* (July 1996). p. 52. Describes accretion disks, jets, Herbig-Haro objects, and the role of angular momentum in star formation.

Greenberg, J. Mayo. "The secrets of stardust." *Scientific American* (Dec 2000). p. 70. Describes studies of the composition of star dust.

Kaisler, Denise. "Cosmic intrigue." *Astronomy* (Oct 2000). p. 42. Describes the characteristics of globular clusters, their formation, and their role in determining the age of the universe.

Kanipe, Jeff. "The giant star pillars of M16." *Astronomy* (Jan 1996). p. 46. Features images and a description of the star farming regions in the Eagle Nebula, M16.

Knapp, Gillian. "The stuff between the stars." *Sky & Telescope* (May 1995). p. 20. Gives an overview of the interstellar medium.

Kurtz, Patti A. "One hot stellar nursery: NGC 604." *Astronomy* (Dec 1996). p. 46. Features an image and discussion of star formation in NGC 604, which is located in the Pinwheel Galaxy, M33.

Lada, Charles. "The hidden treasure of M17." *Sky & Telescope* (Aug 2000). p. 58. A short article featuring images of the emission nebula M17 and its associated molecular cloud.

Ling, Alister. "The secrets of Orion's great nebula." *Astronomy* (Dec 1995). p. 78. Describes the different features of the Orion nebula that can be observed with the aid of different filters.

Meylan, Georges and Brandl, Bernhard. "30 Doradus: birth of a star cluster." *Sky & Telescope* (Mar 1998). p. 40. Describes star formation in the nebula 30 Doradus.

Naeye, Robert. "No globular planets?" *Astronomy* (Oct 2000). p. 24. Reports on a search for planets orbiting stars in the globular cluster 47 Tucanae.

Pommier, Rod. "Seeking star clusters." *Astronomy* (May 2000). p. 84. An observer's guide to open clusters.

Ray, Thomas P. "Fountains of youth: early days in the life of a star." *Scientific American* (Aug 2000). p. 42. Gives an overview of the star-forming process.

Stephens, Sally. "The excesses of youth: T Tauri stars." *Astronomy* (Sept 1996). p. 36. Describes the T Tauri phase of stellar formation.

Notes and Ideas

Class time spent on material: Estimated:_____   *Actual:_____*

Demonstration and activity materials:

Notes for next time:

Chapter 12: Stellar Evolution
The Lives and Deaths of Stars

Outline

Summary

Chapter 12 continues the story of stellar evolution that was begun in Chapter 11. The stages of the evolution of both low-mass and high-mass stars are discussed. Red giants, red supergiants, white dwarfs, planetary nebulae, novae, and supernovae are all objects representing different stages in the life of a star that are explained and described. The evolutionary tracks through these stages are shown on the H–R diagram. The chapter ends with a discussion of the usefulness of star clusters in the study of stellar evolution.

Major Concepts

- Gravity versus gas pressure
- Evolution of low-mass stars
  - Leaving the main sequence
  - Subgiant and red giant branches
  - Helium flash
  - Asymptotic giant branch
  - Planetary nebula
  - White dwarf
  - Nova
- Evolution of high-mass stars
  - Similarities to low-mass stars
  - Heavy element fusion
  - Red supergiants
  - Supernovae – type I and type II
  - Supernova remnants
- Star clusters and stellar evolution
- Evolutionary tracks on the H–R diagram

Teaching Suggestions and Demonstrations

In the last chapter, students learned about the different types of stars, including main-sequence stars, red giants, and white dwarfs. Begin this chapter with a quick review of the different types of stars and their main characteristics. Red giants, for instance, are cool and bright, and therefore they must be very large. Introduce students to the idea that the different classes are different stages in a star's life. Be careful, though, to make sure that students understand that the different types of stars *on the main sequence* do *not* represent different stages. An M star will never evolve into a G star; however, both will evolve into red giants.

Section 12.1

The entire life span of a star, including the stages of stellar formation covered in the last chapter, can be viewed as a balance (or imbalance) between **gravity** and something else. When the star is in equilibrium, the stage of evolution is stable. When something happens to upset the balance, such as depletion of fuel in the core and consequent cessation of core fusion, then the star undergoes a change. For a main-sequence star, the balance is between the inward pull of gravity and the outward push of pressure due to the fusion of hydrogen into helium. A star remains on the main sequence until it begins to run out of fuel in its core. The rest of the chapter deals with the lives of stars after they leave the main sequence. At each stage, remind students of the tug-of-war going on within the star.

If you constructed a timeline for the Sun in the previous chapter, bring it back out and add to it as the later stages are discussed. Students sometimes find it confusing that a total of 13 stages are distinguished in the life of a Sun-like star, but the star spends most of its lifetime in just one of them, stage 7, the main sequence.

Sections 12.2 and 12.3

A good start for this section is "Star Formation and Lifetimes" from *Lecture Tutorials for Introductory Astronomy* by Adams. This activity is good for collaborative small groups and specifically covers **main sequence lifetimes**. Be sure to consider how much time to devote to this exercise, since it normally takes more class time than you'd estimate.

Go through the **stellar evolution stages 7 through 11** carefully. At each one, ask students what they think will happen next. Figures 12.7 and 12.10 show plots of the star on the H–R diagram at each of these stages. Compare the location of each stage to the data given about it in Table 12.1. Then you can consider many different aspects of each stage.

First, ask students to consider the tug-of-war described above for each stage. If the stage is stable, what is supplying the **pressure** to counteract gravity? If the stage is a transition, how is the pressure changing and why? Next, consider the length of **time** the star spends at each stage. Compare to an H–R diagram of a whole cluster of stars. We find the most stars in the longest stages, and very few stars in the stages that a star passes through more quickly. Third, consider **sizes**. Radii are given in Table 12.1 and Figure 12.8 is an excellent illustration of size comparisons of a G star at different points in its evolution. Fourth, use the radii and temperature data from Table 12.1 to calculate the **luminosities** of the star at different stages. Do your results compare reasonably well with the H–R diagram?

Finally, consider core **densities**. The range of densities given in Table 12.1 is impressive, and when neutron stars are added in the next chapter, it will become truly astounding! Help your students relate to these enormous numbers by bringing in an object with a volume of one cubic centimeter. (A die with side length of 1 cm or a marble with a diameter about 1.2 cm works well.) Find the actual mass of the object. Then, calculate what the mass would be if the object had the density listed for each stage in Table 12.1. In other words, if the marble were made of main-sequence star material, what would its mass be? For a main-sequence star, it turns out to be about 100 g. Compare this to a white dwarf; the mass would be on the order of 10,000 kg! For each stage, come up with everyday objects that have the calculated mass, and then imagine compressing them to the size of the marble. Note that the densities are given for the core of the star. The envelope of a red giant is much more diffuse. Do the calculation for the planetary nebula stage as well, for comparison.

Be careful when you introduce **black dwarfs** that students do not confuse them with black holes. Although black holes are not covered until the next chapter, students will certainly have heard of them. A black dwarf is nothing more than an old, burnt out white dwarf, analogous to the ashy coals found in the grill the day after the cookout! It is important to note that black dwarfs are currently a theoretical construct, because the universe isn't old enough for any white dwarfs to have cooled to a point of being close to absolute zero, and thus not giving off any **blackbody radiation.** It's important to mention that anything that has a temperature gives off blackbody radiation, albeit faint and in the infrared.

Show some pictures of **planetary nebulae** and discuss the fact that their name is misleading, as they have nothing to do with planets. Mention that their name comes from the fact that classical planetary nebulae such as the **Ring nebula (M57)** and the **Owl nebula (M97)** appear to have a disc shape, much like a planet. So early observers thought they looked more like a planet than other types of nebula, such as star forming regions which would include the **Orion Nebula (M42). (DEMO⫪)** Use **Starry Night Pro** to show students how to find these nebulae in the sky. Although M42 is the only object visible to the naked eye, M97 and M57 are good objects for 8- to 10-inch telescopes.

Emphasize that in this case, the mass loss is fairly gentle; the planetary nebula is just the escaping outer layers of a red giant. Reconstruct part of the scale model of the solar system to show how the Sun will look as a red giant. Its radius will be perhaps about the same as the radius of Mercury's orbit, but its core will now be a few times larger than Earth. Using these comparisons, it is not hard for students to understand that the core loses its gravitational grip on the outer layers. To demonstrate why planetary nebulae often look like rings when they are actually shells of gas, blow up a balloon and shine a light through it. The edges of the balloon will look much darker than the center. Planetary nebulae are not usually symmetrical like balloons, however, and some may actually *be* rings of gas rather than spheres.

By the time you get to the discussion of the **white dwarf stage**, students will have had lots of practice answering the question "What counteracts gravity?" For the first time, the answer will not be gas pressure. To help students understand, use an analogy. Gas pressure can be visualized as a roomful of flying, bouncing, colliding, Ping-Pong balls (or marshmallows). Imagine sweeping all the Ping-Pong balls into a pile in the center of the room. With the broom, you can "contract" the "gas" so that the balls are all touching each other, but no further. (This analogy becomes useful in the next chapter, also; with a greater force than that supplied by a broom, the Ping-Pong balls or marshmallows would be smashed further, analogous to a neutron star.)

Finish these sections with an examination of Figure 12.10, which shows the **evolutionary track** of a Sun-like star all the way from the main sequence through the white dwarf stage. Project the transparency or slide and informally quiz students about each stage. What is the star called here? What is it doing? How did it get here? You can even include the stages of star formation from Chapter 11 if you wish to do a review.

Sections 12.4 and 12.5

A good start for this section is "Stellar Evolution" from *Lecture Tutorials for Introductory Astronomy* by Adams. This activity is good for collaborative small groups and specifically covers what the stellar remnants from stars of different masses will be. Be sure to consider how much time to devote to this exercise, since it normally takes more class time than you'd estimate.

The **evolution of high-mass stars** is similar to the evolution of low-mass stars in the early stages. Begin with Figure 12.16 and compare the Sun and two high-mass stars. The text points out that the Sun will ascend the red giant branch almost horizontally, but a massive blue main-sequence star will move essentially horizontally to become a red supergiant. Ask students what horizontal motion on the H–R diagram represents; it means constant luminosity. Use the luminosity–temperature–radius relationship to find the radius of the red supergiant compared to the blue giant from which it evolved. (The origin of the name "supergiant" will become obvious.)

Remind students again that motion on the H–R diagram does not mean motion through space. The characteristics of a star change; therefore, its position on a plot of luminosity versus temperature also changes.

The constellation Orion has spectacular examples of both a high-mass, blue main-sequence star (Rigel) and a red supergiant (Betelgeuse). Use a star map to show your students how to find these stars; Orion is one of the easiest constellations to identify, so students should not have any trouble. The colors are noticeable to the naked eye. Aldebaran, another red giant, is nearby in Taurus, and it is sometimes considered the "red eye" of the bull. Antares, a red giant in Scorpio, is interesting because its name, which means "rival of Mars," refers to its color.

Figure 12.17 is a cross-sectional view of an evolved high-mass star with shells of different **heavy elements** fusing. One important idea to point out is that each successive fuel lasts for a shorter time in the core than its predecessor. The timescales become incredibly short compared to almost everything else students have studied so far in astronomy. For instance, silicon burning in the core of a 20 solar-mass star lasts about a week!

Supernovae are another phenomena in astronomy that happen extremely quickly compared to typical astronomical timescales. Notice the scale on the light curves shown in Figure 12.20. Go over Figure 12.21 carefully to distinguish between the two types of supernovae. Because both appear to us as sudden and dramatic increases in luminosity that fade rather quickly, they are both called supernovae. However, they are really quite different. Present some of the observed differences first, such as hydrogen abundance, and discuss how astronomers pieced together the puzzle of supernovae and how the observed characteristics support the theory. Supernova 1987A (see *Discovery 12-1*) is also worth spending time on, as it provided astronomers with some puzzles and a close-up view of this stage of stellar evolution.

Dim the lights when you show pictures of **supernovae remnants**. You can even sprinkle in a few planetary nebulae for review and contrast. You can discuss heavy element formation and distribution while viewing supernovae remnants as well. It can be quite dramatic to point to the wispy, colorful gas and dust in the Crab Nebula or Vela supernova remnant and tell students that they themselves are made of star stuff. In a fundamental sense, they came from material in the interstellar medium and in supernova remnants. All elements other than hydrogen and helium that are in them and in everything around them— their text, their lunch, their shoes—were created and then spewed into space again by stars. Although trace amounts of other light elements (such as lithium) were produced in the primordial nucleosynthesis as discussed in Chapter 17, it's not considered significant for the purposes of this text.

Section 12.6

Now that students understand the different stages in stellar evolution, they can return to an examination of the H–R diagram with new insights. Show again the H–R diagrams of the **globular and open star clusters** from Chapter 11 (Figures 11.28 and 11.29) and have students explain the differences, based on what they know about clusters and about stellar evolution. Figure 12.23 explains the main-sequence cutoff and its relationship with age very nicely. Clusters are also important for testing our theories of stellar evolution; we do not have the opportunity to watch one star evolve through its entire lifetime (or even through a fraction of its lifetime), so instead we watch whole collections of stars. Aliens dropping in on a baseball game would look around the stands and see babies, children, adults, and grandparents and would learn a lot about us, without having to hang around and wait for one of us to individually grow!

More Precisely 12-1 is a wonderful summary of the last few chapters. The idea of recycling (and enriching) matter in the universe is a powerful one. Show the figure and talk about the cycle of stellar birth (from the interstellar medium) back through stellar death, which returns material for more starbirth to the interstellar medium.

Student Writing Questions

1. Describe the 100-million-year period of time *on Earth* when the Sun evolves from the main sequence to the top of the red giant branch. Include how Earth might change and what the Sun will look like as the changes take place.

2. When the Sun is a red giant, describe how this will affect each of the planets. You may need to speculate a bit; just try to make sure there is reasonable scientific merit to your descriptions.

3. Hydrogen, carbon, oxygen, and nitrogen make up 99% of the composition of life-forms on Earth. Trace the path by which these elements have come to you. Begin with their origin and end with how they came to make up your body.

4. Explain why the composition of Earth is not so surprising in light of what you now know about nucleosynthesis and the formation of the solar system.

5. Astronomers typically say that we are overdue for a supernova somewhere in our vicinity of the galaxy. Would you like to search for it? How would you go about it? What do you think your chances for success are? What would you do immediately after discovering it?

Answers to End of Chapter Exercises

Review and Discussion

1. As main-sequence stars, stars like the Sun fuse hydrogen into helium for about 10 billion years. As the hydrogen is depleted in the core, hydrogen fusion continues in a shell around the core for about another billion years.

2. Without the fusion of hydrogen into helium occurring in the core, the core no longer has an energy source. Gravity is then able to collapse the core, forcing major changes in the entire structure of the star.

3. When a star runs out of hydrogen in its core, the core shrinks. As a result, the core's temperature increases and additional energy is radiated away. With a higher temperature, the fusion in the hydrogen shell around the core becomes more efficient. So the core and shell put out even more energy than the core did as a main-sequence star. The increased gas pressure pushes on the outer part of the star, expanding it into a red giant.

4. A star like the Sun will evolve into a red giant and grow to about 100 times its current size. This is equivalent to about half an A.U.

5. It takes a star like the Sun about 100 million years to evolve from the main sequence to the top of the red giant branch.

6. By the time the helium core has formed, the core has a high density of electrons, which produces a pressure unlike that of normal gas. This electron pressure is not influenced by temperature. When the core temperature finally reaches about 100 million K, helium begins to fuse into carbon. Normally the increase in temperature would expand the core and help cool it off. Because of the electron pressure, this does not happen. The fusion of helium raises the core temperature, producing more and more helium fusion, so that over a few hours a large quantity of helium fuses into carbon. This rapid fusion of helium is known as the *helium flash*.

7. Low-mass stars eventually form a carbon core, which collapses but is unable to attain a high enough temperature to allow the fusion of carbon. The outer part of the star continues to expand, and as the final shells of hydrogen and helium fusion die out, this outer part of the star is ejected into space. This cloud of gas is known as a *planetary nebula*. The core of the star remains, continues to cool, and is known as a *white dwarf*. High-mass stars also form a carbon core, which collapses and fuses into still heavier elements. This happens again and again, very quickly. With the formation of the last core, the star suddenly explodes.

8. A planetary nebula is the ejected shell of an evolved giant star. It is in the shape of a spherical shell and is composed of relatively cool, thin gas. It was once the outer part of the star. It is associated with the death of a low-mass star.

9. The remnant of a star at the center of its planetary nebula is the carbon core. As it cools and shrinks in size it becomes a white dwarf. Its size is about that of Earth, its density about a million times that of the Sun, and its luminosity about a thousand times less than the Sun. Although initially rather hot, the white dwarf will cool and fade until it becomes a black dwarf.

10. The primary factor as to whether stars in a binary will affect one another's evolution is the separation of the two stars. If separated by a few A.U., most stars will never expand to a sufficiently large size to ever affect each other. Closer than this and interaction is inevitable. For a given separation, the masses of the stars also play a role. More massive stars have larger Roche lobes than do less massive stars. A larger lobe enhances the possibility that the two stars will interact.

11. A massive star will eventually build up a core of iron. But iron cannot fuse and release energy. As the core collapses under gravity it cannot produce additional energy to stop the collapse. As the collapse proceeds, high-energy photons break up the iron nuclei, further absorbing energy, and neutrinos are released when neutrons are formed from protons and electrons. This further destabilizes the core, producing a catastrophic collapse. A core of neutrons form that oppose any further compression by gravity. The overlying layers of the star collapse and bounce off this core in a catastrophic explosion. This all happens in about a second. This is a core collapse supernova.

12. Type I supernovae are observed to have hydrogen-poor spectra and are fainter than the Type II supernovae. There is also a difference in shape of the light curve, as can be seen in Figure 12.20.

13. In a Type II supernova, the core is surrounded by a hydrogen- and helium-rich layer. The spectrum of such a supernova has lots of lines depicting these two elements. A Type I supernova contains virtually no hydrogen or helium, so the spectrum is very weak in these elements. The light curve of a

Type I supernova is almost totally due to the radioactive decay of elements. Type II supernovae have light curves appropriate for an expanding cloud of gas, blown into space by a shock wave.

14. When the supernova explosion occurs, it rapidly ejects a vast cloud of gas. This is called a *supernova remnant*. Supernova remnants can last for thousands of years and provide evidence of an earlier supernova. Many remnants are observed.

15. A massive star will eventually build up a core of iron. But iron cannot fuse and release energy. The core collapses under gravity; high-energy photons break up the iron nuclei. A core of neutrons forms, and the remainder of the star explodes as a supernova.

Conceptual Self-Test

True or False? 1. T 2. T 3. F 4. T 5. F 6. T 7. T 8. F

Multiple Choice 9. a 10. b 11. a 12. b 13. b 14. c 15. d

Problems

1. The core radius is 1.5×10^7 m, resulting in a volume of $4/3 \, \pi \, (1.5 \times 10^7)^3 = 1.41 \times 10^{22}$ m^3. The mass of the core is $0.25 \times 1.99 \times 10^{30}$ kg $= 4.98 \times 10^{29}$ kg. The density is mass divided by volume; 4.98×10^{29} kg$/1.41 \times 10^{22}$ m$^3 = 3.5 \times 10^7$ kg/m^3.

    For the envelope, convert the radius from A.U. to m: $R = 0.5$ A.U. $\times 1.5 \times 10^{11}$ m/A.U. $= 7.5 \times 10^{10}$ m. Density = mass/volume = $(0.5 \times 1.99 \times 10^{30}$ kg$) \div [4/3 \, \pi \, (7.5 \times 10^{10})^3] = 5.6 \times 10^{-4}$ kg/m^3. The density of the envelope is 1.6×10^{-11} times that of the core.

    The central density of the Sun $(1.5 \times 10^5$ kg/m$^3)$ is smaller than the density of the red giant core by a factor of 4.3×10^{-3} and larger than the density of the red giant envelope by a factor of 2.7×10^8.

2. Find the luminosity of the giant, as compared to when it was on the main sequence. Use the luminosity-radius-temperature relationship: $L = (100)^2 \, (1/3)^4$, $L = 123$. Because of the inverse-square law, this star will appear of equal brightness at a distance that is the original distance times the square root of 123, or 20 pc $\times$ 11 = 220 pc.

3. In solar units, $L = M^4$. Also, lifetime, T, is proportional to M/L, so $T = (M/L)(10^{10}$ years$)$. Substituting for L, $T = (M/M^4)(10^{10}$ years$) = (1/M^3)(10^{10}$ years$)$. Solving for M yields

$$M = \sqrt[3]{\frac{10^{10}}{T}} \text{ in solar masses.}$$

(a) $M = \sqrt[3]{\dfrac{10^{10}}{4 \times 10^8}} = 2.9$ solar masses.

(b) $M = \sqrt[3]{\dfrac{10^{10}}{2 \times 10^9}} = 1.7$ solar masses.

4. Neptune is at 30.1 A.U. This distance is 4.5×10^9 km. At 20 km/s, the time it takes to travel this distance will be $(4.5 \times 10^9 \text{ km})/(20 \text{ km/s}) = 2.25 \times 10^8$ s or about 7.1 years.

    The nearest star is 1.3 pc = 4.02×10^{13} km. The time to reach this distance is $(4.02 \times 10^{13} \text{ km})/(20 \text{ km/s}) = 2.01 \times 10^{12}$ s or about 63,700 years.

5. $v_{esc} = 11.2 \sqrt{\dfrac{M}{R}}$ with mass and radius in Earth units. Table 12.2 gives the mass and the radius of

    Sirius B in solar units. Converting to Earth units gives
    $$v_{esc} = 11.2 \sqrt{\frac{1.1 \times (3.33 \times 10^5)}{0.008 \times 109}} = 7300 \text{ km/s}$$
    Surface gravity is proportional to mass and inversely proportional to radius squared. So, the surface gravity of Sirius B is (M/R^2) times that of Earth, with mass and radius in Earth units.

    surface gravity = $[(1.1 \times 3.33 \times 10^5)/(0.008 \times 109)^2] = $ 500,000 times the surface gravity of Earth.

6. From *More Precisely 10.1*, m – M = 5 log (d/10).
    m = M + 5 log (d/10) = 5 + 5 log (10,000/10) = 20.
    Using the inverse-square law, a nova with a brightness of 10^5 solar luminosities would appear just as bright as the Sun at a distance of $\sqrt{10^5} = 316$ times that of the Sun, or 316 × 10,000 pc = 3.2 Mpc.

    Repeating the calculation for the supernova, the distance is $\sqrt{10^{10}} = 10^5$ times that of the Sun. $10^5 \times 10,000$ pc = 1000 Mpc.

7. The difference in magnitudes is 20 – (–27) = 47 magnitudes. This corresponds to a factor of $2.512^{47} = 6.32 \times 10^8$ times in brightness, which (by the inverse-square law) means that the supernova is 2.51 × 10^9 times closer, which is (1000 Mpc)/(2.51 × 10^9) = 0.4 pc. We would not expect a supernova this close because there are no O or B stars, and, in fact, no stars at all this close to the Sun.

8. For an apparent magnitude *m*, absolute magnitude *M*, and distance *d*, the relationship between these is *m* – *M* = 5log *d* – 5. This gives m = (–20) + 5log 150 – 5 = –14.1 for the apparent magnitude of the supernova. This is about 1.6 magnitudes brighter than the full Moon and 9.7 magnitudes brighter than Venus. Yes, we would expect to (eventually) see a supernova at that distance. See Appendix 3, Table 3, for the distances to candidate stars.

9. Speed is distance divided by time. The distance is 1 pc or 3.1×10^{16} m. The time is about 950 years (using 2004 and 1054). As one year is 3.2×10^7 s, the time is equal to 3×10^{10} s. The speed is then just 1×10^6 m/s or 1000 km/s.

    This answer assumes a constant expansion velocity. The expansion must take place very rapidly at first but then will slow down as the gas runs into the interstellar medium. Gravity probably plays almost no role in slowing it down.

10. The total energy output of the Sun over its lifetime is given by its current luminosity times the number of seconds in a year times its ten billion-year lifetime.

    $$(3.9 \times 10^{26} \text{ W}) \times (10^{10} \text{ years}) \times (3 \times 10^7 \text{ s/yr}) = 1.2 \times 10^{44} \text{ J}$$
    $$m = E/c^2 = 1.2 \times 10^{44} \text{ J}/(3 \times 10^8 \text{ m/s})^2 = 1.33 \times 10^{27} \text{ kg} = 220 \text{ Earth masses.}$$

Resource Information

Student CD Media Resources

Interactive Student Tutorials
Evolution of 1-Solar Mass Star

Movies/Animations
Death of the Sun Part I
Death of the Sun Part II
Helix Nebula Animation
Bi-Polar Planetary Nebula
H–R Diagram Tracks Stellar Evolution
Evolution of a 1-Solar Mass Star
Recurrent Nova
Supernova Explosions

Transparencies

170.	Figure 12.1	Hydrostatic Equilibrium
171.	Figure 12.2	Solar Composition Change
172.	Figure 12.3	Hydrogen Shell Burning
	Figure 12.6	Helium Shell Burning
173.	Figure 12.4	Red Giant on the H–R Diagram
	Figure 12.5	Horizontal Branch
174.	Table 12.1	Evolution of a Sun-Like Star
175.	Figure 12.9	Planetary Nebulae
176.	Figure 12.10	White Dwarf on H–R Diagram
177.	Figure 12.13	Nova
178.	Figure 12.14	Close Binary System
179.	Figure 12.16	High-Mass Evolutionary Tracks
180.	Figure 12.17	Heavy-Element-Fusion
181.	Figure 12.18	Mass Loss from Super Giants
182.	Figure 12.19	Supernova 1987A
183.	Figure 12.20	Supernova Light Curves
	Figure 12.21	Two Types of Supernova
184.	Figure 12.23	Cluster Evolution on the H–R Diagram
	Figure 12.26	Old Cluster H–R Diagram

Materials

A poster-sized periodic table is helpful when discussing core fusion in high-mass stars.

Suggested Readings

Basri, Gibor. "A Decade of Brown Dwarfs." *Sky & Telescope* (May 2005). p. 34. Describes brown dwarfs as the dividing line between stars and planets in terms of mass.

Comins, Neil F. "We are all star stuff." *Astronomy* (Jan 2001). p. 56. Gives an overview of nucleosynthesis in stars.

Croswell, Ken. "Compelling Capella: the brightest star in Auriga." *Astronomy* (Feb 1995). p. 48. Describes the characteristics of the star Capella in the context of stellar evolution.

Croswell, Ken. "White dwarfs confront the universe." *Astronomy* (May 1996). p. 42. Describes using studies of dim white dwarfs to independently determine the age of the universe.

Garlick, Mark A. "Recipe for disaster." *Astronomy* (June 2000). p. 36. Describes cataclysmic variables and the processes leading to novae.

Goldstein, Alan. "Touring a stellar graveyard." *Astronomy* (Dec 1997). p. 84. A guide to observing planetary nebula.

Goodman, Alyssa A. "Recycling in the universe." *Sky & Telescope* (Nov 2000). p. 44. Describes the cycle of stellar evolution and how it enriches the interstellar medium for future generations of stars.

Hayden, Thomas. "Curtain call." *Astronomy* (Jan 2000). p. 44. Describes the life cycle of the Sun from the perspective of the consequences on Earth.

Iben, Icko, Jr. and Tutukov, Alexander V. "The lives of stars: from birth to death and beyond." *Sky & Telescope* (Dec 1997). p. 36. Describes the life cycle of stars.

Kaler James B. "Eyewitness to stellar evolution." *Sky & Telescope* (Mar 1999). p. 40. Describes the life cycle of stars using examples of objects visible in the night time sky.

Kirshner, Robert P. "Supernova 1987A: the first ten years." *Sky & Telescope* (Feb 1997). p. 35. A report on what we have learned about Supernova 1987A.

Krupp, E. C. "Engraved in stone: crab nebula." *Sky & Telescope* (Apr 1995). p. 60. Discusses possible historical observations of the Crab supernova in 1054 A.D.

Kwok, Sun. "What is the real shape of the Ring Nebula?" *Sky & Telescope* (July 2000). p. 32. Describes the structure of the Ring Nebula.

Mohanty, Subhanjoy and Jayawardhana, Ray. "The Mystery of Brown Dwarf Origins." *Scientific American* (Jan 2006). p. 38. Describes the processes and environs that form brown dwarf stars.

Naeye, Robert. "Stars' last gasps." *Astronomy* (Apr 1998). p. 36. Describes HST images of planetary nebula.

Naeye, Robert. "The beginning and the end." *Astronomy* (Sept 1999). p. 36. Features a spectacular HST image of NGC3603 which contains examples of all stages of stellar evolution.

Naeye, Robert. "White dwarfs by the trillions?" *Astronomy* (Apr 2000). p. 22. A brief news report on MACHO results about old white dwarfs in the Milky Way Galaxy.

Parker, Wayne J. "Anatomy of a Crab." *Sky & Telescope* (Jan 1995). p. 38. Discusses what we have learned about the Crab Nebula and pulsar from recent HST images.

Patterson, Joseph. "Our cataclysmic-variable network: Center for Backyard Astrophysics." *Sky & Telescope* (Oct 1998). p. 77. Describes a network of amateur and professional astronomers who routinely monitor cataclysmic variable stars.

Robinson, Leif J. "Supernovae, neutrinos, and amateur astronomers." *Sky & Telescope* (Aug 1999). p. 30. Describes how new neutrino observatories may be used to provide an early alert for new supernovae, and how amateur astronomers can contribute to observations of supernovae.

Sandage, Allan. "Twinkle twinkle." *Natural History* (Feb 2000). p. 64. An overview of stellar evolution and the H–R diagram.

Southwell, Karen. "Inside a star's cocoon." *Astronomy* (May 1997). p. 60. Discusses possible mechanisms for producing the structure seen in HST images of planetary nebula.

Tyson, Neil De Grasse. "Forged in the stars." *Natural History* (Aug 1996). p. 72. Describes the formation of elements in stars and the historical context of our understanding of this topic.

Zimmerman, Robert. "Into the maelstrom." *Astronomy* (Nov 1998). p. 44. Describes our understanding of the Crab Nebula.

Zimmerman, Robert. "When disaster strikes: extraterrestrial risks to Earth." *Astronomy* (Nov 1999). p. 46. Hypothesizes about possible risks to the Earth due to a nearby supernova.

Notes and Ideas

*Class time spent on material: Estimated:*_____   *Actual:*_____

Demonstration and activity materials:

Notes for next time:

Chapter 13: Neutron Stars and Black Holes
Strange States of Matter

Outline

Summary

Chapter 13 explores the final stages in the evolution of massive stars – neutron stars and black holes. The theory of each and observational evidence for each are presented. Pulsars, neutron stars that are visible to us by virtue of the orientation of their radiation beams, are also discussed. The importance of binary systems in detecting neutron stars and black holes is noted. Einstein's special and general theories of relativity are introduced in this chapter and applied to black holes and their effects on space-time.

Major Concepts

- Neutron stars
  - Mass
  - Density
  - Size
  - Formation
  - Pulsars
  - Neutron stars in binaries
- Einstein's theories of relativity
  - Special – speed of light, time dilation, length contraction
  - General – gravity and space-time
- Black holes
  - Theory
  - Escape speed and light
  - Event horizon
  - Schwarzschild radius
  - Tidal forces
  - The singularity
  - Observational evidence

Teaching Suggestions and Demonstrations

Topics such as exotic objects and relativity are topics that many students have a keen interest in. In fact, many students might be taking your astronomy class to specifically learn more about these very topics. The challenge is to show that these objects and concepts are based on observations and are empirical, not just a "philosophy" of the natural world. It is critical to strike a balance between conceptual understanding and the mathematical underpinnings of these topics.

Sections 13.1 through 13.4

Begin your discussion of **neutron stars** by picking up the stellar evolution story from the end of the last chapter. A core-collapse supernova has just occurred… so what's left behind? Go through the extreme characteristics of a neutron star, including its size, density, and rotation. Pull out the marble or cube you used in discussing densities last chapter and calculate the mass it would have if it were made of neutron star material. The result is possibly unimaginable – about 500 *billion* kg. Also remind students of the Ping-Pong ball or marshmallow analogy. The broom is only strong enough to push the Ping-Pong balls into a pile, just as the gravity of a low-mass star is only strong enough to collapse it to a white dwarf, or until the electrons can be shoved together no further. A high mass star has more mass and therefore more gravity, just as you could apply more force with your hands (or feet) and smash the Ping-Pong balls or marshmallows even further.

The lighthouse model of **pulsars** is illustrated in Figure 13.3. Point out that Earth's magnetic and rotational poles do not coincide, either. (Students will have probably heard of Earth's north magnetic pole and how navigators using compasses have to compensate for the fact that it is not located at the north geographic pole.) Possibly the most remarkable feature of pulsars is their rapid rotation. Quickly review the conservation of angular momentum. If you can, find an audiotape that demonstrates the rapidity of the pulses. (Obviously, the pulses are not really sounds, but transforming the electromagnetic pulses into beeps or other sounds with the same frequency of repetition really helps students recognize just how fast pulsar periods are.) Remind students that every pulse represents an entire rotation! As with binary stars, our orientation is what makes a pulsar a pulsar; if we are not in the beam, then we do not see the pulses, and the star is just a neutron star. (**DEMO**) A simple demonstration of the flashing of a pulsar can be made by using a strobe light with a variable flash rate. (Some people are quite bothered by strobe lights, so you should warn students about what you are about to demonstrate.) Set the rate at about one flash per second. Increase the rate until your students agree they cannot make out the individual flashes. Typically, most people cannot see beyond about 10–15 flashes/s. Set the rate at 30 flashes/s to show the Crab Nebula pulsar; there is no way to detect the flashing with the naked eye. (Be sure to emphasize the difference between the model and real pulsars; the strobe light is actually pulsing, whereas pulsars *appear* to be pulsing because of their rotations.)

The **Crab Nebula** (M-1) is associated with a supernova that was chronicled by Chinese astronomers in the year 1054 AD. Today we see this object as a supernova remnant still expanding into space. (**DEMO**) Use **Starry Night Pro** to show students how to find M-1 in the constellation Taurus. Once you find the location of M-1 in Taurus, there is a "zoom" feature that lets you see a telescopic view of the object. This can be a very impressive feature to use, but you should practice before class because the operation can be a bit confusing at times.

What about **millisecond pulsars**? Ask students what could explain the extremely rapid rotations of these pulsars. To give them some ideas, demonstrate an analogy: Have a student sit on a rotating stool with his arms out. Spin him around, and instruct him to pull his arms in; he will noticeably speed up. (Holding weights makes the change in rotational velocity even more dramatic.) This process is what results in normal pulsar rapid rotation. Next, repeat the demonstration, but this time give the student an extra spin after he pulls his arms in as well. Follow-up with a view of Figure 13.8, which shows where the extra angular momentum comes from.

Sections 13.5 through 13.8

Before introducing black holes, spend some time discussing the basics of **Einstein's theories of relativity**. The general concepts can be understood without lots of math, and students typically find the topic fascinating. For **special relativity**, emphasize that Einstein began with two postulates, and remind students just what a postulate is. Einstein did not need to prove them; he accepted them and then determined the consequences that would result from them. The example of the car and bullet versus the spaceship and light beam that is discussed in *More Precisely 13-1* is a good illustration of the postulates and their consequences. Time dilation and length contraction follow. After all, if distance = speed × time and you keep speed constant, then weird things are going to happen to distance and time!

For **general relativity**, emphasize the equivalence principle. If you wake up in a small room with no windows, how do you know if you are on the surface of Earth (gravity) or out in space in an elevator accelerating at 9.8 m/s^2 (acceleration)? You don't.

It is probably easiest to approach the topic of **black holes** with a return to the concept of escape speed. You can use the formula from *More Precisely 5-1* to calculate the radius that the Sun would need in order to have an escape speed equal to the speed of light. This is the Schwarzschild radius. (Calculate it for Earth, too, and have students imagine compressing all of Earth into a sphere with a radius of about 1 cm!)

Emphasize that **gravity** depends on mass and radius. Ask students what would happen to Earth if the Sun were to become a black hole (which it can't). Contrary to common misconceptions, we would not get "sucked" into it. Our orbit wouldn't change, as neither the mass of the Sun nor our distance from it would change. Normal stellar black holes are quite small, another frequently overlooked fact. The Sun's Schwarzschild radius is only about 3 km.

Students understand the concept of escape speed and how decreasing the radius while keeping mass constant increases it. However, they often think that as the escape speed approaches the speed of light, the light (or electromagnetic radiation) trying to leave the surface of the stars moves slower and slower. This, however, contradicts the previous discussion of the constancy of the speed of light. The key is to think of energy, instead of speed. If you throw a ball up it loses kinetic energy as it tries to escape Earth. Light loses energy too, but instead of a reduced speed, the energy loss shows up in a reduced frequency. Smaller frequency means longer wavelength, hence the **gravitational redshift**.

The rubber sheet model of a **black hole** really works well as a demonstration. Sheets of plain rubber can sometimes be located at a dental supply store. Stretch the sheet on an open frame just enough so there are no wrinkles and little sag. Put a mass at the center to warp it. Roll small marbles, ball bearings, or coins tangentially to the center. They will "orbit" around the center, moving faster as the center is approached, and finally spiraling into the center because of friction. Try different speeds and angles to change the trajectories. Small coins often work the best because of the reduced friction. Students will want to play with this demonstration after class. There are also some commercially available plastic models. Small ones are very popular for collecting coins for charities. (It would be best not to compare the charity with a black hole, however!)

To bring the discussion out of the realm of theory and analogy, discuss some of the **tests of the general theory of relativity**. The bending of starlight as it passes the Sun during a solar eclipse is an excellent example. (See *More Precisely 13-2*.) Make sure your students do not think that a solar eclipse is necessary to bend starlight. Starlight bends as it travels by the Sun all the time; we just do not see it because the sky is too bright.

No discussion of black holes would be complete without imagining the **tidal forces** encountered when traveling near one. The charming term "spagettification" to describe what would happen to a person heading feet-first or head-first into a black hole creates an image your students are not likely to forget! Do some calculations to demonstrate. Take the example of a five solar-mass black hole. What would be the tidal force over a distance of one meter if you are 100 km away from the black hole? (Note, the black hole's radius is 15 km, so you are still some distance from the event horizon.) Say you fall feet-first toward the black hole. It is easy to calculate the gravitational force on a 1-kg mass at 100 km and 100 km plus one meter and then simply compare the two. Each kilogram of your body separated by one meter from another kilogram of you would experience a stretching force of 1.3 million Newtons or about 300,000 lbs!

Because no light can escape a black hole, its detection can be somewhat problematic. Before giving **evidence for black holes**, ask your students how black holes could possibly be detected. Refer back to binary systems and to the detection of extrasolar planets for hints regarding one detection method. Figure 13.22 shows an artist's conception of the accretion disk surrounding a black hole. Also, give a preview of chapters ahead by mentioning massive black holes and where they are found.

(DEMO⚡) The **black hole candidate Cygnus X-1** (as shown in Figure 13.21) is a well-known object whose position can be shown using **Starry Night Pro**. Even though Cygnus X-1 is an X-ray object, the B-type giant companion is 8.8 magnitude and can be seen using Starry Night Pro when you zoom in. Visually, Cygnus X-1 is close to the naked-eye star Eta-Cygni, which is 3.9 magnitude.

Student Writing Questions

1. Imagine an environment where the effects of general relativity occur strongly for even weak gravitational fields. What would living in this environment be like?

2. So you just bought a new planet and now you find out it is orbiting a pulsar. What is your planet like? What do you get to see and experience that the rest of us on ordinary planets don't? Was it a good buy?

3. Isolated black holes must exist in the Milky Way Galaxy. What if one of these moved through our solar system? What effect would it have on the solar system? On Earth and its life-forms? Could we capture it? If so, to what use could we put it?

4. Try to trace all the steps in determining distances that finally lead to using supernovae as distance indicators. Start back here on Earth and work your way through the solar system, nearest stars, etc. How accurate do you think supernovae are in calculating distances?

5. Science fiction author Larry Niven wrote a short story titled *Neutron Star*. Find a copy of this and read it. How does this story relate to this chapter? What was the mysterious force encountered around the neutron star? From what you have learned in this chapter, is the physics in the story realistic?

Answers to End of Chapter Exercises

Review and Discussion

1. Some of the basic properties of a neutron star include its high density, rotation, and magnetic field. How these come about to be this way is a direct result of the core collapse that forms the neutron

star. The collapse and shock wave that propagates into the core give the high density. Although the star is rotating initially at a normal rate, the collapse must conserve angular momentum, and this results in the core "spinning up" as it gets smaller. The magnetic field is confined by the gas in the core and is therefore concentrated as the core shrinks.

2. The gravity at the surface of a body depends on the mass of that body and inversely on the square of the distance to the center (i.e., its radius). A neutron star has both a high mass, 1–2 solar masses, and a small size, 10-km radius. Both of these properties result in a very high pull of gravity on its surface. An average human would weight about a million tons on its surface. A person would be flattened out by this huge force.

3. Not all neutron stars are seen as pulsars because their orientation does not allow their beam of radiation to pass in the direction of Earth. The beam can be only a few degrees across, so the alignment must be close to pointing toward Earth in order for us to see it. A neutron star that is not observed as a pulsar by us could be viewed by others in a different direction as being a pulsar.

4. X-ray bursters are found in mass-transfer binary stars where one of the stars is a neutron star and the other is a normal star. The mass transfer forms a disk around the neutron star and slowly accumulates on its surface. Finally, the gas undergoes fusion and there is a burst of X-rays released as a result. This can occur again and again as the mass continues to be transferred to the neutron star.

5. The distribution of gamma-ray bursts is isotropic across the sky, implying they are not associated with our Galaxy. Recently, an Italian-Dutch satellite observed a burst whose position was well-enough determined that optical observations could be made. A redshift was measured and the object was at a cosmological distance. Bursts are very energetic because, at cosmological distances, they must be more powerful than a supernova in order to be observed and have all this energy emitted in just a few seconds.

6. In a mass-transfer binary, something other than just mass is transferred to the neutron star; angular momentum can be transferred too. This results in making the neutron star spin faster and faster. The angular momentum is taken from the orbital motions of the two stars.

7. A supernova explosion should completely destroy any planetary system. However, if the star that goes supernova is in a binary system, the effects of the explosion may destroy most, but not all, of the companion. What is left behind could form a disk of material that eventually accretes to form planetary-sized objects in orbit around the pulsar. This hypothesis is still unproved, though.

8. If an object moves toward me at 10 mph and I move toward it at 5 mph, then the object's speed, relative to me, is 15 mph. If, instead, I am moving 5 mph away from this same object, its speed relative to me is only 5 mph.

   Now, if the object is actually a beam of light moving at the speed of light, the previous example of the addition or subtraction of speeds no longer applies. I will always measure the speed of light to be a constant, independent of my own speed. This was discovered by Michelson and Morley, much to their own amazement, because they believed the speeds would add together. It was a discovery that led Einstein to the special theory of relativity.

9. The escape velocity from the surface of a body depends on both the mass and the radius of that object. It is quite possible for an object to have sufficient mass and small size to have an escape velocity equal to the speed of light. This occurs for a solar mass at a radius of 3 km, or any multiple thereof. What this means is that light itself cannot escape from this object. By definition, this is what

is meant by a black hole. The term "black" comes from the fact that no light can escape from the object, so it appears black.

10. The event horizon is at the Schwarzschild radius of a black hole and defines the region where the escape velocity equals the speed of light. It is also the region of "no return" in that once it is crossed going into a black hole, nothing can return to the outside universe.

11. General relativistic effects, although always present, are not obvious unless a gravitational field is very strong. Most of the gravitational fields we encounter in the solar system, for instance, are fairly weak. But the theory makes predictions that can be tested; it just requires very careful and sensitive measurements to be made.
 The two classical tests of general relativity are the deflection of starlight by the Sun's gravity and the precession of the orbit of Mercury. During a total solar eclipse, stars can be seen near the Sun. However, their positions are slightly altered owing to the fact that their light has skimmed past the Sun, encountering its gravitational field. This bends the path of the light, and we see the stars displaced slightly. Because Mercury has such an elliptical orbit, it moves through varying strengths of the Sun's gravitational field. This causes the orbit to slowly turn or precess. In both cases general relativity accurately predicts the observed effects.

12. Before entering the black hole, tidal forces would pull a person apart. Gravity is so strong near the black hole that the difference in the force on the two sides of the person is sufficient to tear him or her apart. This would be true of any type of matter that would venture close to the black hole.

13. Cygnus X-1 is a good black hole candidate because it is in a binary system; its mass has been determined to be in the range of five to ten solar masses. Mass transfer is occurring and produces X-rays from the black hole candidate. The X-rays vary at a rate suggesting the candidate is small, less than 300 km.

14. About the only way to discover a neutron star from Earth is if it is a pulsar. Traveling through space would allow you to see neutron stars from other directions, and thus as pulsars. One might also encounter neutron stars that are no longer pulsars because they have lost so much energy. Neutron stars are the result of the evolution of massive stars. Wherever the most stars are, there should be many neutron stars. Globular clusters might be a particularly good place to look.

15. Objects are often classified by their mass, such as various types of stars, brown dwarfs, and planets. Because these objects have masses equivalent to planets, the name is appropriate. But they almost certainly are not planets similar to those in our solar system. But then again, the newly discovered planets around other stars (large jovian masses but very near their stars) seem to be rather different from our own, too. What is likely needed here are new names for new types of objects. These might be called planetoids, pulnets, or plansars.

Conceptual Self-Test

True or False? 1. T 2. T 3. T 4. F 5. T 6. F 7. F

Multiple Choice 8. b 9. a 10. b 11. c 12. b 13. c 14. c 15. b

Problems

1. Because angular momentum is conserved, the "before" and "after" values must be equal. Thus, we have:

$$\omega_1 r_1^2 = \omega_2 r_2^2$$

$$\omega_2 = \omega_1 \frac{r_1^2}{r_2^2} r_2^2 = 1 \text{ rev/day} \left(\frac{10{,}000^2}{10^2}\right) = 10^6 \text{ rev/day} = 11.6 \text{ rev/s}.$$

2. Mass = volume × density. An increase in density from 1000 kg/m^3 to 3×10^{17} kg/m^3 is a factor of 3×10^{14}. With a constant volume, the mass increases by this same factor, so a 70-kg person would have a mass of $(70 \text{ kg}) \times (3 \times 10^{14}) = 2.1 \times 10^{16}$ kg.
    (a) The Moon's mass is 7.3×10^{22} kg, greater by a factor of 3.5 million.

    (b) The mass of the asteroid is smaller by a factor that depends on the value chosen for density of the asteroid. For example:
    Assume volume = 4/3 π R^3 For density assume ρ = 3000 kg/m^3
    Mass = volume x density = 1.57 10^{12} kg.
    Asteroid is smaller by a factor of 13,000

3. Surface gravity = $GM/R^2 = (6.67 \times 10^{-11} \text{ Nm}^2/\text{kg}^2)(1.4 \times 1.99 \times 10^{30} \text{ kg})/(10{,}000 \text{ m})^2 = 1.9 \times 10^{12}$ m/s^2. This value is $(1.9 \times 10^{12} \text{ m/s}^2)/(9.8 \text{ m/s}^2) = 1.9 \times 10^{11}$ times the surface gravity of Earth.

$$v_{esc} = 11.2 \sqrt{\frac{M}{R}}$$, with mass and radius in Earth units. One solar mass is 3.33×10^5 Earth masses, and

Earth's radius is 6378 km. Therefore,

$$v_{esc} = 11.2 \sqrt{\frac{(1.4 \times 3.33 \times 10^5)}{(10/6378)}} = 1.9 \times 10^5 \text{ km/s}.$$

For a 1-solar-mass object with a radius of 3 km, the escape speed is

$$v_{esc} = 11.2 \sqrt{\frac{(3.33 \times 10^5)}{(3/6378)}} = 3.0 \times 10^5 \text{ km/s},$$ which is the speed of light.

Recall that 3 km is the Schwarzschild radius of the Sun.

4. $L = R^2 T^4$ in solar units. Using a temperature of 6000 K and a radius of 7×10^3 km, calculate L:
    (a) $L = (10/7 \times 10^3)^2 \times (10^5/6000)^4 = 1.6 \times 10^{-5}$ solar luminosities
    (b) $L = (10/7 \times 10^3)^2 \times (10^7/6000)^4 = 1.6 \times 10^3$ solar luminosities
    (c) $L = (10/7 \times 10^3)^2 \times (10^9/6000)^4 = 1.6 \times 10^{11}$ solar luminosities.

    The coolest could be plotted in the bottom left of the H–R diagram, as a very faint O-type star.

5. Find the total surface area of a sphere with a radius of 1000 Mpc.
    $$\text{Area} = 4\pi \times (10^9 \times 3.09 \times 10^{16})^2 = 1.2 \times 10^{52} \text{ m}^2.$$

    Multiply this area by the energy per area of the detector to get the total energy.
    $$\text{Energy} = (10^{-8} \text{ J}/0.5 \text{ m}^2) \times 1.2 \times 10^{52} \text{ m}^2 = 2.4 \times 10^{44} \text{ J}.$$

Using a distance of 10,000 pc results in an energy of 2.4×10^{34} J, a factor of 10^{10} less. At a distance of 50,000 A.U. = 0.24 pc, the energy is 1.4×10^{25} J.

6. Time is dilated according to the Lorentz Factor.

$$T = \frac{T_o}{\sqrt{1 - \left(\frac{V}{C}\right)^2}} \Rightarrow T = \frac{T_o}{\sqrt{1 - (0.9999)^2}} \Rightarrow T = \frac{2\ \mu s}{0.01414} \Rightarrow T = 141 \mu s$$

7. The Schwarzschild radius is the mass of an object, given in solar masses, times 3 km.
   For the 1-million solar mass black hole: $10^6 \times 3$ km = 3×10^6 km.
   Dividing by the radius of the Sun gives 3×10^6 km$/6.96 \times 10^5$ km = 4.3 solar radii.
   For the 1-billion solar mass black hole: $10^9 \times 3$ km = 3×10^9 km.
   Dividing by the radius of the solar system (= 40 A.U.) gives 3×10^9 km$/(40 \times 1.5 \times 10^8$ km) = 0.5 solar system radii or 20 A.U.

8. The event horizon for a 1-solar-mass black hole is 3 km = 3000 m. Calculate the difference in gravitational accelerations at 3002 m and 3000 m from the center of the black hole.
   $GM/(3000\ \text{m})^2 - GM/(3002\ \text{m})^2 = (6.67 \times 10^{-11}\ \text{Nm}^2/\text{kg}^2)(1.99 \times 10^{30}\ \text{kg})[(1/(3000\ \text{m})^2 - 1/(3002\ \text{m})^2]$
   $= 2 \times 10^{10}\ \text{m/s}^2 = 2 \times 10^9\ g.$
   For a 1-million-solar-mass black hole, the Schwarzschild radius is 3 million km, so the distances 2 m apart are 3,000,000,000 m and 3,000,000,002 km. Using the equation above, the result is 2×10^{-2} m/s^2 = 2×10^{-3} g.
   For a 1-billion-solar-mass black hole, the result is 2×10^{-8} m/s^2 = 2×10^{-9} g.

9. Using the expression from problem 8, $g = GM/[1/r^2 - 1/(r+2)^2]$, where $g = 10(9.8\ \text{m/s}^2)$, $M = 1$-solar mass = 1.99×10^{30} kg, and r is the distance from the black hole. Solving for r gives $r = 1,760,000$ m = 1760 km.

10. The black hole mass is 10 solar masses; the primary star's mass is 25 solar masses. The orbital period is 5.6 days = 0.015 yr. Using Kepler's third law gives:

$$P^2 = (0.015)^2 = a^3/(25+10);\ a = 0.2\ \text{A.U.} = 30\ \text{million km}.$$

Resource Information

Student CD Media Resources

Interactive Student Tutorials
Escape Speed and Black Hole Event Horizons

Movies/Animations
Black Hole Geometry

Transparencies

185.	Figure 13.1	Neutron Star
186.	Figure 13.2	Pulsar Radiation

Materials

A strobe light can be used to demonstrate pulsars.

Use a rubber sheet and small balls or marbles to demonstrate warped space-time and black holes.

Suggested Readings

Charles, Philip A. and Wagner, R. Mark. "Black holes in binary stars: weighing the evidence." *Sky & Telescope* (May 1996). p. 38. Describes the observations used to determine if an object is a black hole.

Ford, Lawrence H.and Roman, Thomas A. "Negative energy, wormholes, and warp drive." *Scientific American* (Jan 2000). p. 46. Discusses the phenomena associated with negative energy

Hawking, Stephen. *The Illustrated a Brief History of Time*. Bantam Books, New York, 1996. An excellent book with superb illustrations.

Irion, Robert. "Pursuing the most extreme stars." *Astronomy* (Jan 1999). p. 48. Describes observations of pulsars.

Lasota, Jean Pierre. "Unmasking black holes." *Scientific American* (May 1999). p. 40. Discusses the accretion of material onto a black hole.

Leonard, Peter J. T. and Bonnell, Jerry T. "Gamma-ray bursts of doom." *Sky & Telescope* (Feb 1998). p. 28. Gives a short overview of gamma ray burst and merging neutron stars, then discusses the potential impact on Earth of a gamma-ray burst from within our part of the galaxy.

Nadis, Steve. "Neutron stars with attitude: magnetars." *Astronomy* (Mar 1999). p. 52. Discusses observations of a class of neutron stars with extremely strong magnetic fields.

Nadis, Steve. "Black Holes in the Middle." *Astronomy* (Mar 2004). p. 36. Discusses how supermassive black holes are from stellar-mass black holes.

Olson, Steve. "Black hole hunters: L. Dressel, T. Heckman, R. van der Marel and M. Urry." *Astronomy* (May 1999). p. 48. Describes the black hole-related research of four different astronomers.

Panek, Richard. "Relativity turns 100." *Astronomy* (Feb 2005). p. 32. Discusses how Einstein sparked a revolution in physics while working at the Swiss patent office.

Pickover, Clifford A. "A black hole user's guide." *Sky & Telescope* (May 1996). p. 92. Describes and gives a program for using a personal computer to investigate the effects of black holes.

Rees, Martin. "To the edge of space and time." *Astronomy* (July 1998). p. 48. Gives an overview of the theory of black holes.

Shipman, Harry L. "How do we know it's a black hole?" *Sky & Telescope* (May 1996). p. 42. Explains how astronomers observe black holes.

Talcott, Richard. "Another record-setting burst." *Astronomy* (Jan 2001). p. 28. Reports on a very distant gamma-ray burst.

Talcott, Richard. "Black holes in all sizes." *Astronomy* (Dec 2000). p. 26. Describes the difference between black holes that form from the evolution of a single star and the massive black holes at the centers of galaxies.

Trefil, James. "Relativity's Infinite Beauty." *Astronomy* (Feb 2005). p. 46. Discusses how relativity will continue to blaze new trails for astronomy and physics.

Tyson, Neil De Grasse. "Flashes of ignorance: gamma-ray bursts." *Natural History* (June 1997). p. 78. Gives a brief discussion of the history of observations of gamma-ray bursts.

Winn, Joshua N. "The life of a neutron star." *Sky & Telescope* (July 1999). p. 30. Summarizes the formation and evolution of neutron stars.

Zimmerman, Robert. "When neutron stars collide." *Astronomy* (Apr 1997). p. 52. Discusses the merging of two neutron stars as a source of gamma-ray bursts.

Notes and Ideas

Class time spent on material: Estimated: _____ *Actual:* _____

Demonstration and activity materials:

Notes for next time:

Chapter 14: The Milky Way Galaxy
A Grand Design

Outline

Summary

Chapter 14 describes the major characteristics of our galaxy as well as the techniques used to determine them. Cepheid variables and RR Lyrae stars are added as the next rung on the cosmic distance ladder. The formation of the Milky Way is discussed. Galactic rotation curves and their role in the discovery of dark matter are explained. The chapter ends with the galactic center and the current theory that a massive black hole resides there.

Major Concepts

- Characteristics of the Milky Way
    - Size and shape
    - Numbers and types of stars
    - Bulge, disk, and halo
    - Orbital motion and differential rotation
    - Structure and spiral arms
- Distance determinations by variable stars
    - Cepheid variable and the period-luminosity relation
    - RR Lyrae stars
- Mass of the Milky Way
    - Rotation curves
    - Dark matter
- Stellar populations I and II
- The formation of the Milky Way
- The center of the Milky Way

Teaching Suggestions and Demonstrations

This point in the course provides another excellent excuse to take your students out for nighttime observing, or to suggest they go themselves. It does not require a telescope to be impressed by the sight of the Milky Way; in fact, a telescope makes the view less dramatic. Choose a dark area and make sure students' eyes are dark-adapted before you begin. Binoculars are nice to have; they will give students a sense of what it was like for Galileo when he first pointed his telescope to the Milky Way and found that it was composed of stars. Viewing the Milky Way is another good exercise in changing point of view. **(DEMO⚡)** Use **Starry Night Pro** to show students how to find both the summer Milky Way (Sagittarius arm) and the winter Milky Way (Perseus arm). Be sure to show them that Sagittarius and Perseus lie within the boundaries of their respective Milky Way bands. Alternatively, students can prepare their own finder charts for the Milky Way bands using **Sky Chart III**.

For beginning astronomy students, connecting the band of light in the sky with a picture or diagram of a spiral galaxy is nontrivial. Ask students to imagine being embedded in a (diffuse) pancake. If they look up or down, away from the plane of the pancake, they are looking through a small thickness of material. But, if they look *along* the plane, they are looking through a great thickness of material. Of course, the "up" and "down" do not correspond to "up" and "down" with respect to standing on Earth. If you are outside with your students, sweep your arm along the Milky Way in the sky; this is the "plane of the pancake" view. Ask them to point to a direction perpendicular to the plane; this view is "out of the pancake." If you are not outside with your students at night, you can still use the pancake analogy and show pictures, such as Figure 14.1. Part *a* is an artist's conception of what our Galaxy would look like from outside, and part *b* is an optical view of the Milky Way from Earth.

Sections 14.1 and 14.2

A good start for this section is using "Milky Way Scales" from *Lecture Tutorials for Introductory Astronomy* by Adams. This activity is good for collaborative small groups and specifically covers distances to well-known objects within our galaxy, location of our solar system in the galaxy, as well as covers the overall size and shape of the Milky Way. Be sure to consider how much time to devote to this exercise, since it normally takes more class time than you'd estimate.

After connecting the view of the Milky Way in the sky with the fact that the Milky Way is the huge collection of stars we call home, give some **basic data**, including size, shape, dimensions, and number of stars. Point out the **galactic disk**, the **galactic bulge**, and the **halo** in a diagram of our Galaxy as well as in photos of external galaxies. Studying external galaxies, such as those shown in Figure 14.2, can help us learn about our own. Just as we cannot study the whole evolution of a single star, we cannot view a single galaxy from many different vantage points. So, we study multiple stars to view the different stages of evolution and, in a similar manner, we study multiple galaxies to help construct our view of what a galaxy is really like. Figure 14.2 shows three spiral galaxies, one face-on, one edge-on, and one tilted. Ask students what pieces of information come from each view, and then combine all the pieces into a coherent picture of a spiral galaxy.

(DEMO⚡) You can construct a **model of the galaxy** to help students visualize its dimensions and the Sun's place within it. Once you have the scale determined, figure out the diameter of the solar system to this same scale. Unless you have an unusually large classroom, the entire solar system will be represented by a dot! Note that standard models do a good job with sizes and/or distances, but do not give any impression at all of motions. If you are feeling really adventuresome, you can try constructing a **moving model of the galaxy**. Assign parts (Sun, Earth, Moon, Jupiter, a couple of other planets and their moons, other stars on our spiral arm, stars on another spiral arm, maybe some extrasolar planets, stars in the nuclear bulge, etc.). Go out to a large field, have your cast take their places and shout "go!" The result may be chaos, but sometimes groups can maintain a semblance of order for about half a galactic year! One point of this exercise is to emphasize to students all the motions that Earth undergoes. It rotates on its axis, revolves around the Sun, and follows the Sun on its orbit around the center of the galaxy. If you try this, be sure to follow-up with a discussion of models. This type obviously is no help at all in the discussion or demonstration of sizes and distances. However, it does offer some advantages not available with standard models.

Briefly discuss historical changes of the **view of our place in the universe**. The belief that Earth was the center of the universe prevailed until Copernicus moved it into orbit around the Sun. Then, bolstered by Hershel's star counts, people believed for many years that the solar system was the center of the Milky Way Galaxy. Discuss the observational evidence for these views and why observation can be misleading. In the case of the galaxy, astronomers were unaware of the effect of interstellar dust. For an analogy, ask students to imagine being in a large parking lot, say, at a mall. On a clear day, the view from your spot shows you cars in every direction, but, unless you are in the center, you will see more cars in some directions than in others and be able to determine where you are with respect to the center. If a dense fog rolls in, however, and you are neither at the center nor all the way at an edge, you will probably look around and see about the same number of cars in all directions, concluding, falsely, that you are indeed at the center.

Harlow Shapley's "brilliant intellectual leap," as described in the text, was to connect the **globular cluster distribution** he observed to the actual extent of the galaxy. You can extend the parking lot analogy (though it is a bit of a stretch!) to illustrate. You need to imagine that the dense fog is a layer extending from the ground to just over your head and the tops of the cars. So, when you look up, you can see the light posts extending up above the fog in all directions. If you are not at the center, more light posts will be visible in some directions than in others. Shapley's interpretation is an excellent example of how "thinking outside the box" can result in tremendous advances in scientific understanding.

To determine the distances to the globular clusters, Shapley needed to use **RR Lyrae variable stars**, which, along with **Cepheid variables**, form the next rung on the distance ladder, as shown in Figure 14.7. As an activity, find data on Cepheid variables and have students plot their own period-luminosity graphs to discover the relationship. Then show a graph of another Cepheid's apparent brightness and have students determine its distance. This exercise will clarify the procedure for them. Henrietta Leavitt was one of the Harvard observatory workers called "computers, along with Annie Jump Cannon, discussed in Chapter 10.

Sections 14.3 through 14.5

Before discussing information about the two **stellar populations** or the theory of the **formation of the Milky Way**, present observational comparisons of the disk, the halo, and the bulge. (See Table 14.1.) Then see if students can come up with possible explanations for the observed characteristics. Use Figure 14.9 to distinguish among the various areas. One very common misconception among students regards the relationship between the metallicities and the ages of stars. Students often assume that older stars will have more elements heavier than hydrogen and helium, because such stars are further along in their evolution. However, the opposite is true. Very old stars were formed at an earlier time in the universe when the interstellar matter was less enriched; therefore, their envelopes will be made primarily of hydrogen and helium. Younger stars were formed more recently, after earlier generations of stars spewed forth elements manufactured during their lifetimes. Consequently, their envelopes will show more evidence of heavier elements. Also, be sure your students understand how the fact that the globular clusters are mostly reddish stars indicates that they are old. Refer back to the main-sequence turnoff points discussed earlier and to the relationship between lifetime and original main-sequence mass. Finally, show how the theory of the formation of the Milky Way Galaxy accounts for the observed differences in the disk and halo, from the compositions of stars to their orbits. You can mention conservation of angular momentum yet again; students should be quite comfortable with this concept by now!

We see **spiral arms** in external galaxies, but how do we know that *our* Galaxy has them? Discuss the "tracers," including molecular clouds, young star associations, and 21-cm observations. The traffic jam explanation for the density wave theory explained in *Discovery 14-2* is excellent and will help students understand why the arms of galaxies are not wrapping up tighter and tighter.

Sections 14.6 and 14.7

A quick review of Kepler's third law is warranted at the beginning of these sections, because it is significant in the determination that much of our Galaxy must be made of **dark matter**. Students may have heard the term "missing mass" used in this context; the problem with this term is that the *mass* is not missing; we have too much mass and cannot account for it all. Also point out that "dark" does not mean just a lack of visible light. The galaxy has been probed in all wavelengths of the electromagnetic spectrum and still we cannot explain the rotation curve. Have students look up some information about Vera Rubin, an astronomer who was very influential in the initial study of galactic rotation curves and the determination of dark matter.

A typical **galactic rotation curve** (velocity versus distance) for a spiral galaxy or the Milky Way can be described as follows: From the center the velocity increases rapidly, starts to drop off slowly, then rises slowly or becomes constant. Some may show a final slow drop. Examine the reasons behind these shapes with students. Let us assume that the stars and gas clouds are all moving in circular orbits around the center of the galaxy. This is not a bad assumption. Then we already know that gravity from inside the orbit must balance the centripetal force: $GM/R^2 = v/R$. So the velocity simply equals $v = (GM/R)^{1/2}$. But the mass, M, increases with radius R unless there is negligible mass outside of R. Mass, (M), can be thought of as varying three different ways with respect to R. For a spherical distribution of mass, $M \propto R^3$; for a disk, $M \propto R^2$; with little or no mass outside of R, M is a constant.

In these three cases, the velocity v will vary with R as either $\propto R$, $\propto R^{1/2}$, or $\propto R^{-1/2}$. Coming out from the center, the nuclear bulge is like a spherical distribution of mass, and so the velocity varies linearly with R. As R increases and the disk is entered into, the velocity varies as $R^{-1/2}$ because it "sees" the bulge as one large mass and does not yet see much mass in the disk. As more disk is encountered, the velocity varies as $R^{1/2}$ and therefore increases slowly with distance. Sooner or later, at some large value of R, the velocity should return to a $R^{-1/2}$ dependence and slowly drop off. This is not always seen, and often the velocity remains constant. This implies $M \propto R$, which is somewhere between a disk and a central distribution of mass, the additional mass coming presumably from the outer halo or corona. There is more mass there than meets the eye (or detector). Use Figure 14.19 and interpret the ups and downs of the curve using the previous explanations. Ask your students how they would interpret the relatively constant velocity at large distances.

Figure 14.20 illustrates **gravitational lensing**. This technique will come up again in the study of external galaxies and quasars, so take a little time to introduce it now.

Finally, end the chapter with a "trip" to the **center of the galaxy** and a discussion of the Sagittarius A (Sgr A*) radio source. **(DEMO⚡)** Use **Starry Night Pro** to show students how to find the position Sgr A*. Even though it's a radio source, the location is easy to find just above the "spout of the teapot" in Sagittarius. Draw on knowledge students now have of black holes as you describe the observations and interpretations. Wrap things up by emphasizing that this area of astronomy still has a lot of unanswered questions and exciting puzzles associated with it.

Student Writing Questions

1. It is not uncommon for science fiction stories to talk about "galactic empires." Considering the size of the galaxy, number of stars, and motions within the galaxy, discuss some of the difficulties in

having an empire such as those suggested in these stories. Do you think it would be ultimately possible to have such an empire? What would be needed for such an empire to remain as a cohesive unit?

2.   It takes the Sun about 225 million years to go once around the Milky Way Galaxy. This means that the Sun and the solar system have gone over 20 times around the galaxy. Look up information on the development of life on Earth, such as when it first existed, developed nucleated cells, multicellular life, etc. Give this history and when these events occurred, not in millions or billions of years, but in revolutions around the galaxy (i.e., "galactic years"). For example, life first arose on Earth after 2 GY.

3.   Describe the Milky Way from the vantage point of a planet located around a star in the halo.

4.   What will be the conditions in the solar system when the Sun becomes an RR Lyrae star? What would it be like in the inner solar system? The outer solar system? What would the Sun look like?

5.   We often think of Earth as providing the conditions necessary for life. But are there places in the galaxy that provide good or bad environments for life? Where in the galaxy is it safest for life to exist on a planet? Where is it the least satisfactory? Evaluate the Milky Way with regard to the question of providing an environment supportive for life on a planet.

Answers to End of Chapter Exercises

Review and Discussion

1.   Globular clusters occur only in one half of the sky. This peculiar situation was recognized early-on in their study. They also appear "clustered" around one part of the Milky Way. It was correctly concluded that the globular clusters form a halo around the galaxy; the center of their distribution is also the center of the Milky Way Galaxy. Astronomers can determine the distance to the center of the distribution of globular clusters and therefore determine the distance to the center of the galaxy. We can therefore determine our place within the galaxy by observing the distribution of globular clusters.

2.   Cepheids have the unique property of a relationship between their period of pulsation and their luminosity or absolute magnitude. By observing the Cepheid and determining its period of variation, its absolute magnitude is known. Comparing the absolute magnitude with the apparent magnitude allows the distance to be determined.

3.   Because of their intrinsically high luminosity, Cepheids can be seen, and therefore used, out to a few million parsecs. They are used to determine distances to the nearest galaxies.

4.   RR Lyrae variables are very useful for determining distances to globular clusters. By knowing how the globular clusters are distributed in the galaxy, the halo is mapped out. But most importantly, the distribution of globular clusters gives the distance to the center of the Milky Way Galaxy from the Sun. This also helped tell astronomers how large the Milky Way actually is.

5.   The central regions of the galaxy are obscured by thick clouds of interstellar dust. Visible light cannot penetrate these clouds. However, infrared and especially radio waves can easily penetrate these clouds, and so we can "see" the center of the galaxy at these wavelengths.

6. In the radio part of the spectrum, atomic hydrogen gas emits 21-cm radiation. Because its long wavelength allows it to travel throughout the galaxy without absorption by dust, astronomers can use it to map the structure of gas clouds in the galaxy. Molecular hydrogen is very difficult to observe, but other molecules, such as carbon monoxide, are used to map molecular clouds. Radio sources are often more useful than observations made in visible light because the radio waves penetrate the dust that obscures the visible wavelengths.

7. The stars in the Galactic disk move in roughly circular orbits around the center of the Milky Way. The orbits all lie in the plane of the disk. The halo stars have approximately the same velocities as the disk stars, but are moving in various directions relative to the disk, forming a spherical halo around the galaxy. These stars pass in and out of the disk, toward the center of the galaxy and back out again into the halo. When seen locally, they appear to have high velocities relative to the Sun and other disk stars, and the direction of their motion is at an angle to the plane of the disk.

8. The spiral arms of a galaxy are bright and contain very luminous stars, open star clusters, and emission nebulae. All these objects are found in star formation regions and are all considered young objects.

9. The gas and dust enter the spiral arm from behind and become compressed as they encounter the density wave. Star formation starts from the compressed gas and dust. The stars and unused gas and dust move on through the spiral arm and continue with their normal orbital motion around the galaxy.

10. Imagine a group of newly formed massive stars somewhere in the Galactic disk. When these stars form, the H II regions, or emission nebulae, that appear around them send shock waves through the surrounding gas. These waves can trigger new star formation. Similarly, when the stars explode in supernovae, more shock waves are formed. The formation of one group of stars provides the mechanism for the formation of more stars.

11. The stars in the halo have orbits that form a spherical halo around the galaxy. This tells us the original shape of the cloud of gas that was the galaxy before stars formed. The entire halo appears to rotate, which further tells us that this cloud was rotating. The formation of a disk is the result of the cloud having some initial rotation. The stars in the halo are red, which tells us they are old. All the high-mass stars have already evolved away from the main sequence. The cloud from which the Milky Way formed was therefore probably spherical, then collapsed. The red halo stars were formed in the earlier days of the galaxy.

12. Different parts of the galaxy rotate at different rates. The rotation is actually the motions of the stars and gas around the galaxy. Because the Milky Way is not a solid body, like Earth, different parts of it move at different rates. The orbital motions are determined strictly by the amount of mass interior to the orbit. The velocity of the orbits at differing distances gives us the rotation curve of the galaxy. By looking at the outermost orbits, the total mass of the galaxy can be determined. For the Milky Way, the rotation curve indicates that there is substantially more mass than can be accounted for by stars, gas, and dust.

13. The rotation curve of the galaxy provides strong evidence for dark matter. By studying the motion of stars around the galaxy, the mass interior to their orbits can be determined. However, more mass is found, by about a factor of two, than can be accounted for by ordinary matter. Furthermore, the galaxy seems to be larger than previously known. The rotation curve of the outer part of the Milky Way continues to show greater and greater amounts of matter, extending out to what is known as the Galactic corona.

14. Possible explanations for dark matter make a long list. Some are: brown dwarfs, black dwarfs, black holes, WIMPS, and MACHOS.

15. From a disk of hot gas spanning 10 pc across the center of the Milky Way Galaxy, infrared spectral lines are broadened, indicating the motion of the gas. For this motion to be possible, there must be a massive central body. Yet it must be of small size and very faint or nonluminous. This is best explained by there being a 1-million-solar-mass black hole at the center of our galaxy.

Conceptual Self-Test

True or False? 1. T 2. T 3. F 4. F 5. F 6. T 7. F 8. T

Multiple Choice 9. b 10. c 11. a 12. b 13. d 14. b 15. c

Problems

1. If the radius of the nebula is 100 A.U., then its diameter is 200 A.U.
$$(\text{angular diameter})/360° = (\text{diameter})/[2\pi(\text{distance})].$$
   Angular diameter $= [(200 \text{ A.U.} \times 1.5 \times 10^8 \text{ km/A.U.})(360°)] \div [2\pi(100 \text{ pc})(3.09 \times 10^{13} \text{ km/pc})] =$
   5.46×10^8 degrees $= 2.0''$, which is much less than the angular diameter of Andromeda.

   Solve the above formula for the distance at which Andromeda would have an angular diameter of 6°.
   Distance $= [(200 \text{ A.U.} \times 1.5 \times 10^8 \text{ km/A.U.})(360°)]/(2\pi \times 6°) = 2.9 \times 10^{11}$ km $= 1900$ A.U.

2. A difference of 5 magnitudes corresponds to a factor of 100 in brightness. So, a difference of 20 magnitudes corresponds to a factor of $100^4 = 10^8$ in brightness. By the inverse-square law, the distance will be a factor of the square root of $10^8 = 10^4$ times greater than 10 pc. 10 pc $\times 10^4 = 100,000$ pc $= 100$ kpc.

3. Using the inverse-square law, if a Cepheid is 100 times brighter than an RR Lyrae variable, it should be visible at 10 times the distance. In other words, placing the Cepheid 10 times farther away will make it 10^2 times fainter, or 100 times fainter. Therefore, it would equal the RR Lyrae star's brightness.

4. Every factor of 100 in luminosity corresponds to a difference of 5 magnitudes, as $2.512^5 = 100$. If x is the number of magnitudes corresponding to a luminosity difference of 30,000 times, then $2.512^x = 30,000$, and $x = 11.2$. The absolute magnitude of such a Cepheid would therefore be $5 - 11.2 = -6.2$.

   Using the inverse-square law, if a Cepheid is 30,000 times brighter than the Sun, it should be visible at a distance of the square root of $30,000 = 173$ times farther than the Sun would be. If the *Hubble Space Telescope* could see the Sun at 100,000 pc, then it should be able to see a Cepheid at 173 $\times$ 100,000 pc $= 1.7 \times 10^7$ pc or 17 Mpc.

5. Set up a ratio: (transverse velocity)/(circumference) = (angular velocity)/(360°).
   Then angular velocity $= [(200 \text{ km/s})/(2\pi \times 3000 \text{ pc} \times 3.09 \times 10^{13} \text{ km/pc})] \times 360° =$
   1.2×10^{-13} degrees/s $= 0.014''$/year. Yes, this motion would be measurable.

6. At 20 kpc, the circumference of the orbit is $2\pi \times 20,000$ pc $= 126,000$ pc. A parsec $= 3.1\times10^{13}$ km, so the circumference is 3.9×10^{18} km. At a rate of 240 km/s it will take 1.6×10^{16} s to orbit once. A year has 3.2×10^{7} s in it, so the period of the orbit is 509 million years.

    Use Kepler's third law; we have the period in years but we need the size of the orbit in A.U. There are 206,000 A.U. in 1 pc, so 20 kpc $= 4.12\times10^{9}$ A.U. Finally, we can apply Kepler's third law; the result will be in solar masses: $(5.09\times10^{8}$ yr$)^2 = (4.12\times10^{9}$ A.U.$)^3/M$; $M = 2.7\times10^{11}$ solar masses.

7. The Sun makes one orbit around the center of the galaxy in $t = d/v = (8$ kpc$)/(220$ km/s$)$. The stars at 15 kpc are moving at about 250 km/s, so they complete one orbit in $(15$ kpc$)/(250$ km/s$)$. Let n be the number of orbits that the Sun has made when it laps the stars at 15 kpc. Then $(n - 1)$ is the number of orbits made by the stars at 15 kpc in this same time. So:
    $$n[(8 \text{ kpc})/(220 \text{ km/s})] = (n - 1)[(15 \text{ kpc})/(250 \text{ km/s})], \text{ or } n = 2.54.$$

    Therefore, the Sun has orbited 2.54 times when it laps the stars at 15 kpc. To find out how long this is in years, determine the period of the Sun's orbit:
    $t = d/v = (2\pi \times 8$ kpc $\times 1000$ pc/kpc $\times 3.09\times10^{13}$ km/pc$)/(220$ km/s$) = 7.06\times10^{15}$ s $= 224$ million years.
    Therefore, the Sun laps the stars at 15 kpc in 224 million years $\times 2.54 = 570$ million years.

    Repeat for matter at 5 kpc, which appears to be moving at about 205 km/s:
    $$n[(8 \text{ kpc})/(220 \text{ km/s})] = (n + 1)[(5 \text{ kpc})/(205 \text{ km/s})], \text{ or } n = 2.0.$$
    Therefore, the Sun is lapped by the stars at 5 kpc in 224 million years $\times 2.0 = 450$ million years.

8. Let's try an easy approach to this question. The Sun is moving at 220 km/s around the Milky Way Galaxy but is approaching spiral arms at a speed of $220 - 120 = 100$ km/s. This is about half its speed. We also know from the text that it takes the Sun 225 million years to go around the galaxy once. Think about the Sun moving half as slow now. But the distance to be covered between spiral arms is also half its normal orbit because there are two spiral arms. So the Sun must cover half the distance with half the speed; it will take about as long as a normal orbit does, 225 million years. In 4.6 billion years the Sun has gone around 20.4 times, so it should have passed through a spiral arm about 20 times.

    If you want a more precise measure of this, just realize the previous calculation is correct for a speed of 110 km/s, not 100 km/s. The Sun is really moving $100/110 = 0.91$ times *slower* than what we had assumed, meaning it will take *longer* to move between spiral arms and complete 0.91 *fewer* passes than we had calculated. This gives $0.91 \times 20 =$ about 18 passes instead of 20.

9. The difference in the speed of the star and the speed of the density wave is 100 km/s. In 10 million years this will amount to 100 km/s $\times 10\times10^{6}$ yr $\times 3.2\times10^{7}$ s/yr $= 3.2\times10^{16}$ km. This is equivalent to 1000 pc, or 1 kpc.

10. An angle of 0.2" will subtend 0.2 A.U. at 1 pc. At 8000 pc this distance will be 1600 A.U., which is the radius of the circular orbit.
    The period of the orbit is circumference divided by velocity:
    $$P = (2\pi r)/v = (2\pi \times 1600 \text{ A.U.} \times 1.5\times10^{8} \text{ km/A.U.})/(1200 \text{ km/s}) = 1.26\times10^{9} \text{ s} = 39.8 \text{ years.}$$

    Using Kepler's third law,
    $$(39.8 \text{ yr})^2 = (1600 \text{ A.U.})^3/M; \qquad M = 2.6 \text{ million solar masses.}$$

Resource Information

Student CD Media Resources

Interactive Student Tutorials
Gravitational Lensing

Movies/Animations
Cepheid Star in Distant Galaxy
Stellar Motion in Center of Milky Way; Proof of a Black Hole?

Transparencies

194.	Figure 14.1	Galactic Plane
195.	Figure 14.3	Hershel's Galaxy Model
196.	Figure 14.4	Variable Stars
	Figure 14.5	Variable Stars on the H–R Diagram
197.	Figure 14.6	Period–Luminosity Plot
	Figure 14.7	Variable Stars on Distance Ladder
198.	Figure 14.8	Globular Cluster Distribution
199.	Figure 14.9	Stellar Populations in Our Galaxy
200.	Figure 14.10	Infrared View of the Milky Way
201.	Figure 14.11	Orbital Motion in the Galactic Disk
	Figure 14.12	Stellar Orbits in Our Galaxy
202.	Figure 14.13	Milky Way Formation
	Figure 14.14	Gas in the Galactic Disk
203.	Figure 14.15	Milky Way Spiral Structure
	Figure 14.16	Differential Galactic Rotation
204.	Figure 14.17	Density Wave Theory
	Figure 14.18	Self-propagating Star Formation
205.	Figure 14.19	Weighing the Galaxy
206.	Figure 14.20	Gravitational Lensing
207.	Figure 14.23	Orbits Near the Galactic Center

Materials

A four-foot long panorama poster of the Milky Way is available from the Astronomical Society of the Pacific, www.astrosociety.org.

Suggested Readings

Adams, Amy. "The triumph of *Hipparcos*." *Astronomy* (Dec 1997). p. 60. Describes *Hipparcos* observations of Cepheid variable stars.

Bartusiak, Marcia. "Gravity's rainbow." *Astronomy* (Aug 1997). p. 44. Describes gravitational lenses, and how this effect is used to map dark matter.

Binney, James. "The evolution of our galaxy." *Sky & Telescope* (Mar 1995). p. 20. Describes the formation and evolution of the Milky Way.

Birriel, Jennifer. "The Milky Way's Age." *Mercury* (Jan/Feb 2005). p. 8. A very good discussion about how radioactive isotopes provide a means of determining the age of the Milky Way.

Croswell, Ken. "To kill a galaxy." *Astronomy* (Dec 1996). p. 36. Describes the interaction between the Milky Way and its near neighbors.

Croswell, Ken. "What lies at the Milky Way's center?" *Astronomy* (May 1995). p. 32. Describes observations of the radio source Sagittarius A*.

Di Cicco, Dennis. "There's no place like home: panorama of the Milky Way." *Sky & Telescope* (Nov 1999). p. 137. Describes features seen in a stunning panorama of the Milky Way.

Eicher, David J. "Meet the Milky Way." *Astronomy* (May 1996). p. 72. A guide to observing the Milky Way with the naked eye, binoculars, and small telescope.

Jayawardhana, Ray. "Destination: galactic center." *Sky & Telescope* (June 1995). p. 26. Describes a virtual journey from the Sun to the center of the galaxy.

Mateo, Mario. "Bonuses of the microlensing business." *Sky & Telescope* (Sept 1997). p. 38. Describes gravitational microlensing and the search for dark matter.

Russell, David. "Island universes: from Wright to Hubble." *Sky & Telescope* (Jan 1999). p. 56. Traces the history of the concept of galaxies.

Schulkin, Bonnie. "Does a monster lurk close by? Massive black hole at galactic center." *Astronomy* (Sept 1997). p. 42. Discusses the evidence that the center of our galaxy contains a massive black hole.

Szpir, Michael. "Passing the bar: the Milky Way Galaxy is a barred spiral." *Astronomy* (Mar 1999). p. 46. Describes the evidence that the Milky Way is a barred spiral galaxy.

Tyson, Neil De Grasse. "The Shapley-Curtis debate." *Natural History* (May 1995). p. 66. Summarizes the key points in the historic Shapley-Curtis debate on the nature of the Milky Way.

Waller, William H. "Redesigning the Milky Way." *Sky & Telescope* (Sept 2004). p. 50. Over the past two decades various galactic surveys have changed how astronomers describe our Milky Way.

Notes and Ideas

Class time spent on material: Estimated:_____   Actual:_____

Demonstration and activity materials:

Notes for next time:

Chapter 15: Normal and Active Galaxies
Building Blocks of the Universe

Outline

Summary

Chapter 15 explores the wide variety of galaxies found in the universe. "Normal" galaxies are treated first; topics include Hubble's classification scheme, the characteristics of spiral, barred-spiral, elliptical, and irregular galaxies, and the organization of galaxies into clusters and superclusters. The Hubble Law, which describes the expansion of the Universe is introduced. The chapter continues with a discussion of active galaxies, quasars, radio galaxies, and the supermassive black holes in galactic nuclei.

Major Concepts

- Classification of galaxies
    - Spirals
    - Barred spirals
    - Ellipticals
    - Irregulars
    - Hubble's "tuning fork" diagram
- Distances to galaxies—additional methods
    - Tully-Fisher relation
    - Supernovae as standard candles
- Clusters of galaxies
    - Rich and poor clusters
    - Superclusters, or clusters of clusters
    - The Local Group
    - The Virgo Supercluster
- Hubble's law
    - Expansion of the universe
    - Redshifts and recessional velocities of galaxies
    - Relationship between recessional velocity and distance
    - Value of Hubble's constant
    - Using Hubble's law to determine distances
- Active galaxies and quasars
    - Seyferts
    - Radio galaxies
    - Quasars
    - Characteristics of active galaxies
    - Energy source

Teaching Suggestions and Demonstrations

The Andromeda Galaxy is a good place to begin the discussion of galaxies in general. It is shown in Figure 14.2 from the previous chapter. Have your students construct a finder chart for the **Andromeda Galaxy (M-31)** using **Sky Chart III**. It is easily visible with binoculars and even visible with the naked eye from a reasonably dark site. Also, spend a little time on the Shapley-Curtis debates regarding the nature of the "spiral nebulae." We take for granted now that galaxies are at great distances from us, but when they were first discovered their distances were unknown, and many astronomers believed galaxies were nebulae inside our own Milky Way Galaxy. A good start for this chapter is using "Looking at Distant Objects" from *Lecture Tutorials for Introductory Astronomy* by Adams. This activity is good for collaborative small groups and specifically covers our perspective of how external galaxies appear from our vantage point within the Milky Way. Be sure to consider how much time to devote to this exercise, since it normally takes more class time than you'd estimate.

Section 15.1

You may want to begin this section with a slide show of lots of different **galaxies**. Show individual images as well as clusters of galaxies and deep-field images. Darken the room and ask students to concentrate on similarities and differences, and specifically on characteristics that could be used to categorize galaxies into different types. List their suggestions for characteristics and discuss. For instance, characteristics like size can be problematic because sizes are not known unless distances are. Chances are, your students will come up with the same major three groups that Hubble did: **spirals, ellipticals,** and **irregulars**. (Of course, they may not come up with the same names.) Go over the comparisons in Table 15.1 and then return for a reexamination of the slides. Students can classify each galaxy shown and justify their classification based on the properties in the table.

Next, concentrate on the **spiral galaxies** and **barred-spiral galaxies**. After showing photos, ask students to describe any relationships they see between different galaxy characteristics. They will probably notice that the galaxies with the most tightly wound arms tend to have the largest nuclei. Discuss the criteria for classification and give students more examples to classify. The line dividing the different subclasses is vague, since, for instance, the nuclear bulges come in a continuous range of sizes, not just small, medium, and large.

Use Figure 15.9 to illustrate **Hubble's "tuning fork" scheme**. Emphasize that it does *not* represent an evolutionary sequence. Also discuss how the orientation of a particular galaxy with respect to our line of sight can present a problem for classification. Two paper plates taped together can represent a disk; tilt it to show how it will appear at different orientations. An elliptical galaxy can be represented by a football or a cigar. Each of these items could appear spherical if viewed "end on."

Irregulars are particularly interesting because they tend to have lots of star formation. See if students can come up with a reason for a relationship between an irregular shape and vigorous star formation. Remind them of the necessity to trigger star formation in interstellar clouds. What could possibly be the trigger in the case of these galaxies?

Section 15.2

This section provides the next two rungs for the cosmic distance ladder, the **Tully-Fisher relation** and **standard candles**, in particular, supernovae. (See Figure 15.11.) Discuss both of these methods and compare them to the earlier methods. Point out again how important distance determinations are to astronomy.

Tell your students to imagine getting an intergalactic letter. What would the address be? So far, students know the first several lines: "Earth, the Solar System, the Milky Way Galaxy." Now is time to add the next two: "the **Local Group**, the **Virgo Supercluster**." Discuss clusters and superclusters of galaxies. Show Figure 15.12 and discuss our neighbors in the Local Group. Contrast it with a rich cluster of galaxies. **(DEMO**‼**)** Create a scale model showing the distance between the Milky Way and Andromeda in relation to their sizes. Surprisingly, the distance between them is only about 25 times the diameter of either one. Compare this to stars, which are tiny compared to the distances between them. A collision between stars would be very unlikely; collisions between galaxies, in contrast, likely happen regularly. Go back to the discussion of the shapes and star formation rates associated with irregular galaxies and ask students if they see any possible evidence for galactic collisions.

Section 15.3

Hubble's law is extremely important to the understanding of both this chapter and Chapter 17, so be sure to spend sufficient time on it. One point to make in the beginning of your discussion is that Hubble's law itself is empirical, that is, it is based on observations. Although it is just one part of the **Big Bang Theory** and is based on **inference**, the expansion of the universe is based on **observations** and is known as the **Hubble Law**.

In every direction we look on a large scale, we see galaxies receding from us. (The "large scale" qualification means that this does not apply to nearby galaxies within the Local Group, which is gravitationally bound.) Furthermore, the *farther* the galaxy is from us, the *faster* it is receding. This relationship between recessional velocity and distance is **Hubble's law**. The observation implies cosmic expansion, which will be discussed further in the next chapter. For now, we will use Hubble's law as the final rung in the distance ladder.

Show the spectra in Figure 15.15 and explain how the **recessional velocities** are obtained. Revisit the Doppler shift here, but point out that there is a fundamental difference between the cosmological redshift and the Doppler redshift. The galaxies are not moving through space away from us; they are being carried away by an expanding space-time. (This concept will also be further discussed in Chapter 17.) Have students plot the galaxy data from Figure 16.1 and obtain the graph of Figure 15.16a. Then show the addition of more values in Figure 15.16b.

Show your students how Hubble's law provides a straightforward method of obtaining **distances** to very faraway objects, since recessional velocities can be found from spectra, and distance is just the recessional velocity divided by Hubble's constant. The catch is that enough objects with already *known* (and agreed upon!) distances must be used to determine the value of **Hubble's constant, H_0**. Also point out that this final rung on the cosmic distance ladder does not work for objects nearer than about 100 Mpc. The **units** of Hubble's constant, k/s/Mpc, can also be confusing for students. Distance divided by time divided by distance actually leaves you with the inverse of time, a point that will come up in connection with the age of the universe in the next chapter. In the meantime, remind students that the units represent a speed per unit distance. So, a galaxy 1 Mpc away will be receding from us with a velocity of 70 km/s, whereas a galaxy 2 Mpc away will be receding at 140 km/s.

Sections 15.4 and 15.5

In these sections, concentrate on the characteristics that distinguish **active galaxies** from normal galaxies. Active galaxies, including Seyferts, radio galaxies, and others, emit tremendous amounts of energy from fairly compact nuclei. The energy also usually spans the electromagnetic spectrum rather than following a blackbody curve as stellar radiation would. Show pictures of active galaxies and always point out the wavelength range in which the image was made. Remind students to consult the icons underneath the figures in the text to show what type of electromagnetic radiation is represented. In addition to illustrating important information about active galaxies, you can use these pictures as an opportunity to remind students of the importance of observing in different regions of the spectrum. A galaxy that appears quite normal in the visible may turn out to be spectacularly energetic in radio observations.

Quasars are now considered to most likely be the very bright cores of distant galaxies. The discovery of quasars and their identification as extragalactic objects is another example of the success that can come from thinking "outside the box." The spectral lines of quasars were not recognizable at first; because the objects appeared to be starlike, no one considered that the lines could be redshifted by such large amounts.

As discussed in the text, the large distances to quasars and the finite speed of light combine to imply that when we look at quasars (or other very distant objects) we are **looking back** to an earlier time in the history of the universe. Although light-years have already been discussed, students may not yet be completely comfortable with this important concept. Usually, for instance when we climb to the top of a mountain for a good view, what we expect (and get) at the top is a view of a large distance at a particular moment in time—now. Looking out in space is different because of the tremendous distances involved. As an analogy, have your students imagine the classroom as the universe. You are looking out over the people but do not see them as they are now. The ones in the back row appear as babies, then progress through childhood as they get closer, and finally you see college students in the front rows. Often this is seen as a disadvantage. After all, don't we want to know how things are *now*? Show your students how it can be an advantage for the astronomer. You can learn something about the childhood of the universe even if you were not there to experience it. If quasars really do represent an earlier stage of our universe, then we have the finite speed of light to thank for being able to study it.

Section 15.4 begins with an excellent list of the properties of active galactic nuclei. Go through this list carefully, and as you present the theory for the **energy production**, point out how the theory explains some of the properties listed. Figure 15.30 is a good place to start. Figure 15.33 will also help explain the formation of jets and the radiation observed at different viewing angles. Students may be confused by the fact that black holes are "engines" powering these nuclei. After all, nothing can escape from a black hole. Remind students that the material spiraling toward a black hole but not yet at the event horizon can emit radiation that will reach us as it is heated up to high temperatures. As mentioned in the text, 10 to 20 percent of the total mass–energy of the in-falling matter can be radiated away. Calculate with students the amount of energy that would come from the equivalent of one solar mass falling into the central black hole. Because the constant c is such a large number, the amount of energy is impressive! Non-thermal synchrotron radiation is a sure sign of the strong magnetic fields around a black hole. Discuss figure 15.34 which compares thermal (blackbody) radiation to non-thermal (synchrotron) radiation. Emphasize that synchrotron doesn't have the familiar blackbody curve associated with blackbody radiation. There is a linear relationship between frequency and intensity.

Student Writing Questions

1. You live in a spiral galaxy much like the Milky Way and, being an observant student of astronomy, you know that the huge nearby galaxy you see in your night sky will soon collide with your galaxy. Describe what it will be like to be in a galaxy as such a collision takes place. What will you see occurring? How long will it all take? What will be the fate of your star and planetary system? You may need to extend your lifetime a bit in order to witness the entire event. You can choose the type of galaxy that collides with you and whether there is a direct collision or a near-miss. Both types produce interesting effects.

2. Elliptical galaxies are mostly made up of lower-mass old stars. For this reason they do not look very interesting. But sometime in the past they must have had lots of gas, bright young stars, and so forth. Describe what a young elliptical galaxy might have looked like back then.

3. Most civilizations on Earth have some type of mythology based on the stars and planets. But imagine if we were in the center of our galaxy or some other galaxy that has an extremely rich sky, filled with hundreds of times the stars we see in our sky. How do you think the mythologies of these civilizations would be affected? Would they develop an awareness of astronomy sooner than we did? Or would the "heavens" play an even greater role in their daily lives, their religions, and their culture?

4. In 1978 Drs. Stephen Gregory and Laird Thompson announced their discovery of *voids*. Such structures had never before been seen. What do you think it would be like to make a discovery like this? Do these discoveries come slowly with lots of work or quickly, as in a moment of insight? Is this discovery typical of most discoveries being made in science? How do you feel about making discoveries yourself? Do you have the determination?

Answers to End of Chapter Exercises

Review and Discussion

1. Sa galaxies have large nuclear bulges and tightly wound arms. Sb galaxies have smaller bulges and less tightly wound arms, and Sc galaxies have the smallest bulges and least tightly wound arms. SBa, SBb, and SBc galaxies are the barred counterparts to Sa, Sb, and Sc classifications. Their arms originate from a "bar" of matter passing through the bulge and extending into the disk.

2. Like the halo of our Galaxy, elliptical galaxies are made primarily of old, reddish, low-mass stars with disordered orbits. There is no overall rotation scheme to either elliptical galaxies or to our halo. Another similarity between the Galaxy's halo and elliptical galaxies is lack of cool gas, dust, and star formation. One major difference is that ellipticals do have large amounts of hot gas, unlike our halo.

3. Radar ranging is used to establish distances within the solar system and gives us the size of the A.U.

   Parallax uses triangulation to measure distances to the nearest stars. The radius of Earth's orbit, 1 A.U., is one side of the triangle. Distances are good out to about 200 pc.

   Spectroscopic parallax utilizes the properties of stars in the H–R diagram. Using parallax, the absolute luminosities of some types of stars are established. When identified in the H–R diagram, similar stars at unknown distances can have their distances determined by comparing their apparent luminosities with those that are known. Distances can be determined to about 10,000 pc.

   Pulsating variable stars such as Cepheids have a strong relationship between the period of their pulsations and their absolute luminosities. Once established using nearby Cepheids, this method can be extended to the nearest galaxies. Distances to about 25 Mpc are possible.

4. The Tully-Fisher relation is a correlation between a galaxy's luminosity and its rotational velocity. The rotational velocity is determined from the broadening of the 21-cm line width. Here is a way in which a galaxy's total luminosity can be independently determined and, when compared to its apparent luminosity, the distance can be calculated. This relation is also independent of many of the other methods in its calibration.

5. The Virgo Cluster is one of the nearest rich clusters of galaxies. It contains about 2500 galaxies and is about 20 Mpc distant.

6. Galaxies are observed to have redshifted spectra, which is interpreted as meaning that all galaxies are receding from us. Hubble discovered that the recessional velocity is proportional to the distance for all galaxies. This is known as Hubble's law.

    Once Hubble's law is known, it is almost trivial to use for determining distances to galaxies. The spectrum of a galaxy will reveal its recessional or radial velocity. Hubble's law states how this velocity is proportional to the distance; the distance is immediately determined once the velocity is known.

7. In order to establish Hubble's law, each galaxy observed must have its velocity and distance determined. The velocity is relatively easy to determine because it comes directly from the spectrum of the galaxy. The distance, however, is much more difficult and uncertain. Hubble's constant is the constant of proportionality between the distance and the velocity of galaxies. Its value ranges between 50 and 80 km/s/Mpc. With distances uncertain, Hubble's constant remains uncertain too. The value adopted by the text is 70 km/s/Mpc.

8. Redshifts are observed; they have not been interpreted as anything like velocity or distance. When the latter is done, Hubble's constant must be used, and there is still uncertainty about its value.

9. Active galaxies are different from normal galaxies in at least two ways. First, they emit much more radiation than do normal galaxies, up to thousands of times more. Second, the nature of the radiation is different. Normal galaxies emit most of their radiation around and near the visible part of the spectrum. This is because they are composed of stars that are all emitting light at various wavelengths of the visible spectrum. But active galaxies emit most of their radiation at infrared or radio wavelengths. The source of these emissions must be other than stars, and this radiation may be referred to as nonstellar radiation.

10. The lobes of a radio galaxy are aligned on either side of the nucleus; a straight line joining the lobes would always pass through the nucleus. In some lobe radio galaxies a filament of radio-emitting material can be traced connecting the lobes to the nucleus.

11. Optical and radio interferometric observations show the energy-producing regions of active galaxies to be small. In addition, many are variable over time; the time for the variation to occur sets an upper limit to the size. A flickering over a period of a week means the size must be smaller than a light-week.

12. In the nucleus of an active galaxy is a massive black hole surrounded by an accretion disk. Gas moving in this disk emits large quantities of radiation before entering the black hole. Up to 20% of the rest mass of the gas can be emitted as energy before entering the black hole. This model can also account for the small size of the central engine, the rapid motions, and possibly jets coming out of the disk.

13. Spectra of active galaxies tend to be non-stellar in nature; rather than following a blackbody curve, they indicate that active galaxies emit substantial amounts of radiation at wavelengths longer and shorter than visible as well as visible. Non-thermal synchrotron radiation is one explanation.

14. Synchrotron radiation requires both high-energy charged particles, most likely electrons, and a strong magnetic field. As the particles spiral around the magnetic field lines, they lose energy and

emit synchrotron radiation. That this is the form of radiation emitted by active galaxies suggests that the source is very energetic. Ejected jets contain highly ionized gas and strong magnetic fields. Radio radiation increases its intensity with decreasing frequency; it is not blackbody radiation. All of this is consistent with synchrotron radiation.

15. Quasars appear as faint stars, yet their redshifts indicate enormous distances. The luminosity of quasars was calculated from these two facts and turned out to be extremely high.

Conceptual Self-Test

True or False? 1. F 2. T 3. T 4. T 5. T 6. T 7. T

Multiple Choice 8. a 9. c 10. b 11. b 12. a 13. b 14. c 15. c

Problems

1. Distance divided by velocity gives time. Convert 800 kpc to kilometers. Also, convert final answer in seconds to years: 800,000 pc × 3.1×10^{13} km/pc = 2.5×10^{19} km; 2.5×10^{19} km/266 km/s = 9.3×10^{16} s; 9.3×10^{16} s/3.2×10^{7} s/yr = 2.9×10^{9} years, or about 3 billion years. (The Sun will not have evolved to a red giant yet by this time!)

2. From Figure 14.6, a Cepheid with a period of 20 days has a luminosity of 10,000 solar luminosities. This is exactly 10 magnitudes brighter than the Sun (5 magnitudes = a factor of 100, 10 magnitudes = 100 × 100 = 10,000) or an absolute magnitude of 4.85 – 10 = – 5.15. Rearranging the magnitude formula given in *More Precisely 10-1* gives:

$$d = 10^{\frac{m-M+5}{5}} = 10^{\frac{26-(-5.15)+5}{5}} = 1.7 \times 10^{7} \text{ pc} = 17 \text{ Mpc.}$$

3. A factor of 1 billion in brightness means the supernova is the square root of 1 billion = 32,000 times as far: 32,000 × 10,000 pc = 320 Mpc.

4. According to Hubble's law, the recessional velocity of a galaxies increases as a function of its distance from the Earth. The value of the Hubble constant also determines this velocity.

$$V = H_0 \times D = 70 Km/s/Mpc \times 200 Mpc = 1.4 x 10^4 km/s$$

$$D = \frac{V}{H_0} = \frac{4000 km/s}{70 km/s/Mpc} = 57.1 Mpc$$

a. $$V = H_0 \times D = 50 Km/s/Mpc \times 200 Mpc = 1.0 x 10^4 km/s$$

$$D = \frac{V}{H_0} = \frac{4000 km/s}{50 km/s/Mpc} = 80.0 Mpc$$

b. $$V = H_0 \times D = 80 Km/s/Mpc \times 200 Mpc = 1.6 x 10^4 km/s$$

$$D = \frac{V}{H_0} = \frac{4000 km/s}{80 km/s/Mpc} = 50.0 Mpc$$

5. The distance to the Virgo cluster of galaxies is 18 Mpc, so the time for doubling the distance would simply be the time it would it take to travel another 18 Mpc.

   a. $V = H_0 \times D = 70 \, Km/s/Mpc \times 18 Mpc = 1260 km/s \times \dfrac{1pc}{3.09x10^{13} km} = 4.08x10^{-11} \, pc/s$

   $T = \dfrac{D}{V} = \dfrac{18 Mpc}{4.08x10^{-11} \, pc/s} = 4.4x10^{17} \, s = 14 \, Billion \, Years$

   b. $V = H_0 \times D = 70 \, Km/s/Mpc \times 100 Mpc = 7000 km/s \times \dfrac{1pc}{3.09x10^{13} km} = 2.27x10^{-10} \, pc/s$

   $T = \dfrac{D}{V} = \dfrac{100 Mpc}{2.27x10^{-10} \, pc/s} = 4.4x10^{17} \, s = 14 \, Billion \, Years$

6. Convert the distance to A.U.: 0.1 light year = 9.46×10^{11} km = 6.3×10^3 A.U. Next, find the period of the orbit: $(2\pi \times 9.46 \times 10^{11}$ km$)/5000$ km/s = 1.2×10^9 s = 38 years. Kepler's third law gives:

$$(38 \text{ yr})^2 = (6300 \text{ A.U.})^3/M; \qquad M = 1.8 \times 10^8 \text{ solar masses.}$$

7. The lobe is 250 kpc from the nucleus, which is 815,000 light-years. At a velocity of 0.9 c it will take 815,000 ly/0.9 ly/yr = 900,000 yr to travel this distance.

8. Use $E = mc^2$, divided by the time of one day, 86,400 s; use one Earth mass, 6×10^{24} kg, and an efficiency of 20%, or 0.2.

$$L = (.2)(6 \times 10^{24} \text{ kg})(3 \times 10^8 \text{ m/s})^2 / 86,400 \text{ s} = 1.3 \times 10^{36} \text{ W.}$$

The luminosity of the Sun is 3.9×10^{26} J/s, so this is 3.2 billion solar luminosities.

9. Use the equation for the velocity of an object in a circular orbit. Convert 0.25 pc to m and the mass of M87 from solar masses to kg.

$$v = \sqrt{\dfrac{GM}{R}} = \sqrt{\dfrac{(6.67 \times 10^{-11} \text{ Nm}^2/\text{kg}^2)(3 \times 10^9 \times 1.99 \times 10^{30} \text{ kg})}{0.25 \text{ pc} \times 3.09 \times 10^{16} \text{ m/pc}}} = 7.2 \times 10^6 \text{ m/s} = 7200 \text{ km/s.}$$

10. The amount of energy received per unit area per unit time from the Seyfert nucleus is

$$\dfrac{\text{J/s}}{\text{m}^2} = \dfrac{10^{37} \text{ W}}{4\pi(8000 \text{ pc} \times 3.09 \times 10^{16} \text{ m/pc})^2} = 1.3 \times 10^{-5} \text{ W/m}^2.$$

Sirius A has a luminosity of 23.5 solar luminosities and is 2.7 pc away. The amount of energy per area per time from it is

$$\dfrac{\text{J/s}}{\text{m}^2} = \dfrac{23.5 \times 3.90 \times 10^{26} \text{ W}}{4\pi(2.7 \text{ pc} \times 3.09 \times 10^{16} \text{ m/pc})^2} = 1.0 \times 10^{-7} \text{ W/m}^2.$$

The power per area from Sirius A is 120 times smaller than that from the Seyfert nucleus. It is reasonable to ignore interstellar extinction if much of the emission is in the infrared.

Resource Information

Student CD Media Resources

Interactive Student Tutorials
None

Movies/Animations
Birth of a Quasar
Active Galaxy
Cosmic Jets
Black Hole in M87
Supermassive Black Hole

Transparencies

208.	Figure 15.3	Sombrero Galaxy
209.	Table 15.1	Basic Galaxy Properties by Type
210.	Figure 15.9	Galactic "Tuning Fork"
211.	Figure 15.10	Galaxy Rotation
212.	Figure 15.11	Extragalactic Distance Ladder
213.	Figure 15.12	Local Group
214.	Figure 15.13	Virgo Cluster
215.	Figure 15.15	Galaxy Spectra
216.	Figure 15.16	Hubble's Law
217.	Figure 15.17	Cosmic Distant Ladder
218.	Figure 15.20	Seyfert Time Variability
219.	Table 15.2	Redshift, Distance, and Look-Back Time
220.	Figure 15.25	Radio Galaxy
221.	Figure 15.28	Quasar Spectrum
222.	Figure 15.30	Active Galactic Nucleus
223.	Figure 15.32	M87 Disk
224.	Figure 15.33	Dusty Donut
225.	Figure 15.34	Nonthermal Radiation

Suggested Readings

Bartusiak, Marcia. "A beast in the core." *Astronomy* (July 1998). p. 42. Describes the search for "fossil quasars," or supermassive black holes at the center of normal galaxies.

Bechtold, Jill. "Shadows of creation: quasar absorption lines and the genesis of galaxies." *Sky & Telescope* (Sept 1997). p. 28. Describes how absorption features in quasar spectra can be used to probe the early universe.

Bothun, Gregory D. "Beyond the Hubble sequence." *Sky & Telescope* (May 2000). p. 36. Discusses the limitations on galaxy classification based on observed morphology, and suggests alternatives related to galactic evolution.

Charlton, Jane C., Gallagher, Sarah C., and Palma, Christopher. "Galaxy Train Wrecks." *Sky & Telescope* (Nov 2004). p. 30. New observations are helping to unravel the turbulent histories of compact galaxy groups.

Croswell, Ken. "How far to Virgo?" *Astronomy* (Mar 1995). p. 48. Describes measurements of the distance to the Virgo cluster using Cepheid variable stars.

Disney, Michael. "A new look at quasars." *Scientific American* (June 1998). p. 52. Summarizes Hubble Space Telescope results about quasars.

Finkbeiner, Ann K. "Cosmic yardsticks: supernovae and the fate of the universe." *Sky & Telescope* (Sept 1998). p. 38. Describes the use of Cepheid variable stars and type Ia supernova for measuring distances in the universe.

Ford, Holland and Tsvetanov, Zlatan I. "Massive black holes in the hearts of galaxies." *Sky & Telescope* (June 1996). p. 28. Discusses observations of supermassive black holes in the centers of ordinary and active galaxies.

Graham, David. "Clusters in collision." *Astronomy* (May 1999). p. 58. Discusses the interaction of galaxies in clusters.

Henry, J. Patrick, Briel, Ulrich G., and Bohringer, Hans. "The evolution of galaxy clusters." *Scientific American* (Dec 1998). p. 52. Describes X-ray observations of the dynamics of galaxy clusters.

Kinney, Anne L. "When galaxies were young: the Next Generation Space Telescope promises to decipher the origins of stars and galaxies." *Astronomy* (May 1998). p. 44. Profiles the plans and capabilities of the Next Generation Space Telescope.

Martin, Pierre and Friedli, Daniel. "At the hearts of barred galaxies." *Sky & Telescope* (Mar 1999). p. 32. Summary of our knowledge of barred spiral galaxies.

Nadis, Steve. "Here, there, and everywhere?" *Astronomy* (Feb 2001). p. 34. Discusses supermassive blackholes and the formation of galaxies.

Shaffer, Rick. "Observer's challenge: hunt down a quasar: 3C273." *Astronomy* (Apr 1996). p. 64. A guide to observing the quasar C3273 with a small telescope.

Stephens, Sally. "Hubble warrior." *Astronomy* (Mar 2000). p. 52. Profiles the life and work of Wendy Freedman, the leader of the Hubble Space Telescope Key Project.

Tyson, Neil de Grasse. "Between the galaxies." *Natural History* (June 1999). p. 34. Describes the intergalactic medium .

Tyson, Neil De Grasse. "Galactic engines." *Natural History* (May 1997). p. 66. Describes energy production in active galaxies and quasars.

Voit, G. Mark. "The rise and fall of quasars." *Sky & Telescope* (May 1999). p. 40. Discusses the connection between quasars and collisions of galaxies.

West, Michael. "Galaxy clusters: urbanization of the cosmos." *Sky & Telescope* (Jan 1997). p. 30. Describes the characteristics of galaxy clusters.

Notes and Ideas

Class time spent on material: Estimated:_____   *Actual:_____*

Demonstration and activity materials:

Notes for next time:

Chapter 16: Galaxies and Dark Matter
The Large-Scale Structure of the Cosmos

Outline

Summary

Chapter 16 introduces galactic structure as related to dark matter. Masses of galaxies, dark matter, the large-scale structure of the universe, and our techniques for probing and mapping it are all discussed. Theories of galaxy formation and evolution are discussed. Black holes and active galaxies, as related to earlier epochs, are also discussed. The discussion of earlier epochs leads to the discussion of the universe on very large time scales.

Major Concepts

- Dark matter in the universe
  - Galaxy masses
  - Visible matter and dark halos
  - Intra-cluster gas
- Galaxy collisions
  - Observed collisions
  - Computer simulation of collisions
- Galaxy formation and evolution
  - Mergers and acquisitions
  - Galaxy interactions
  - Making the Hubble Sequence
- Black holes and active galaxies
  - The quasar epoch
  - Active and normal galaxies
  - Active galaxy evolution
- Universe on very large scales
  - Clusters of galaxies
  - Redshift surveys
  - Quasar absorption lines
  - Gravitational lensing

Teaching Suggestions and Demonstrations

Sections 16.1 and 16.2

By now, students should be able to make a pretty good guess regarding some of the methods of determination of **galaxy masses**. Using rotation curves (see Figure 16.1) and applying Kepler's third law to binary galaxies are two of the familiar methods that students will come up with. Discuss analysis of motions of galaxies within clusters as well. As with the measurement of mass of the Milky Way, there is a large discrepancy between what we see and how much mass these dynamical measurements tell us there should be.

Galaxy collisions have been observed and are viewed as being a normal stage of galaxy formation. In fact, our Milky Way galaxy and the Andromeda galaxy are heading towards each other and will collide within the next 4 billion years. **(DEMO!)** As in Chapter 15, use a scale model showing the distance between the Milky Way and Andromeda in relation to their sizes. Surprisingly, the distance between them is only about 25 times the diameter of either one. Initially students might think it's not likely that these two galaxies would ever collide, but it seems much more likely when the scale model is displayed.

Section 16.3

Figures 16.9 and 16.17 show a possible **evolutionary sequence for galaxies**. Emphasize to students that the details are yet far from certain in this active and exciting area of astronomy. Also point out the difference between galaxy evolution as described, which hinges on chance encounters, mergers, and collisions, and stellar evolution, which relies on the intrinsic properties of the stars. The Hubble deep field in Figure 16.10 was very important in our understanding of how very distant galaxies appear as "fragments" of more modern galaxies. Remind students again of the typical sizes of galaxies compared to the distances between them to justify the assumption that galaxy interactions, mergers, and collisions are not uncommon events. The roles of quasars and active galaxies in the sequence is consistent with our observations as we look out in space and back in time. Compare Figure 16.13, a computer simulation in which spiral arms are formed, with the photo of the Whirlpool galaxy, Figure 15.2b.

Section 16.4

Emphasize that young galaxies, such as quasars, are very different than modern galaxies in that the black hole in their centers are active, which makes them very luminous compared to modern galaxies. This is because there was much more available material in the early universe for the black holes to "feed" upon. These very luminous galaxies are referred to as being **"active" galaxies** and the less luminous galaxies, such as the Milky Way, are referred to as being **"normal" galaxies**. The central engine of all galaxies is a **super massive black hole.** As shown in Figure 16.17, the black hole mass is directly proportional to the mass of the galactic bulge. The mechanism for this luminosity is the accretion disc for the visible light and the polar jets for the radio emission as shown in Figure 15.29 and Figure 15.31.

Section 16.5

We have now reached examination of the **large-scale structure** of the universe. Try to find several slices of the **redshift survey** to give your students a better feel for the voids, filaments, and bubble-like patterns. Some 3-D pictures that can be rotated on a computer screen are available. Remind students of the scale; it is truly remarkable that we can make such plots!

In order to probe space at such great distances, it has been necessary to devise new techniques. Discuss **gravitational lensing** (as shown in Figure 16.25) and the **absorption lines in quasar spectra** (as shown in Figure 16.23). Point out that what could have been considered an annoyance to the study of quasars (intervening galaxies and dust clouds) actually became very valuable for probing space and learning about the distribution of mass.

Student Writing Questions

1. Much of the material of this chapter is at the cutting edge of astronomical research. Discuss all the topics you have encountered here that are still not understood or about which there are some significant uncertainties. Some of this may also pertain to recent chapters; that would be good to include, too.

2. Are quasars at the distances calculated from Hubble's law or are they much closer to us? Take one side and give evidence to support your case. In particular, try to answer the objections made by the other side.

3. What would it be like to live in an active galaxy? Assume you lived on a planet orbiting a star about half-way out from the center of the galaxy. The galaxy has an active nucleus and ejects plasma jets every few hundred million years. What impact would there be on life or its development? Would life be wiped out by these events? What do you think you would experience during one of these episodes?

4. Quasars were originally named "radio stars" because they looked optically like stars but emitted radio waves. But stars implied they were local, in our Galaxy. Maarten Schmidt, while looking at the unidentifiable lines in a radio star's optical spectrum, considered for a moment a possibility "outside of the box." In so doing he discovered the cosmological distances to quasars. Find examples where the label or name we give to something biases our thinking to the point that we completely miss what it is we are experiencing. Examples outside of science are appropriate.

5. Describe what the universe must have been like during the age of quasars. If you were a life-form back then, what kind of universe was it? What did it look like and how was it different from today's universe? Would planets and life even have been possible back then?

Answers to End of Chapter Exercises

Review and Discussion

1. The mass of a galaxy can be determined in several different ways. The rotation curve is the most accurate method. By measuring the velocity of rotation, Kepler's third law can be applied to calculate the mass. If the galaxy is part of a binary galaxy system, Kepler's third law can be applied again, but now to the orbit of the galaxies around each other. There are some uncertainties in this method, and it is best applied to a large number of binaries in order for a statistical result to be obtained.

2. The motion of galaxies within a cluster must be balanced by the total gravitational field produced by all the mass in the cluster. When traditional methods are applied to determining the total mass of the galaxies in a cluster it always results in total masses that are 10 to 100 times too little compared to the mass necessary to hold the cluster together. But because the cluster is a cluster, it must be held together by its own gravity. The question arises: Where is the extra mass?

3. The X-rays emitted by clusters of galaxies originate from very hot intracluster gas. This gas has a temperature of about 10 million K and emits strongly in the X-ray region of the spectrum.

4. Figure 16.13 gives one example. Two disk galaxies interact and the smaller one distorts the larger one, causing spiral arms and structure to appear where none existed before. Another example is the "antenna galaxy" as shown in Figure 16.8.

5. Collisions between galaxies can be partly evolutionary. The large central galaxies found in clusters certainly share an evolutionary history; they have cannibalized many smaller galaxies in their cluster. But collisions and close encounters are random processes, each case being a little or a lot different from the next. The result is that each galaxy may have, to some degree, a uniqueness to it— a structure unlike any other—that disallows any discussion of evolution. The evolution of a 1-solar-mass star will be just like any other star of the same mass and composition; this cannot be said for any Sb, E3, or any other type of galaxy.

6. It now appears that large galaxies grow through repeated mergers or collisions with smaller galaxies. This process is not at all like star formation, but in many ways is more similar to planetary formation. We do not know how this process affects the type of galaxy that results. Certainly this process continues today; interacting galaxies are relatively common.

7. Starburst galaxies have vigorous star formation and therefore are "bluer" than normal galaxies because of their numerous high-mass stars. This star formation can be triggered by gravitational interactions between galaxies and is related to galaxy evolution because mergers and collisions between galaxies are part of galaxy evolution.

8. Although the lifetime of quasars is unknown, we know it can be neither very short nor very long. If quasars existed for just a few years, we probably would not see any. Records indicate quasars on old photographs dating back many decades. If quasars last billions of years then there are two problems. First, where would they get all the mass to feed their energy needs? Some quasars are using between 10 and 100 solar masses a year. Over 10 billion years would require between 10^{11} and 10^{12} solar masses, in other words, the mass of an entire large galaxy. Second, if quasars lasted this long, we should see many more of them near to us, which we do not. It is reasonable to expect that quasars last just a few tens of millions of years; it is consistent with the numbers and distances of quasars.

9. The supermassive black hole in a quasar used up most of the available matter in the central portion of the galaxy. With less material entering it, the energy source surrounding the black hole becomes inactive. Modern "normal" galaxies are thought to have dormant supermassive black holes still lurking at their centers.

10. Evidence for supermassive black holes at the centers of galaxies include the extreme luminosity of quasars and the very fast rotation of the accretion disk at the center of galaxies that is associated with these supermassive black holes as shown in Figure 15.32.

11. A normal galaxy can become active if it receives an influx of new material, which could happen during a collision between 2 (or more) galaxies.

12. A redshift study of galaxies determines the recessional velocity of these galaxies as observed from the vantage point of Earth by observing the Doppler shift of certain spectral lines. This velocity can be used with the Hubble law to calculate the distances to these galaxies.

13. Two discoveries led astronomers to the "soap bubble" distribution of galaxies. First, voids were discovered. They are large, roughly spherical regions that do not contain any galaxies. Second, galaxies seemed to group in sheets of galaxies, as if they were the surface of giant bubbles.

14. Clouds of gas between quasars and us will produce absorption lines in the spectrum of the quasar. These can be distinguished from the quasar absorption lines (if any exist) by their different redshifts, corresponding to their respective distances. The quasar can also be gravitationally lensed by a galaxy or cluster of galaxies lying between it and us. Study of the lensing pattern can provide information regarding the mass and mass distribution of the galaxy or cluster.

15. The gravitational lensing of background quasars and galaxies by foreground galaxy clusters provides evidence of dark matter on large scales.

Conceptual Self-Test

True or False? 1. F 2. F 3. F 4. T 5. T 6. F 7. T 8. T

Multiple Choice 9. b 10. c 11. d 12. a 13. d 14. b 15. a

Problems

1. Convert 500 kpc to A.U. as follows: 500 kpc × 1000 pc/kpc × 206,000 A.U./pc = 1.03×10^{11} A.U. Set up Kepler's third law as usual:

   $$P^2 = a^3/M$$

   $(30 \times 10^9 \text{ yr})^2 = (1.03 \times 10^{11} \text{ A.U.})^3/M;$ $M = 1.2 \times 10^{12}$ solar masses.

2. At 20 kpc, the circumference of the orbit is $2\pi \times 20{,}000$ pc = 126,000 pc. A parsec = 3.1×10^{13} km, so the circumference is 3.9×10^{18} km. For NGC 4984, the velocity is 340 km/s; it will take 1.6×10^{16} s to orbit once. A year has 3.2×10^7 s in it, so the period of the orbit is 348 million years.

   Use Kepler's third law; we have the period in years but we need the size of the orbit in A.U. There are 206,000 A.U. in 1 pc, so 20 kpc = 4.12×10^9 A.U. Finally, we can apply Kepler's third law; the result will be in solar masses:

   $(3.48 \times 10^8 \text{ yr})^2 = (4.12 \times 10^9 \text{ A.U.})^3/M;$ $M = 5.78 \times 10^{11}$ solar masses.

3. At a recessional velocity of 6500 km/s, the distance (obtained from Hubble's law) is 6500 km/s ÷ 70 km/s/Mpc = 92.8 Mpc. The true separation between the satellite and the parent, in Mpc, is

   $(0.1/360)(2\pi \times 93 \text{ Mpc}) = 0.162 \text{ Mpc} = 3.34 \times 10^{10}$ A.U.

   The period of the satellite galaxy around the parent is $(2\pi r)/v$.

   $(2\pi \times 0.162 \times 10^6 \text{ pc} \times 3.09 \times 10^{13} \text{ km/pc})/(50 \text{ km/s}) = 6.29 \times 10^{17} \text{ s} = 1.99 \times 10^{10}$ years.

   Using Kepler's third law, $P^2 = a^3/M$, gives

   $(1.99 \times 10^{10} \text{ years})^2 = (3.34 \times 10^{10} \text{ A.U.})^3/M;$ $M = 9.4 \times 10^{10}$ solar masses.

4. For hydrogen and $T = 20$ million K, *More Precisely 5-1* gives:

   $$v_{avg} = 0.157\sqrt{\frac{2 \times 10^7}{1}} = 702 \text{ km/s}$$

   702 km/s compares closely to 660 km/s, which is the velocity of a galaxy orbiting around a cluster.

5. Total distance covered is 200 kpc. Convert 200,000 pc to kilometers: 200,000 pc $\times$ 3.1$\times$10^{13} km/pc = 6.2$\times$10^{18} km. Dividing this distance by the velocity will give the amount of time: 6.2$\times$10^{18} km/1500 km/s = 4.1$\times$10^{15} s. A year has 3.2$\times$10^7 s. Making the conversion to years gives 4.1$\times$10^{15} s/3.2$\times$10^7 s/yr = 1.3$\times$10^8 yr or 130 million years.

6. From Table 15.2, a redshift of 0.25 corresponds to a distance of 999 Mpc.
   From *More Precisely 10-1*, m – M = 5 log (d/10 pc), so
   $$M = m - 5 \log (d/10 \text{ pc}) = 13 - 5 \log (999,000,000 \text{ pc}/10 \text{ pc}) = -27.2$$

   This is close to the Sun's apparent magnitude, – 26.8. The quasar at 10 pc would appear 0.4 magnitudes = 1.45 times as bright as the Sun at 1 A.U. The quasar is actually (4.8 – (– 27.2)) = 32 magnitudes brighter, which is a factor of $(2.512)^{32}$ = 6.3 trillion. The luminosity of the quasar is 6.3 trillion solar luminosities.

7. From Table 15.2, a redshift of 5 corresponds to 7940 Mpc.
   From *More Precisely 10-1*, m – M = 5 log (d/10 pc), so
   $$M = m - 5 \log (d/10 \text{ pc}) = 22 - 5 \log (7,940,000,000 \text{ pc}/10 \text{ pc}) = -22.5$$

   $$L = (2.512)^{(4.85 - (-22.5))} = 8.7 \times 10^{10} \text{ solar luminosities.}$$

8. The energy available is $E = 0.2mc^2$; $E = 0.2 \times (2 \times 10^{30} \times 10^8) \times (3 \times 10^8)^2 = 3.6 \times 10^{54}$ J. Dividing this by the power output gives (3.6$\times$10^{54} J)/(1040 W) = 3.6$\times$10^{14} s = 11 million years.

9. Because the redshifts of 0.15 and 0.155 are fairly low, a non-relativistic solution is a reasonable approach. Using the classical redshift formula and c = 300,000 km/s, the velocities will be:
   $$v = 0.15 \times 300,000 = 45,000 \text{ km/s}$$
   $$v = 0.155 \times 300,000 = 46,500 \text{ km/s.}$$

   These two velocities will correspond to distances, using Hubble's law, of:
   $$d = (45,000 \text{ km/s})/(70 \text{ km/s/Mpc}) = 643 \text{ Mpc}$$
   $$d = (46,500 \text{ km/s})/(70 \text{ km/s/Mpc}) = 664 \text{ Mpc}$$

   The two galaxies are 21 Mpc apart.

10. From Table 15.2, a redshift of 3 corresponds to 6460 Mpc. The galaxy lies midway between the Earth and the quasar, at a distance of 6460 Mpc/2 = 3230 Mpc. Find the distance which corresponds to 3" observed from 3230 Mpc.
    $$3"/(360 \times 60 \times 60) = x/(2\pi \times 3230 \text{ Mpc}); \qquad x = 47 \text{ kpc.}$$

Resource Information

Student CD Media Resources

Interactive Student Tutorials
None

Movies/Animations
Dark Matter
Collision of Two Spiral Galaxies

Hubble Deep Field Zoom
Starburst Galaxy
Interacting Galaxies
Cluster Merger
Gravitational Lensing

Transparencies

Suggested Readings

Bartusiak, Marcia. "What makes galaxies change?" *Astronomy* (Jan 1997). p. 36. Discusses the mechanisms for galactic evolution.

Christianson, Gale. "Mastering the universe: Edwin P. Hubble." *Astronomy* (Feb 1999). p. 60. Profiles the life and work of Edwin P. Hubble.

Djorgovski, S. George. "Fires at cosmic dawn." *Astronomy* (Sept 1995). p. 36. Discusses the connection between quasars and galaxy formation.

Eicher, David J. "Galactic genesis." *Astronomy* (May 1999). p. 38. Describes the formation and evolution of galaxies.

Keel, William. "Before galaxies were galaxies." *Astronomy* (July 1997). p. 58. Describes how observations of radio galaxies are used to probe galactic formation.

Parker, Samantha and Roth, Joshua. "To see the world in a grain of sand: the Hubble Deep Field." *Sky & Telescope* (May 1996). p. 48. Describes results obtained from the Hubble Deep Field.

Shara, Michael. "Cannibals of the cosmos." *Natural History* (Feb 2000). p. 70. Describes how collisions between galaxies influence galactic evolution.

Strauss, Michael A, and Knapp, Gillian R. "The Sloan Digital Sky Survey." *Sky & Telescope* (Feb 2005). p. 34. An unassuming 2.5 meter telescope is rewriting the textbooks on asteroids, quasars, and everything in between.

Notes and Ideas

Class time spent on material: Estimated:_____   *Actual:_____*

Demonstration and activity materials:

Notes for next time:

Chapter 17: Cosmology
The Big Bang and the Fate of the Universe

Outline

Summary

The origin, history, and fate of our universe are the topics of Chapter 17. The Big Bang theory and observational evidence in support of it are discussed. New data regarding a possible acceleration of the expansion of the universe are presented, and dark energy is introduced.

Major Concepts

- Cosmological principle
  - Homogeneity
  - Isotropy
  - No edge or center to the universe
- Expansion and the Big Bang
  - Hubble's law
  - Cosmological redshift
  - Olbers's paradox
  - The Big Bang
- Cosmic dynamics and the geometry of space
  - Two futures
  - Shape of the universe
- The fate of the universe
  - Critical density
  - Models: unbound, marginally bound, bound
  - The age of the universe
  - Cosmic accceleration
- The history of the universe
  - The Big Bang and cosmic background radiation
  - Radiation-dominated era
  - Primordial nucleosynthesis
  - Formation of atoms and decoupling
  - Inflation
  - Formation of large-scale structure

Teaching Suggestions and Demonstrations

Cosmology is mind-boggling. Tell students that if they leave class with no questions and with a sense of complete understanding, they must not have been paying attention! Encourage discussion and questions, and remind students that all the puzzles are certainly not yet solved in this field. Cosmology requires students to imagine both incredibly short and incredibly long times, to think outside our world of three dimensions, and to consider the most fundamental questions, such as, "How did the universe begin and how will it end?"

Sections 17.1 through 17.2

Students may at first balk at the assumptions of the **cosmological principle**. After all, we have been discussing all semester how matter is organized and clustered. Assure them that the homogeneity requirement applies to large scales only, not to our immediate neighborhood, galaxy, or cluster of galaxies. Show the galaxy survey in Figure 17.1. The idea that the universe has no edge follows directly from the cosmological principle. (Besides, how could it have an edge? Edges are boundaries and what could be on the other side that we would not include as part of our universe?) Then, the idea that there is no center follows directly from the idea that there is no edge. Challenge students to find the center of the room with no references to the edges.

Pose Olbers's paradox to see if any students can come up with a solution. Remind them of Hubble's law relating recessional velocity to distance, which was described in Chapter 16. To explain why this observation implies **cosmic expansion** (and to also explain why it does not imply that we are at the "center"—a common student misconception) use an analogy. For example, draw three cars in a row traveling down the highway. Imagine that the first one is going 80 mph, the second 60 mph, and the third 40 mph. Then ask students to imagine the view from any one of the vehicles. People in the last car see both of the others receding from them, with the first one receding at a greater rate. People in the middle car also see both vehicles receding, one in each direction. And, those in the front car see the other two cars moving away also, as they fall farther and farther behind. The space between the vehicles is expanding, and each observer sees the more distant car moving the fastest.

The most common analogy used in astronomy is usually called the **"raisin cake" model**. You mix up batter for a raisin cake and put it in the oven. The raisins are spread throughout the batter. As the cake bakes and expands, the raisins are carried apart from each other. If two raisins begin, say, 2 cm apart and spread to 6 cm apart by the end of a certain time, then two raisins that were originally 4 cm apart will spread to 12 cm in the same time. The recessional velocity in the second case was greater. The batter expanded, carrying the raisins with it. In a similar way, space expands, carrying the galaxies with it.

A good start for this section is using "Expansion of the Universe" from *Lecture Tutorials for Introductory Astronomy* by Adams. This activity is good for collaborative small groups and is a straightforward activity dealing with the expansion of the universe which will promote student engagement. Be sure to consider how much time to devote to this exercise, since it normally takes more class time than you'd estimate.

(DEMO 17) Show the demonstration illustrated in Figure 17.3, in which you tape objects onto a balloon, blow it up, and show that the view from any one object is the same as from any other: All the others are receding and the most distant ones are receding the fastest. You can try drawing galaxies on the balloon, but then the galaxies themselves expand, which is not the case in the universe. Gravitationally bound galaxies and clusters of galaxies do not expand; they just get farther away from each other. Stickers work well if you cannot get the coins shown in the figure to stay on. Also note that there is no center to the expansion and no edge. Hang on to the balloon and repeat the demonstration when you discuss possible curvatures of space.

Now you can also return to the comparison of the **cosmological redshift** and the Doppler redshift. As a photon travels to us through space, its wavelength is stretched as the space itself expands. Try the demonstration shown in Figure 17.4. Now you do want to draw on the balloon itself.
Blow up the original balloon (with the sticker galaxies) one more time; then slowly release the air and ask students to watch the galaxies as the expansion of the universe is played backwards. If you could remove all the air, then the galaxies would all land back in one spot. So, Hubble's law and the expansion of the universe imply that the universe all began in one spot. All of matter and space was one point that exploded in an event named the **Big Bang**, which marked the beginning of the universe. Students will almost certainly have heard of the Big Bang; thus, present the current observation of the expansion of the universe as the first piece of evidence in support of the Big Bang theory.

A limit to the **time that has elapsed since the Big Bang** can be estimated, as described in the text, from $1/H_0$. To show students why this is true, do some other examples. If you drive 120 miles at a velocity of 60 mph, how long ago did you start? To get 14 billion years from $1/(70$ km/s/Mpc$)$ you need to do some unit conversions. Take the time to do it; an estimation of the age of the universe is fundamentally important, and students should see where the value of 14 billion years comes from. Also discuss that this estimate depends critically on the value chosen for the Hubble constant *and* also on an assumption that this value has been constant over time. What if the expansion of space has slowed over time, for instance? Imagine your friend traveling 120 miles to see you. You have a view of the highway and notice she is going 40 mph as she approaches the exit. If you assume she went 40 mph the whole time, then you calculate that she took 3 hours to make the trip. If, however, she was going 60 mph earlier and slowed later, then the trip took less time.

There is certainly a lot of uncertainty about **when** the Big Bang occurred, but astronomers are in general agreement that it did occur and it marks the beginning of the universe. Very likely, at least one of your students will ask the question, "What happened *before* the Big Bang?" One answer is simply that there is no such thing as *before* the Big Bang – time started with it. An brilliant analogy for a similar type of question given by Stephen Hawking (paraphrased) is the following: Imagine standing exactly on the North Pole of Earth. Where is 2 miles north of your location?

The question "**where** was the Big Bang?" can be even tougher than "when was the Big Bang?" for students to grapple with. Pull out the balloon again, inflate it, and then deflate it. Ask students which sticker or coin represents the center of the expansion. The answer is that none of them represents the center. All space was at one point at the time of the Big Bang. The explosion did not fling matter through space, originating at one point; it flung space itself.

(**DEMO**) As an easy way to represent that there is no center of the universe a series of enlargements of a star field made on overhead transparencies can be used. Make an inverted image of any star field (black on white). This can be easily done using **Starry Night Pro**. Now make 5 or 6 copies at various magnifications using a photocopier. Label individual stars with letters. These stars will represent galaxies. If a galaxy field (such as the Virgo cluster) is used, the galaxy images will also be enlarged. This isn't ideal for this demonstration because the expansion of the universe doesn't overcome the gravitational field of a galaxy, so galaxies don't expand along with the universe. Ideally, all the stars (or dots) should be the same size on each image, but the distances should be different. Start placing the overheads on the projector one at a time starting with the smallest scale. Be sure to align one of the stars (galaxies) in the field with each new image. What you'll be able to show your students is that the "galaxy" that was used for aligning seems to be at the center, with all other "galaxies" seem to be rushing away from it. Now try it with another "galaxy" on the image, and then another. What you'll be able to show your students is that each position seems to be at the center, and thus there is no center.

Sections 17.3 and 17.4

Use lots of diagrams and analogies in discussing these sections, which can be very difficult for students to understand, but also very exciting as they involve research at the forefront of astronomy. Figure 17.5 and the analogy of the spacecraft leaving the planet helps students understand the difference between a bound and an unbound universe. Explain the concept of **critical density** carefully, because the density of the universe plays such an important role in its evolution and fate. Figure 17.6 looks fairly simple but will require explanation. Point out that we are stuck at our current spot in time; all three lines pass through that point because that represents the rate of expansion we now experience. What the universe was like in the past or will be like in the future is not known positively; different options are shown by the different curves.

Figure 17.8 is another very important one, as it represents observational evidence that the universe's expansion is **accelerating**. This fairly new idea surprised astronomers; it should sound surprising to students as well because it does not at all fit the gravity-dominated scenario we have assumed up to now. Gravity is apparently *not* slowing down the rate of expansion as predicted; something else must be involved. (What if you threw a ball up in the air, and instead of slowing down because of gravity, it sped up?) Introduce **dark energy** and the uncertainties that surround it. Go over the excellent discussion of the age of the universe and Figure 17.10 carefully.

Bring the balloon back out as an example of positive **curvature**. Of course, its surface is two-dimensional, so it is only an analogy of what positively curved space-time would be like. Explain to students that as three-dimensional (3-D) creatures ourselves, it is very difficult for us to imagine curved 3-D space. So, we imagine a 2-D universe instead. Blow the balloon up and notice not only the expansion but also that this balloon-surface universe is bounded, has no center, and has no edge. The 2-D analogies for flat and negatively curved space are a plane and a saddle. (See *More Precisely 17-1*.)

Sections 17.5 through 17.8

The final sections of the chapter outline the history of the universe from the Big Bang to the formation of the large-scale structure of the universe. Present the **cosmic background radiation** as another important piece of evidence supporting the Big Bang theory. The *COBE* (Cosmic Background Explorer) satellite data shown in Figure 17.13 is compelling. Note that we do not see all the way back to the Big Bang itself, but rather back to the epoch of **decoupling** when the universe became transparent. This concept is shown in Figure 17.16, but be careful using this illustration—some students may interpret it as representing Earth at the center of the universe!

Make a chart of the major epochs in the history of the universe with the events that were going on at each time. The following is an example:

Era	Epoch	Time (from Big Bang)	Events
Radiation	Planck	0 sec	Unknown
	GUT (Grand Unified Theory)	10^{-34}	Unification of forces
	Inflation	10^{-32}	Rapid expansion
	Baryonic	10^{-4}	Protons and neutrons formed
		10 sec	Electrons formed
Matter	Atomic	100	Helium and deuterium formed
		1000 yrs	Matter dominates radiation
		200,000	Decoupling of matter and radiation
	Galactic	10^8 yrs	Formation of galaxies
	Stellar	10^9 yrs	Beginning of star formation

Point out observations that support this understanding of the evolution of the universe. For instance, the abundance of primordial helium matches that predicted by the theory. The percent of matter that is dark matter also agrees with the theory.

The epoch of **inflation** is a particularly interesting one. To explain how it solves the flatness problem use the analogy of the ant on the balloon shown in Figure 17.20. To explain how it solves the horizon problem, use an analogy. Imagine a few students spread out in the classroom. Someone comes in the door and whispers a message to a student, who then passes it to the next, and so forth until it has reached the other side of the room. This process would take a certain amount of time. In the inflation model, the students would all be clumped together in the middle of the room, would receive the message, and then (somehow) spread very quickly (that is "inflate") to opposite sides of the room. Hence, two people on opposite sides of the room would both know the message, even if not enough time had passed for the message itself to travel from one side to the other.

The ripples in the background radiation found by the *COBE* satellite are yet another piece of evidence in support of both the Big Bang and the theory of the early evolution of the universe. They are consistent with the current structure of voids and filaments. As you discuss this chapter, constantly relate the material to observations and remind students that the theories are trying to reproduce and interpret what is seen observationally.

Student Writing Questions

1. What kind of universe do you want to live in: open, closed, or flat? Why? Scientists also have their preferences (we prefer to say preference rather than bias), and this can influence how they may interpret observations. It is a part of being human. The question "Why?" is important. Why should you or anyone prefer the universe to be one way or the other? Try to explain your personal feelings about this.

2. What if a significant part of the redshift measured for all extragalactic objects was actually non-Doppler, that is, instead of the redshift being interpreted as completely due to motion or even the Hubble flow, a significant part of it was due to some unexplained phenomenon? How would this affect the Hubble constant? Would dark matter be "necessary"? Would clusters of galaxies be unstable? What would be the effects on the cosmic density parameter? What else would be affected by this discovery?

3. Your body is made up of various molecules that contain a lot of hydrogen. Each of these hydrogen atoms was created during the Big Bang. Briefly trace the history of a typical hydrogen atom from its origin to you. Will all your hydrogen atoms share this exact same history?

4. About 500 years ago people struggled with the concept of a curved surface for Earth. (Even longer ago than this, but at this time more people were affected. Sailors feared falling off the edge of Earth.) Relate the difficulty in understanding this concept with the current problem of understanding the concept of the curvature of space. How are they similar and how are they different? What role does human experience play in understanding these concepts?

5. You now have a perspective on the evolution of the entire universe, and you are here studying it. What do you believe have been the most critical events over the past 13 billion to 15 billion years that have made it possible for you to be studying astronomy at this time?

6. Look at the Hubble Ultra Deep Field-South photograph at the beginning of the chapter. Write your impressions of what you see and what this image means to you.

Answers to End of Chapter Exercises

Review and Discussion

1. Pencil-beam surveys extending to a distance of 2000 Mpc suggest that the universe is uniform on a large scale. There do not appear to be any structures larger than about 200 Mpc.

2. The cosmological principle is made up of two assumptions fundamental to cosmology. They are homogeneity and isotropy. At a large enough scale, the universe is homogeneous; one part is pretty much like any other part. Isotropy means that it looks the same in all directions. The cosmological principle tells us there can be no edge to the universe and there is no center to it either.

3. According to the cosmological principle, the universe is homogeneous and isotropic. If it is also infinite in extent and unchanging in time, then the universe is uniformly populated with galaxies filled with stars. In that case, when you look at the night sky, your line of sight must eventually encounter a star; the sky should appear as bright as the surface of the Sun. This was first proposed by Heinrich Olbers and is known as Olbers's paradox. Because this is not what is observed, however, something must be different from what was assumed. The resolution lies in the fact that the universe is expanding. Whether the universe is finite or infinite, we only see a finite portion of it. The expansion also redshifts the radiation to longer wavelengths, so distant stars will not be seen in the visible part of the spectrum.

4. Hubble's law is a relationship between velocity of recession of objects in the universe and their distance, $v = H_0 d$. Because we know that velocity is distance divided by time, Hubble's constant, H_0, is a measure of 1 divided by time, the time of the expansion of the universe to its present size. It turns out that this time gives a maximum age for the universe.

5. Although we appear to be at the center of the Hubble flow, it turns out that all other locations in the universe appear to be at the center too. This is due to the fact that the Hubble flow is not due to the motion of objects into the universe; rather, it is an expansion of the universe itself. Space itself is expanding. Because the Hubble flow is an expansion of space itself, galaxies are not rushing outward into unoccupied parts of the universe. The universe is evenly filled with matter, but space is expanding, which gives rise to an appearance of galaxies flying outward from us.

6.   Supernovae are a standard candle by which astronomers can examine Hubble's law at great distances and therefore at a time when the universe was much younger. Instead of finding a universe that appears to be slowing down with time, the supernovae data suggest a universe that is accelerating. If confirmed, this discovery would necessitate a cosmological constant, whose origin is unknown at this time.

7.   Where did the Big Bang occur? In a word, everywhere. It was an explosion of all of space and time, not an explosion in space. When it occurred is given by the age of the universe, about 14 billion years ago.

8.   A wave of electromagnetic radiation, as it moves through the universe, will experience the same expansion of the space experienced by the universe. As the wave travels farther and farther, it expands more and more. By the time it is observed, it appears redshifted in proportion to the distance it has traveled.

9.   Just after the Big Bang occurred, the universe was filled with X-ray and gamma-ray radiation. Since that period, this radiation has traveled through the universe, its wavelength expanding as the universe has expanded. It is now observed in the microwave part of the spectrum. It provides us with information about the very early universe; it is the light from the very oldest object visible in the universe—the universe itself!

10. When the universe was about 100 s old, conditions such as temperature and density were just right for the fusion of protons and neutrons to form helium. Twenty-five percent of matter by mass was converted into helium at that time. Not until stars started nucleosynthesis did hydrogen fuse into helium again. But all matter in the universe contains at least this 25% helium; any more than this is due to stellar nucleosynthesis.

11. If the density of the universe is sufficiently high, the universe will eventually stop expanding and start collapsing. If the density of the universe is sufficiently low, the universe will continue to expand forever. Between these two extremes is the critical density, Ω_0; the universe will stop expanding after an infinite amount of time. The value of the critical density depends on Hubble's constant.

The amount of deuterium that remains today depends on the amount that remained after helium was formed. That amount was very sensitive to the conditions of the universe at that time, particularly the density. The greater the density, the less deuterium that should have been left over.

12. When the universe cooled to the point where electrons could recombine with nuclei, neutral atoms started to appear. Radiation no longer interacted strongly with matter and the universe became transparent. The universe was a few hundred thousand years old at the time.

13. When the universe was 10^{-35} s old, the strong force froze-out or separated from the superforce. The universe briefly entered a high-energy state called the *false vacuum*. Empty space pulled the universe outward in an extremely rapid, but brief, period of expansion. This period of time is referred to as the *period of inflation*. The universe expanded by a factor of 10^{50} in size.

The horizon problem is solved through inflation by taking points that were close together and in communication with each other and quickly separating them. They are the same today because they were the same then.

The flatness problem is also solved by inflation. Although space was curved, at the time of inflation the universe grew so large that the curvature is now no longer significant.

14. Fluctuations in baryonic matter could not have formed large-scale structures in as short a time as is observed. Dark matter decoupled very early from normal matter, and its fluctuations had time to grow. Gas was later attracted to these regions, producing the large-scale structure now observed. Hot dark matter can produce large-scale structures but not small-scale structures. Cold dark matter can produce both.

15. Inflation theory predicts a Ω_0 of 1. The *COBE* data on the angular size of the fluctuations verify that this parameter is very close to 1.

Conceptual Self-Test

True or False? 1. F 2. F 3. F 4. T 5. T 6. F 7. T 8. T

Multiple Choice 9. a 10. d 11. c 12. d 13. b 14. c 15. a

Problems

1. $m - M = 5\log(d/10)$; $20 - (-20) = 5\log(d/10)$; $d = 10^9$ pc $= 1000$ Mpc.

2. The volume of space out to a distance of 1 billion parsecs is $4/3\pi(10^9 \text{ pc})^3 = 4 \times 10^{27} \text{ pc}^3$. There are $(10^6 \text{ pc})^3 = 10^{18} \text{ pc}^3$ in 1 cubic megaparsec. Dividing this into the previous volume gives $4 \times 10^9 \text{ Mpc}^3$. With 0.1 Milky Way-like galaxies per Mpc^3 there should be a total of **400 million** galaxies of this size in this volume of space.

3. The diagonal of any one of the 10-by-10 Mpc squares is $\sqrt{200} = 10\sqrt{2} = 14.1$. The right triangle to be solved has sides of 10 and 14.1. The hypotenuse is the distance from one corner to the other corner.
$$d = \sqrt{(10^2 + 14.1^2)} = 17.3 \text{ Mpc}.$$
The recessional velocity at this distance is 70 km/s/Mpc × 17.3 Mpc = 1200 km/s in a direction directly away from the opposite corner.

4. In order for the units to work out for the age of the universe, the H_0 Mpc part of km/s/Mpc must be converted to Km as follows. 1 Mpc = 3.1 x 10^{19} km   (See footnote 3 on page 458 of *BG5*.)

For $H_0 = 50$ km/s/Mpc, T = $1/H_0$ = 1/(50 km/s/Mpc) = 3.1 x 10^{19} km/50 km/s = 20 billion years

For $H_0 = 70$ km/s/Mpc, T = $1/H_0$ = 1/(70 km/s/Mpc) = 3.1 x 10^{19} km/70 km/s = 14 billion years

For $H_0 = 80$ km/s/Mpc, T = $1/H_0$ = 1/(80 km/s/Mpc) = 3.1 x 10^{19} km/80 km/s = 12 billion years

5. Mass = density × volume = $(9 \times 10^{-27} \text{ kg/m}^3)$ (1 A.U.^{3})$(1.5 \times 10^{11} \text{ m/A.U.})^3 = 3.04 \times 10^7$ kg.

Volume = mass/density = $(5.98 \times 10^{24} \text{ kg})/(9 \times 10^{-27} \text{ kg/m}^3) = 6.64 \times 10^{50} \text{ m}^3$. This volume is a cube that is 8.7×10^{16} m = 2.8 pc on a side.

6. The velocity divided by the Hubble constant gives the distance to the Virgo Cluster; (1200 km/s)/(70 km/s/Mpc) = 17.1 Mpc. The volume within this distance is $4/3\pi(17,100,000 \text{ pc})^3$ = 2.09×10^{22} pc^3. Converting this to cubic meters gives 6.17×10^{71} m^3. Multiplying by the critical density gives 5.54×10^{45} kg = **2.8×10^{15} solar masses.**

Find the escape speed, converting the mass to kg and the distance to m.

$$v_{esc} = \sqrt{\frac{2GM}{R}} = \sqrt{\frac{2(6.67\times10^{-11})(2.8\times10^{15})(1.99\times10^{30})}{(17.1\times10^6 \times 3.09\times10^{16})}} = 1.2\times10^6 \text{ m/s} = 1200 \text{ km/s.}$$

7. (a) From Wien's law, λ_{max} = (0.29 cm)/T. For a background radiation temperature of 2.7 K, λ_{max} = (0.29 cm)/2.7 = 0.107 cm = 1.07 mm, or about 1.1 mm.

The ratio of the sizes of the universe at the two different times is equal to the ratio of the wavelengths of the peak radiation.
(b) 10 μm/1.07 mm = 10×10^{-6} m/0.00107 m = 0.0093

(c) 100 nm/1.07 mm = 100×10^{-9} m/0.00107 m = 9.3×10^{-5}

(d) 1 nm/1.07 mm = 1×10^{-9} m/0.00107 m = 9.3×10^{-7}.

8. First, some theory. Mass density is mass divided by volume; $\rho_m \propto m/R^3$. $E = mc^2$. Solving for m gives $m = E/c^2$ so $\rho_E \propto E/R^3$, where this is now the energy density. The energy of a photon is given by $E = hf$, where f is the frequency. So $E \propto 1/\lambda$. As the universe expands, wavelengths expand in proportion; the cosmological redshift. So, $\lambda \propto R$ and $E \propto 1/R$. Substituting for E in the density expression finally gives $\rho_E \propto 1/R^4$. Note that we started with mass density, which has a $1/R^3$ dependence. These two different relationships give rise to the two curves in Figure 17.14.

For matter density: the density scales as $1/R^3$. $1000^3 = 10^9$. The density then will be the density now times this factor; 9×10^{-27} kg/m$^3 \times 10^9$ = **9×10^{-18} kg/m^3.**

For equivalent mass density of the cosmic radiation: the density scales as $1/R^4$. $1000^4 = 10^{12}$. Using the current energy density from the text, 5×10^{-31} kg/m$^3 \times 10^{12}$ = **5×10^{-19} kg/m^3.**

9. According to the text, decoupling occurred when the universe was 1100 times smaller than it is today. 100 Mpc/1100 = 91 kpc.

10. Estimating from Table 15.2, the distance to decoupling must be around 14,000 Mpc (redshift of 1100).
diameter/($2\pi\times$distance) = (angular diameter)/$360°$.

Diameter = ($2\pi \times$ 14,000 Mpc) $\times$ [(20'÷60'/°)/360°] = 81 Mpc. This is the size as it appears now. At decoupling, the universe was 1100 times smaller, so the size would have been 81 Mpc/1100 = **74 kpc.**

Resource Information

Student CD Media Resources

Interactive Student Tutorials
None

Movies/Animations
Cosmic Structure

Transparencies

242.	Figure 17.1	Galaxy Survey
243.	Figure 17.2	Olbers's Paradox
244.	Figure 17.3	Receding Galaxies
245.	Figure 17.4	Cosmological Redshift
246.	Figure 17.5	Escape Speed
247.	Figure 17.6	Model Universes
248.	MP 17-1	Curved Space
249.	Figure 17.8	Accelerating Universe
250.	Figure 17.10	Cosmic Age
251.	Figure 17.12	Cosmic Blackbody Curves
252.	Figure 17.13	Microwave Background Spectrum
253.	Figure 17.14	Radiation–Matter Dominance
254.	Figure 17.15	Helium Formation
255.	Figure 17.16	Radiation–Matter Decoupling
256.	Figure 17.17	Horizon Problem
257.	Figure 17.19	Cosmic Inflation
258.	Figure 17.20	Inflation and the Flatness Problem
259.	Figure 17.21	Structure Formation
260.	Figure 17.24	Early Structure

Materials

A chart entitled "The History and Fate of the Universe" is available from The Contemporary Physics Education Project. It is also included as a supplement to the March 2003 issue of *The Physics Teacher*. Check http://UniverseAdventure.org for more details.

Be sure to bring a balloon to class for performing some classic cosmology demonstrations.

The video *Creation of the Universe* (PBS Home Video) is an excellent exploration of many topics in cosmology.

Suggested Readings

Adams, Fred C. and Laughlin, Greg. "Embracing the end." *Astronomy* (Oct 2000). p. 48. Describes the "Degenerate Era," the ultimate end of the universe when all that remains are the remnants of stars.

Adams, Fred C. and Laughlin, Gregory. "The future of the universe." *Sky & Telescope* (Aug 1998). p. 32. Provides an overview of the entire life of the universe.

Arkani Hamed, Nima, Dimopoulos, Savas and Dvali, Georgi. "The universe's unseen dimensions." *Scientific American* (Aug 2000). p. 62. Describes recent advances in string theory related to cosmology.

Caldwell, Robert R. and Kamionkowski, Marc. "Echoes from the big bang." *Scientific American* (Jan 2001). p. 38. Describes small flucuations in the cosmic microwave background that would be formed by gravitational waves from the early universe.

Donahue, Megan. "Cosmology with Galaxy Clusters." *Sky & Telescope* (Dec 2004). p. 32. Discusses how astronomers are using super clusters of galaxies to measure the properties of dark matter in the universe.

Falk, Dan. "An interconnected universe? Exploring the topology of the cosmos." *Sky & Telescope* (July 1999). p. 44. Discusses the topology of the universe.

Gallmeier, Jonathan, Grilley, David, and Olson, Donald W. "How old is the universe?" *Sky & Telescope* (Jan 1996). p. 92. Gives a computer program which calculates the age of the universe for different input values of the Hubble constant, the density parameter, and the cosmological constant.

Glanz, James. "Accelerating the cosmos." *Astronomy* (Oct 1999). p. 44. Describes observations of distant supernovae, the cosmological constant, and the acceleration of the universe.

Glanz, James. "On becoming the material world." *Astronomy* (Feb 1998). p. 44. Discusses primordial nucleosynthesis.

Guth, Alan H. "Genesis: the sequel." *Natural History* (Feb 2000). p. 77. Provides an updated summary of cosmic inflation.

Hogan, Craig J. "Primordial deuterium and the big bang." *Scientific American* (Dec 1996). p. 68. Describes measurement of the abundance of deuterium in the universe and how this value constrains theories of cosmology.

Jayawardhana, Ray. "In search of the first stars." *Astronomy* (Dec 2005). p. 42. Discusses how the detection of the first stars will help astronomers unlock the secrets of the infant universe.

Kaku, Michio. "What happened before the Big Bang?" *Astronomy* (May 1996). p. 34. Discusses the idea of parallel universes.

Krauss, Lawrence M. "Cosmological antigravity." *Scientific American* (Jan 1999). p. 52. Discusses explanations for the observed expansion of the universe.

Krauss, Lawrence M. "The history and fate of the universe: a guide to accompany the contemporary physics education cosmology chart." *The Physics Teacher* (Mar 2003). p. 146. An excellent summary of current understanding of the history and future of the universe, with resources for teachers.

Landy, Stephen D. "Mapping the universe: large-scale structures." *Scientific American* (June 1999). p. 38. Describes the results of the Las Campanas Redshift Survey with an emphasis on cosmology and the structure of the universe.

Luminet, Jean Pierre, Starkman, Glenn D., and Weeks, Jeffrey R. "Is space finite?" *Scientific American* (Apr 1999). p. 90. Describes possible topologies of the universe.

Ostriker, Jeremiah P. and Steinhardt, Paul J. "The quintessential universe." *Scientific American* (Jan 2001). p. 46. Describes our understanding of the structure of the universe.

Nadis, Steve. "Before there was light." *Astronomy* (Aug 2005). p. 46. Discusses how astronomers are poised to explore the mysterious cosmic Dark Ages.

Nadis, Steve. "Sizing up Inflation." *Sky & Telescope* (Nov 2005). p. 32. Discusses the mysterious force that initiated cosmic inflation.

Parker, Samantha and Roth, Joshua. "To see the world in a grain of sand: the Hubble Deep Field." *Sky & Telescope* (May 1996). p. 48. Describes results obtained from the Hubble Deep Field.

Rees, Martin. "Just 6 numbers." *Astronomy* (July 2000). p. 54. Describes six numbers that determine the nature of the universe.

Rees, Martin. "Exploring our universe and others." *Scientific American* (Dec 1999). p. 78. Looks at our state of understanding the universe and discusses direction for future research.

Roth, Joshua. "The race to map the microwave background." *Sky & Telescope* (Sept 1999). p. 44. Discusses the nature of the cosmic microwave background.

Steele, Diana. "Unveiling the flat universe." *Astronomy* (Aug 2000). p. 46. Describes BOOMERANG results which support the idea of a flat universe.

Tyson, Neil De Grasse. "On being dense." *Natural History* (Jan 1996). p. 66. Gives examples of the densities of different components of the universe.

Weil, Thomas A. "Looking back cosmologically." *Sky & Telescope* (Sept 1997). p. 59. Discusses the concept of the "lookback time" and provides a computer program to calculate the lookback time of an object as a function of the redshift of the object and the value of the Hubble constant.

Notes and Ideas

*Class time spent on material: Estimated:*_____   *Actual:*_____

Demonstration and activity materials:

Notes for next time:

Chapter 18: Life in the Universe

Are We Alone?

Outline

Summary

The possibility of, and search for, extraterrestrial life are the topics of Chapter 18. First, characteristics of life and its development are discussed. Then, the questions of life elsewhere in our solar system and elsewhere in the universe are addressed. The Drake equation for predicting the number of intelligent, technological civilizations in the Milky Way is examined, and each factor within it is discussed. Finally, the chapter concludes with the search for extraterrestrial life and the difficulties in communicating with other technological civilizations, should they exist.

Major Concepts

- Cosmic evolution
- The definition of life and life "as we know it"
- Candidates for life in the solar system
  - Mars
  - Moons of outer planets—Europa, Enceladus, and Titan
  - Cometary and meteoritic debris
- The Drake equation for number of technological, intelligent civilizations in the Milky Way
  - Rate of star formation
  - Fraction of stars having planetary systems
  - Number of habitable planets per system
  - Fraction of habitable planets on which life arises
  - Fraction of life-bearing planets on which intelligence arises
  - Fraction of planets on which civilization becomes technological
  - Average lifetime of a technological civilization
  - Uncertainties and estimates of factors
- Communication with extraterrestrial, intelligent life
  - Distances
  - Radio leakage from Earth
  - SETI, the search for extraterrestrial intelligence
  - The water hole

Teaching Suggestions and Demonstrations

Asking the question "Are we alone?" is indeed a powerful way to conclude a course! Students may well have thought about this question before, but likely not from the perspective of astronomy or by using a tool such as the Drake equation. In addition to discussing the science involved in attempting to answer this question, be sure to save time for the philosophical implications as well. If we were to find another intelligent civilization, what would it mean for us? How would this knowledge change us, if at all?

Sections 18.1 and 18.2

Project and discuss Figure 18.1, the **arrow of time**. (Make sure your students recognize that it is not to scale!) It is a powerful statement of how we got to where we are today, and is a nice way to summarize some of the big ideas from the course and add to them what students already know about the development of life on Earth.

Before proceeding with the **definition of life** as given in the textbook, ask your students to define life. What conditions must be met in order to classify something as alive? Record responses on the board. There will probably be some disagreement on some of the conditions; open the discussion and get students to try to convince each other of their point of view. When the class is satisfied with the list, play devil's advocate and try to come up with something that meets the conditions but would not be considered "alive." The example of stars given in the book is a good one; stars react to their neighbors, grow, generate energy, and (in a sense) reproduce. The main point of this exercise is to demonstrate that distinguishing between living and nonliving is not as trivial as students probably will think at first. We tend to think of life in terms of things like trees, bugs, giraffes, people. Point out the less clear-cut possibilities as well.

The course so far has covered the first four stages in the arrow of time diagram. Touch briefly on the next two, **chemical evolution** and **biological evolution**, now. Explain the Urey-Miller experiment and its significance. All life-forms on Earth are 99% hydrogen, oxygen, carbon, and nitrogen, in order of decreasing abundance. This certainly is not the makeup of Earth's crust or atmosphere. What object(s) have a composition similar to this? It is a good question to ask your students because they have the information to answer it. It is the Sun (and typical stars and interstellar clouds of gas and dust). With the exception of two inert gases, helium and neon, life's elemental abundance reflects that of stars and interstellar matter from which they all formed! This is hardly a coincidence, and is a good topic for discussion.

(DEMO⚡) Make a **timeline** of the about 4.6 billion years of Earth's history, and indicate when life first appeared, when the dinosaurs roamed Earth, and when humans appeared. This can be done on a long strip of paper, such as adding machine or receipt tape. Another common approach is to compress the history of Earth into a single year. If Earth formed on New Year's Day and today is midnight on the next New Year's Eve, when did life appear? When were the dinosaurs around? When did humans appear? When did Galileo use a telescope to view the stars? When were you born? This exercise puts history into perspective; it is amazing how much happens in that last day, and even in the last seconds of the last day. Alternatively, you can discuss Figure 18.6 with your class.

When we talk about **life in the universe** (other than our own), we often look at one extreme or the other. On the one hand, we are intrigued by the possibility of there being other intelligent life "out there." On the other hand, we are looking for *any* life, including the simplest, single-celled form of life imaginable. Such a finding would be incredibly exciting, partly because we know that single-celled life-forms can, eventually, evolve into higher life-forms. Even finding fossil evidence of past simple life would be a major discovery, as it would show us that the development of life is not unique to our planet. In this realm, the search is mainly taking place in our solar system. Mars has been considered the best candidate, but so far life has not been discovered on Mars. Ask students to apply their knowledge of the solar system and suggest other places where life may have developed. A meteorite found in Antarctica has been studied, and some scientists believe they have found fossil evidence of simple worms.

The moons of the outer solar system have become very promising destinations in the search for extraterrestrial life. Europa, and perhaps Ganymede, of Jupiter and Enceladus of Saturn are promising because there is thought to be liquid subsurface water. Titan of Saturn, on the other hand, is interesting because the complex hydrocarbons present in the dense nitrogen atmosphere are thought to mimic the chemistry of the early Earth.

Sections 18.3 and 18.4

The **Drake equation** addresses the question at the other extreme, the possible existence of *intelligent* life. It calculates the number of technological, intelligent civilizations now present in the Milky Way Galaxy. Point out to students that the certainty of the result of an equation is no better than the certainty of the data entered into it. In this case, the values of some of the factors of the Drake equation are far from certain. However, it is still a useful tool because it helps us to examine the factors necessary for the development of advanced civilizations and to address them individually. As you go through a discussion of the Drake equation, have students debate and come up with their own estimates for each term and calculate the class's result for the number of intelligent, technological civilizations. You can also present the "liberal" or optimistic view given in the text; students typically are very conservative with some of their estimates. Let the lifetime, L, remain an open question after it has been thoroughly discussed (and this term usually produces the liveliest discussion). Putting all the factors together, the number of technical civilizations in the galaxy, N, will be $N = L$ from the text and maybe something like $N = 0.000000001\ L$ from your students (depending on how unlikely they feel some of the factors are).

Now put in a low value for L, like $L = 100$, which is about where we are at this time. In the case of the text, $N = 100$, but for a student estimate like the one above, $N = 0.0000001$. But this cannot be right because they have not managed to predict their own existence! Thus, $N = 1$ should be a minimum result. Try different values of L and discuss why the value of L has such a enormous potential range. This last term in the Drake equation brings up a fundamental question for civilization—do civilizations wipe themselves out when they become technologically advanced? Are we doomed, or can we overcome environmental, political, and social problems and last for millions or perhaps even billions of years?

As done in the text, take the result from the Drake equation and assume these civilizations are spread reasonably uniformly throughout the Milky Way Galaxy, then calculate the distance to the closest one. Clearly, the greatest obstacle in communicating with other intelligent civilizations is **distance**. Discuss the limitations of space travel, science fiction notwithstanding! Even the travel time of a *message*, sent at the speed of light, is enormous. Nevertheless, we are putting effort into looking for extraterrestrial life. Discuss SETI (the search for extraterrestrial intelligence) and its implications. What if we find extraterrestrial, intelligent, technologically competent beings? Will they be more advanced than us? (Most likely, the answer is yes. We have been technological for only 100 years; chances are, any civilization communicating with us would have been at it a lot longer.) Ask your students how they, individually, would react to such a discovery. How do they think our planet's civilization as a whole would react?

In addition to looking for messages, we have sent out our own messages both in the form of radio waves escaping from Earth and as plaques and records with interstellar probes, as shown in Figure 18.11 and discussed in the context of the *Voyager* spacecraft. Perhaps this would be a good time to return to the exercise mentioned earlier, in which student teams plan the sounds and images that would be sent into space to represent Earth. The topic of extraterrestrial life provides not only an intriguing way to view the cosmos, but also an opportunity to think about our own home in space.

Student Writing Questions

1. Assuming contact has been made with beings from another civilization at a distance of, say, 100-light years, what sort of information would you like to know about them? What would you like or want to say about us to them in return? Keep in mind that a question-and-answer format is not really practical with a 200-year interval between question and answer.

2. What impact would the discovery of an advanced alien civilization have on civilization here on Earth? Assume the contact is made through radio communications with beings on their home planet at a distance of 100 light-years or more. Consider the effects, if any, on our political, social, and religious institutions.

3. Reflect for a moment on the word "alien" in terms of how it is used when referring to extraterrestrial life-forms and its meaning when used in reference to people from countries other than our own. Keep in mind the varieties of environments and evolutionary possibilities when thinking about life on planets orbiting other stars. Consider, too, the differences among humans on Earth that make one group "alien" from another. What is the significance of the differences in these two cases?

4. Look up the meaning of "panspermia." Write a scenario in which life on Earth is seeded from life on Mars. How unlikely a possibility is this? Can this "new panspermia" be easily dismissed? If this is actually how life began on Earth, what effects do you believe this would have on how we think about ourselves?

5. The Drake equation tells us our Galaxy could contain as few as one technical civilization (us!) or possibly some other, potentially large, number. Take the latter number to be something not too large, like 100,000. What are our responsibilities, if any, with regard to either of these two situations; we are the lone technical civilization in the entire galaxy or we are among 100,000 other civilizations? Keeping in mind that $N = L$, what is the implication with regard to our lifetime as a civilization? In the case of $N = L = 100,000$, how would our technology compare to most other technologies?

6. Imagine that you could carry on a conversation with another intelligent species on Earth, such as a dolphin. What would you ask a dolphin? What would they ask us? What communication obstacles would we have with dolphins? Would we even have anything in common? How might our communications with dolphins give us insight into communicating with an extraterrestrial species or civilization?

Answers to End of Chapter Exercises

Review and Discussion

1. Characteristics of life are reaction, growth, reproduction, and evolution. Although other characteristics might be listed, most life-forms have these four characteristics in common. Life is difficult to define because not all forms of life share the same traits.

2. Chemical evolution is a process by which life develops from the natural environment of Earth (or anyplace else, for that matter). The chemistry of life, to some degree, depends on the material present on Earth's surface and on the environment of the surface.

3. The Urey-Miller experiment tries to re-create the conditions on Earth before life existed, with the purpose of producing molecules necessary for life. Using ingredients like water, methane, ammonia,

and carbon dioxide, and by adding energy, essential organic molecules for life, such as amino acids and nucleotide bases, have been formed.

4. The basic ingredients are water, methane, carbon dioxide, and ammonia.

5. The fossil record dates back to at least 3.5 billion years ago, when Earth was just over a billion years old. The fossil record, although at times unclear, is continuous up to the present time.

6. Language may be the direct result of the development of human intelligence. With language, information could be passed on from generation to generation. Ideas could be developed and exchanged. Cultural evolution is the changes in ideas and behavior of society and is likely linked to the appearance of language.

7. Organic molecules have been found in meteorites and in molecular clouds of interstellar matter. Comets and the surface of Titan likely contain some organic molecules. Many other solar system objects may also contain such molecules, but they have not been sufficiently explored.

8. The possibility of life cannot be excluded from places such as Jupiter's atmosphere, Europa's liquid ocean, or the surface of Titan.

9. The *Viking* landers on Mars found no evidence of life as we know it. However, several possibilities remain before anyone can say for certain that life does not (and did not) exist on Mars. The landers were in very desolate, mid-latitude sites that may be quite inhospitable for life. Better locations might be near the poles where water, mostly frozen, exists in greater abundance. Life might also exist below the immediate surface of Mars, deeper in the soil where water may be abundant and life is shielded from the harsh surface environment. The landers could only look for life as we know it to be, and could not look for alternate forms of life. Fossil evidence of life might also exist, telling of times in the past when the Martian environment was favorable for life. These questions have yet to be investigated.

10. "Life as we know it" means life based on organic molecules in a mostly water environment. When searching for life we must remember that "life as we know it" may not be the only possibility for life to have. Life might be based on atoms other than carbon, or it may have a carbon base but function radically differently from our own life-forms.

11. The Drake equation has been devised as a way to estimate the abundance of life outside the solar system. The result depends on seven factors: (1) rate of star formation, (2) fraction of stars having planetary systems, (3) number of planets in a solar system with a suitable environment for life, (4) fraction of suitable planets on which life actually develops, (5) fraction of life-bearing planets on which intelligence evolves, (6) fraction of intelligent-life planets that develop a technology, and (7) average lifetime of a technological civilization.

    Factors 1 and 2 are fairly well known. Factor 3 could also be included in this group, although it is not as well known as factors 1 and 2. Factors 4, 5, and 6 really require some guesswork. We really have no other examples other than ourselves. Factor 7 has the widest range of values possible, and is therefore the least well-known.

12. When the lifetime of a civilization approaches the time it takes for one two-way communication, then such communication becomes impractical if not impossible. This occurs for lifetimes of less than about 3000 years. If these civilizations were separated by 1500 light-years, then one two-way communication would require 3000 years. By the time one of the civilizations sends a message by

radio waves to the other and receives a reply, it would be just dying out.

13. Radio transmissions from Earth would vary significantly over a 24-hour period. This is the result of Earth's rotation and various groups of transmitters coming into view. Most of the transmissions would be in the FM and television frequencies.

14. The advantages of radio waves for interstellar communication are several. Radio waves travel just as fast as all other electromagnetic waves—the speed of light. They can penetrate dust clouds and can reach anywhere in the galaxy. Being the lowest energy waves, they are cheap to produce and do not require a high level of technology either to produce or to receive. The background noise level at radio wavelengths is minimal, allowing signals to be detected over large distances.

15. The water hole is a section of radio wavelengths between 18 and 21 cm. This region of the radio spectrum would be the best for interstellar communications because it has the least amount of naturally occurring radio noise. These wavelengths also pass easily through interstellar dust clouds and are least affected by planetary atmospheres.

Conceptual Self-Test

True or False? 1. F 2. F 3. T 4. F 5. T 6. T 7. T

Multiple Choice 8. b 9. c 10. c 11. b 12. d 13. a 14. d 15. d

Problems

1. In 46 years there are $46 \times (60 \times 60 \times 24 \times 365)$ s $= 1.45 \times 10^9$ s. Dividing this by the 4.6-billion-year age of Earth gives 0.315 s/yr.

Age of a 20-year-old person:	6.3 s
End of WW II:	18 s
Declaration of Independence:	72 s
Columbus' voyage:	161 s
Extinction of dinosaurs:	237 days

2. The energy received will be inversely proportional to the square of the distance. Set up a ratio comparing the K-star to the Sun. The ratio of the luminosities is 1:0.1.

$$\frac{1}{0.1} = \frac{d_{sun}^2}{d_{star}^2}.$$

   For the inner boundary, $d = \sqrt{(0.6^2 \times 0.1)} = 0.19$ A.U.

   For the outer boundary, $d = \sqrt{(1.5^2 \times 0.1)} = 0.47$ A.U.

3. If 10 stars per year is the average formation rate of stars, if each is able to form a planetary system, and if 1 in 10 have a suitable environment for habitability, then over a period of 5 billion years there should now be $10 \times 1 \times 0.1 \times 5$ billion = 5 billion habitable planets in the Milky Way Galaxy.

4. Using the scale from Figure 18.12a, the distance between the 2 stars would be ~4.5 A.U. apart.

It is also reasonable to compare the force of gravity on the planet from its parent star to that from the companion star. If the latter force is 0.01% of the former, then the former is 10,000 times the latter. Thus, by the inverse-square law, the parent star must be 100 times closer. The companion star would be 100 A.U. from the planet, or 101 A.U. from the parent star.

5. no. of technological civilizations = $20 \times 0.1 \times 1 \times 0.1 \times 0.1 \times 0.1 \times$ average lifetime of civilization
    no. of technological civilizations = $0.002 \times$ average lifetime of civilization

    (a) no. of technological civilizations = $0.002 \times 100 = 0.2$
    (b) no. of technological civilizations = $0.002 \times 10,000 = 20$
    (c) no. of technological civilizations = $0.002 \times 1,000,000 = 2000$

6. Let A be the area of the galaxy, R its radius in light years, and N the number of civilizations. The area per civilization will be A/N. If r is the dimension of the civilization's area, then

    $A/N = r^2$ and since $A = \pi R^2$, $r = R(\pi/N)^{1/2}$.

    The distance to the nearest neighbor is going to be r and for a round-trip conversation, the total distance will be $2r$. The communication will be at light speed, $c = 1$ ly/yr and must be completed in the lifetime of the civilization, L. So, $L = 2r/c$. From the Drake Equation, $N = L$.

    $$L = 2r/c = 2\ [R(\pi/N)^{1/2}]/c = 2\ [R(\pi/L)^{1/2}]/c$$

    $R = 15,000$ pc = 49,500 light-years and $c = 1$ ly/year

    $$L^{3/2} = 2R(\pi)^{1/2}/c;\ L = 3100 \text{ years}.$$

    Traveling at 50 km/s is 6000 times slower than light speed. So a civilization must last 6000 times longer, or about 20 million years, to complete a trip at this speed.

7. 1.3 pc is 4.0×10^{13} km. 80 years is 2.5×10^9 s. The total distance for the round trip would be 8.0×10^{13} km. The average speed would be distance/time = $(8.0 \times 10^{13}$ km$)/(2.5 \times 10^9$ s$) = 32,000$ km/s.

8. 10,000 stations $\times$ 50,000 W/station = 5×10^8 W. This is 5×10^8 W/10^6 W = **500 times more** power radiated than the Sun in this same frequency range.

9. The water hole ranges from 18 to 21 cm in wavelength. Because $c = \lambda f$, the corresponding frequencies are $(3 \times 10^{10}$ cm/s$)/18$ cm = **1.67×10^9 Hz** and $(3 \times 10^{10}$ cm/s$)/21$ cm = **1.43×10^9 Hz**.

    Subtracting these two frequencies gives 2.4×10^8 Hz. Dividing by 100 Hz per channel gives **2,400,000 channels.** This is how many channels would have to be searched when observing throughout the water hole.

10. 20,000 stars $\times$ 1 hour/star = 20,000 hours = 833 days = 2.3 years;

    20,000 stars $\times$ 1 day/star = 20,000 days = 55 years.

Resource Information

Student CD Media Resources

Interactive Student Tutorials
None

Movies/Animations
None

Transparencies

261.	Figure 18.1	Arrow of Time
262.	Figure 18.2	DNA Molecule
263.	Figure 18.3	Miller-Urey Experiment
264.	Figure 18.6	Life on Earth
265.	Figure 18.9	Drake Equation
266.	Figure 18.10	Stellar Habitable Zones
267.	Figure 18.11	Galactic Habitable Zone
268.	Figure 18.12	Binary-star Planets
269.	Figure 18.13	Pioneer 10 Plaque
270.	Figure 18.14	Earth's Radio Leakage
271.	Figure 18.15	Water Hole
272.	Figure 18.16	Project Phoenix

Materials

Two interesting videos which deal with the possibility of finding life elsewhere in the galaxy are *Contact: The Search for Extraterrestrial Intelligence* (Space Viz Productions), and *Hunt for Alien Worlds* (NOVA).

Suggested Readings

Crawford, Ian. "Where are they?" *Scientific American* (July 2000). p. 38. Examines possible explanations for the absence of detected signals from extraterrestrial civilizations.

Davies, Paul. "Interplanetary infestations." *Sky & Telescope* (Sept 1999). p. 32. Discusses the hypothesis that life is brought to planets by microbes from space.

LePage, Andrew J. "Habitable moons." *Sky & Telescope* (Dec 1998). p. 50. Discusses the conditions necessary for the moons of extrasolar giant planets to harbor life.

LePage, Andrew J. "Where they could hide." *Scientific American* (July 2000). p. 40. Displays diagram summarizing the SETI search results in terms of distance from Earth and total radiated power.

Marchand, Peter J. "Windows on the desert floor: desert life may give hint of what extraterrestrial life may be like." *Natural History* (May 1998). p. 28. Describes microbes that exist under harsh conditions on Earth.

McInnis, Doug. "Wanted: life-bearing planets." *Astronomy* (Apr 1998). p. 38. Describes plans to search for Earth-like extrasolar planets.

Naeye, Robert. "OK, where are they?" *Astronomy* (July 1996). p. 36. Takes a look at all the conditions necessary for a planet to harbor an advanced civilization.

Paque, Julie. "What makes a planet a friend for life?" *Astronomy* (June 1995). p. 46. Discusses the origin of life on Earth.

Pendleton, Yvonne J. and Farmer, Jack D. "Life: a cosmic imperative?" *Sky & Telescope* (July 1997). p. 42. Evaluates conditions for sustaining life on planets and moons in the solar system.

Schilling, Govert. "The chance of finding aliens: reevaluating the Drake equation." *Sky & Telescope* (Dec 1998). p. 36. Reevaluates the factors in the Drake equation.

Seager, Sara. "Unveiling Distant Worlds." *Sky & Telescope* (Feb 2006). p. 28. Discusses the physical characteristics of the roughly 160 known extra-solar planets.

Shostak, Seth. "Listening for a whisper." *Astronomy* (Sept 2004). p. 34. A general overview of status of the SETI project as of 2004.

Swenson, George W., Jr. "Intragalactically speaking." *Scientific American* (July 2000). p. 44. Discusses the transmission of radio signals and the limitations on communication with extraterrestrial civilizations.

Tyson, Neil de Grasse. "Goldilocks and the three planets." *Natural History* (May 1999). p. 92. Discusses the many factors that affect the suitability of a planet for life.

Notes and Ideas

Class time spent on material: Estimated:_____   Actual:_____

Demonstration and activity materials:

Notes for next time: